ABYSSAL CRUSTACEA

VEMA RESEARCH SERIES

NUMBER I

ABYSSAL CRUSTACEA

J. Laurens Barnard   Robert J. Menzies

[Jerry]

Mihai C. Băcescu

COLUMBIA UNIVERSITY PRESS

New York and London   1962

THE PUBLICATION OF THIS VOLUME WAS MADE POSSIBLE BY
A GIFT FROM THE G. UNGER VETLESEN FOUNDATION

CONTENTS

FOREWORD

This is the first volume of the VEMA REPORTS, a series of papers based upon the work done aboard the Columbia University research vessel *Vema*. The series is designed for publication of papers whose length, requirements for illustration, or subject matter would make publication in existing journals difficult.

Over the past eight years a major part of the Lamont Geological Observatory's research program has been based upon data gathered by *Vema*. Her seventeen cruises to date have been planned primarily for investigation of fundamental problems in marine geophysics and submarine geology. Limited attention has been given, however, to areas of oceanography and marine biology with an application to our fields of principal interest. In addition, considerations of national defense, the obligation to take basic observations when visiting unknown parts of the oceans, and the personal interests and capabilities of the investigators who have worked aboard *Vema* have played a part in determining our program.

The publication of the VEMA REPORTS was made possible by support from the G. Unger Vetlesen Foundation. Previously the work done on *Vema* has been reported solely in standard scientific journals. Unfortunately, this has left many serious gaps in the record. For example, we have found it difficult to publish adequate descriptions of many of the new instruments and techniques devised and perfected on *Vema*. Extensive reports containing large quantities of data are likewise difficult to publish in standard journals. Large numbers of excellent ocean-bottom photographs have had to await some special medium of publication, owing to the difficulty and cost of making large numbers of engravings. Extensive studies of submarine canyons and a large part of our work on bathymetry and physiography require large charts and drawings that are beyond the scope of most scientific journals. Cruise narratives—those documents which seem so inconsequential when related to recent cruises and so precious for those that preceded them—cannot be preserved and made available except by publication in a series like VEMA REPORTS. Opinions of readers will differ regarding the relative importance of the various types of publication mentioned. To me, the most important advantages of this series are that it provides for papers too long for the journals and too short for issuance as individual monographs, and that the series will place on the same shelf in many libraries papers that will often need to be consulted together.

Perhaps a few words about *Vema* are in order in this first volume of VEMA REPORTS. We consider her to be one of the most versatile and able of research vessels. Her history is interesting. She was designed by Cox and Stevens and built in 1923 by Burmeister and Wain in Copenhagen for Mr. and Mrs. E. F. Hutton. Christened *Hussar*, she was one of the finest of yachts—a three-masted schooner with wrought-iron hull, 734 tons in displacement, 202 feet long, and very fast. In 1934, by which time the ship had been purchased by Mr. and Mrs. Vetlesen and been renamed *Vema*, she crossed the Atlantic from Montauk Point to Bishop's Rock in ten days and ten hours.

As did all ocean-going yachts in this country, the *Vema* passed into government ownership when the United States entered World War II. In government hands she underwent a drastic conversion to a floating barracks for use in the training program of the U.S. Merchant Marine Academy.

After the war she suffered several years of ruinous neglect, then narrowly escaped the shipbreakers through purchase by a private owner for use as a charter vessel or light cargo carrier. We at Columbia chartered *Vema* for use on an expedition in 1953. We saw such great possibilities in the vessel that we arranged for the purchase of this beautiful ship by the University.

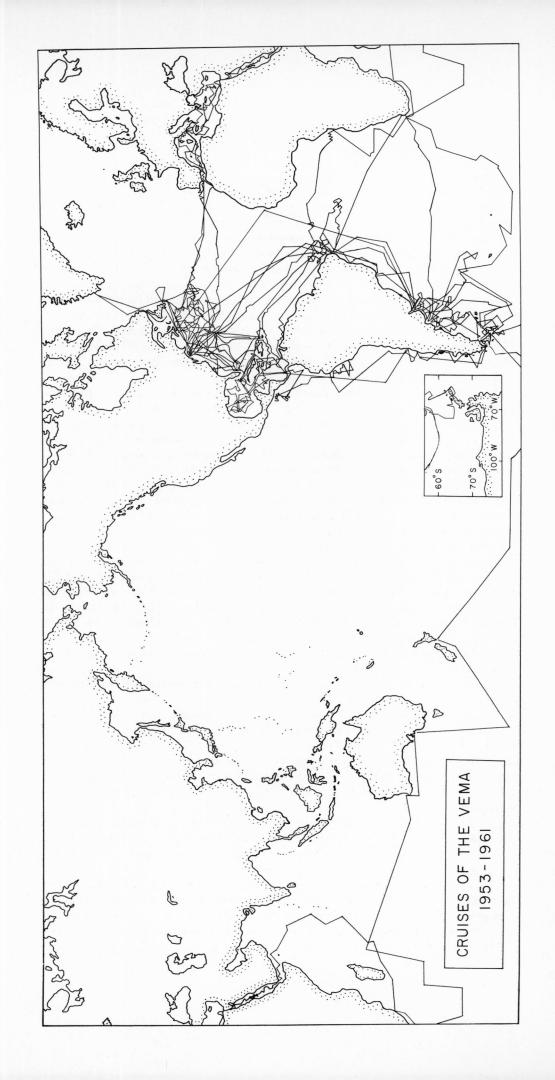

CRUISES OF THE VEMA
1953 - 1961

During the years since, *Vema* has made seventeen cruises. They have included most of the major passages of the world. Cape Horn, the Strait of Magellan, Drake Passage, Deception Island, Valparaiso, the South Sandwich Islands, the Panama Canal, the River Plate, Gibraltar, Suez, the Red Sea, the Gulf of Aden, the Cape of Good Hope, Mauritius, Freemantle, Adelaide, Wellington, Rio de Janeiro, Recife, the Strait of Belle Isle, Davis Strait, the Grand Banks, and many other waters have seen her pass. One of her voyages was a circumnavigation of the globe, during which she reached the ice-covered seas of both the northern and southern hemispheres.

On *Vema* Cruise No. 1, the charter cruise in 1953, the vessel was in poor condition. The engine was unreliable, the decks leaked in so many places that neither men nor instruments could escape dripping sea water either by day or by night in heavy weather, and installations of scientific instruments and machinery as well as living and working space for the scientific party were of the most makeshift character. Generous support, principally from the Navy Department and the National Science Foundation, has enabled us both to improve her steadily and to keep her constantly busy. Since becoming a Columbia vessel she has averaged ten months a year at sea and covered an average of thirty thousand miles a year. Major improvements include replacement of the deck, deck houses, and engine and the addition of a stabilizing tank. She now has fine equipment for acoustic, seismic, gravity, magnetic, and thermal studies and for much of the work of chemical, physical, biological, and geological oceanography.

Vema's wide-ranging voyages have been planned to permit cooperation with the vessels and scientists of other nations. Among those with which we have engaged in joint researches are *Bahia Blanca, Sanaviron,* and *Capitan Canepa* of the Argentine Navy, *Forte de Quimbra* of the Brazilian Navy, *Casma* and *Yelcho* of the Chilean Navy, *Sackville* of the Fisheries Research Board of Canada. *Vrystaat* of the Union of South Africa, Launch V-17 of the Spanish Navy, *Arar* of the Turkish Fishery Research Centre, and H.M.A.S. *Diamentina* of Australia. The contributions to international understanding as well as to scientific knowledge from these cooperative programs have been important.

We believe that there are many great expeditions in the future for *Vema*, and through the wise and generous action of the Trustees of the Vetlesen Foundation, established by the ardent sailor who once owned the *Vema*, the VEMA REPORTS will play an essential part in making the results of her work available to scientists of the world.

MAURICE EWING

New York   Higgins Professor of Geology in Columbia University
July, 1961   Director, Lamont Geological Observatory

South Atlantic Abyssal Amphipods
Collected by R. V. *Vema*

by J. LAURENS BARNARD

Institute of Marine BioResearch, Beaudette Foundation, Solvang, California

TABLES

INTRODUCTION

This is a report on the amphipod crustaceans collected by abyssal benthic trawling from fifteen stations made by the R.V. *Vema* in the South Atlantic Ocean (Table 1). It is the first in a planned series treating the extensive amphipod collections gathered by the *Vema* from several abyssal areas, such as the Caribbean, eastern Pacific, Indian Ocean, and Red Sea. Only Amphipoda of the suborder Gammaridea are considered.

The objectives of this study are: the discovery and documentation of deep sea amphipods; the determination of their habitats, whether benthic, demersal, or pelagic, by a study of morphology and food habits; a search for pandemism or endemism in the abyssal basins; and the collection of data on the relationship of animal size and systematic diversity to depth.

Amphipoda are an important and a diversified part of the abyssal fauna. They reproduce by brooding their young, so that dispersal is limited by the lack of free larval stages. Many are nektonic and are dispersed by migration and water mass movements. Others presumably are obligatorily benthic, swimming only small distances; these species offer the best potential cases of abyssal endemism.

Open benthic trawls collect both benthic and pelagic animals. Most animal groups are readily classified as either one or the other, but amphipods are ambivalent and habitat classification simply by appearance is not possible. The analysis of gut contents provides certain clues to habitat, but, as discussed later, it is not altogether satisfactory.

I have worked according to the hypothesis that degrees of endemism in restricted abyssal areas might provide clues to the relative ages of basins and their barriers. At the same time the origin of the abyssal fauna has to be considered by a study of phylogenetic diversity, comparative morphology, and zoogeography.

Zoologists seek primitive and ancient forms in the deep sea. Amphipods are poor material for this study because they are not a part of the fossil record, except

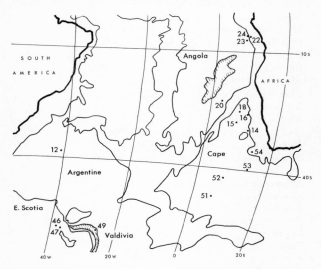

Figure 1. South Atlantic Ocean, showing basins and stations analyzed in this report. Contours are 2000 fathoms, hatched contours are 3000 fathoms.

Table 1

STATION DATA OF BOTTOM TRAWLS IN THE SOUTH ATLANTIC OCEAN BY LAMONT GEOLOGICAL OBSERVATORY

Biotrawl No.	Gear	Dates	Research Vessel	Latitude	Longitude	Corrected Meters	Surface Sediment	Basin
12	LBT	6 April '57	*Vema* 12	38° 58.5′ S.	41° 45′ W.	5041	Red clay	Argentine
14	SBT	30 April '57	*Vema* 12	30° 14.9′ S.	13° 03′ E.	3045	Foraminifera	Cape
15	SBT	2 May '57	*Vema* 12	28° 25.2′ S.	8° 28.5′ E.	4986	White clay	Cape
16	SBT	3 May '57	*Vema* 12	25° 33′ S.	12° 27′ E.	2972	Cream forams	Cape
18	SBT	7 May '57	*Vema* 12	23° 00′ S.	8° 11′ E.	4050	Foraminifera	Cape
20	SBT	9 May '57	*Vema* 12	22° 41′ S.	3° 16′ E.	4981	Red clay	Angola
22	SBT	21 May '57	*Vema* 12	5° 53.5′ S.	9° 51.5′ E.	3015	Greenish lutite	Angola
24	SBT	24 May '57	*Vema* 12	5° 45′ S.	8° 29′ E.	3951	Tree leaves and sand	Angola
46	SBT	6 March '58	*Vema* 14	55° 19′ S.	37° 57′ W.	3725		East Scotia
47	SBT	6 March '58	*Vema* 14	55° 29′ S.	37° 57′ W.	3770		East Scotia
49	SBT	9 March '58	*Vema* 14	56° 43′ S.	27° 41′ W.	2747		Valdivia
51	SBT	28 March '58	*Vema* 14	45° 34′ S.	6° 02′ E.	4618		Cape
52	SBT	30 March '58	*Vema* 14	41° 03′ S.	7° 49′ E.	4961		Cape
53	SBT	4 April '58	*Vema* 14	36° 34′ S.	14° 08′ E.	4983		Cape
54	SBT	6 April '58	*Vema* 14	34° 35′ S.	17° 31′ E.	1861		Cape Slope

Table 2

LIST OF STATIONS AND SPECIES

EAST SCOTIA BASIN
Station 46, 3725 meters, 14 specimens
    Necochea pardella, n.gen., n. sp. (1)
    Rhachotropis anoculata, n. sp. (1)
    Photis coecus, n. sp. (4)
    (lysianassid, tironid, tironid, tironid, 4 others)
Station 47, 3770 meters, 3 specimens
    Figorella tanidea, n. gen., n. sp. (1)
    (phoxocephalid, lysianassid)

VALDIVIA BASIN, slope of South Sandwich Trench
Station 49, 2747 meters, 12 specimens
    Uristes typhlops mediator, n. ssp. (1)
    Harpinia wandichia, n. sp. (4)
    Urothoe vemae, n. sp. (1)
    (tironid, 2 others, 3 similar rear ends)

ARGENTINE BASIN
Station 12, 5041 meters, 5 specimens
    Clepidecrella cabinda, n. sp. (1)
    (*Vibilia* unknown, *Lepechinella*, acanthonotozomatid)

CAPE BASIN
Station 51, 4618 meters, 9 specimens
    (lysianassid, *Rhachotropis* [2 fronts, and one], lysianassid,
    lysianassid, unknown, hyperiid, hyperiid)
Station 52, 4961 meters, 5 specimens
    Chironesimus adversicola (K. H. Barnard) (1)
    Harpinia laevis capensis, n. ssp. (1)
    Leptophoxoides molaris, n. gen., n. sp. (1)
    (tironid, *Rhachotropis*)
Station 54, 1861 meters, 67 specimens
    Chironesimus rotundatus (K. H. Barnard) (1)
    Tryphosa biloba (Stephensen) (2)
    Tryphosa caecoides, n. sp. (2)
    Lepidepecreum clypodentatum, n. sp. (1)
    Uristes antennibrevis, n. sp. (2)
    Uristes typhlops mediator, n. ssp. (5)
    Phippsiella nipoma J. L. Barnard (1)
    Harpinia excavata Chevreux (3)
    Harpinia cinca, n. sp. (18)
    Carangolia mandibularis J. L. Barnard (1)
    Urothoe rotundifrons, n. sp. (4)
    Ampelisca byblisoides K. H. Barnard (6)
    Jeddo simplisyrrhis, n. gen., n. sp. (2)
    Kindia sorpresa, n. gen., n. sp. (1)
    (lysianassid, lysianassid [3], oedicerotid, *Rhachotropis* [2]
    synopiid?, photid, photid, photid?, unknown, caprellid
    [4], *Vibilia*)
Station 14, 3045 meters, 8 specimens
    Tryphosites coxalis, n. sp. (1)
    Kindia lorida, n. gen., n. sp. (1)
    Syrrhoites torpens, n. sp. (2)
    (lysianassid, andaniexid, *Rhachotropis*)
Station 15, 4986 meters, 3 specimens
    Proboloides aequalis, n. sp. (1)
    Stenopleura atlantica Stebbing (1)
    (*Vibilia*)

Station 16, 2972 meters, 50 specimens
    Lysianella mimica, n. sp. (1)
    Tryphosa biloba (Stephensen) (2)
    Tryphosa triplans, n. sp. (8)
    Phippsiella nipoma J. L. Barnard (1)
    Harpinia excavata Chevreux (3)
    Harpinia cinca J. L. Barnard (2)
    Urothoe rotundifrons, n. sp. (8)
    Carangolia mandibularis, n. gen., n. sp. (1)
    Bruzelia diodon K. H. Barnard (1)
    Syrrhoites torpens, n. sp. (2)
    (oedicerotid, stilipedid?, stegocephalid, tironid,
    Rhachotropis [5 fragments], unknown, 5 other fragments,
    Vibilia [6])
Station 18, 4050 meters, 10 specimens
    Chironesimus rotundatus (K. H. Barnard) (1)
    Cyphocaris challengeri Stebbing (1)
    Lysianella mimica, n. sp. (2)
    Stegocephaloides katalia, n. sp. (1)
    Lepechinella echinata (Chevreux) (1)
    Bruzelia cuspidata, n. sp. (1)
    Pseudotiron golens, n. sp. (1)
    (neohelid, fragment)
Station 53, 4893 meters, 61 specimens
    Chironesimus adversicola (K. H. Barnard) (4)
    Cyphocaris richardi Chevreux (1)
    Tryphosa quadrata, n. sp. (1)
    Andaniexis australis K. H. Barnard (5)
    Harpinia laevis capensis, n. ssp. (2)
    Urothoe vemae, n. sp. (1)
    Pseudotiron golens, n. sp. (1)
    Harpinioidella fissicauda Schellenberg (3)
    Liljeborgia zarica, n. sp. (9)
    Lepechinella pangola, n. sp. (13)
    Atylus aberrantis, n. sp. (1)
    Lembos lobata, n. sp. (1)
    Podoceropsis lapisi, n. sp. (6)
    Bogenfelsia incisa, n. gen.; n. sp. (1)
    Neoxenodice caprellinoides Schellenberg (2)
    (oedicerotid, calliopiid, *Rhachotropis* [2], podocerid,
    6 fragments of 5 species)

ANGOLA BASIN
Station 20, 4981 meters, 1 specimen
    (hyperiid)
Station 23, 3916 meters, 2 specimens
    Elimedon cristatus, n. gen., n. sp. (1)
    (*Harpinia*)
Station 22, 3015 meters, 7 specimens
    Tryphosa kergueleni (Miers) restricted (1)
    Uristes typhlops mediator, n. ssp. (1)
    Harpinia excavata, var. (3)
    Urothoe simplignathia, n. sp. (1)
    Bonnierella angolae, n. sp. (1)
Station 24, 3951 meters, 8 specimens
    Stenopleura atlantica Stebbing (2)
    (*Rhachotropis*, oedicerotid [3], unknown, fragment.)

in Tertiary ambers and rare rock records. Thus, comparative phylogeny, using living species, is the zoologist's only tool.

Not all of the stated objectives have been accomplished, for the present study included only a small number of samples from South Atlantic basins. The high proportion of new species and genera described herein indicates the continuing necessity for further exploration of the abyss. Shallow water faunas surrounding the South Atlantic are still poorly known, so that comparative studies cannot be made with any assurance of completeness.

However, the several objectives and the studies they entail are discussed at length below, and the following results are briefly stated: thirty-eight new species and nine new genera are described and fourteen other species are recorded; the large number of new entities, especially in Cape Basin, not recorded from other abyssal areas by previous expeditions indicates high endemism; the conclusion by Zenkevich and Birstein (1956, p. 54) that abyssal animals are larger than their shallow water relatives cannot be substantiated for benthic amphipods, whereas the inverse relationship is indicated; the study of gut contents reveals several pelagic species as bottom feeders; selective feeding on organic deposits is shown, rather than gross mud ingestion, suggesting considerable efficiency of abyssal feeding; and extensive compilation of factual information on previously known abyssal amphipods is provided.

None of the information in the various tables of this paper includes new species and new records described in the recently published paper on *Galathea* Amphipoda by Barnard (1961).

ACKNOWLEDGMENTS

I am greatly indebted to Dr. C. Lalor Burdick and the Lalor Foundation of Wilmington, Delaware, for a summer fellowship which provided support for this study at the Lamont Geological Observatory. Dr. Robert J. Menzies of L.G.O. provided the original impetus for this research and the facilities of the L.G.O. laboratories, for which I am very grateful. Mr. Thomas G. Dow of L.G.O. inked my pencil drawings. The library research, writing, and plating were done at the Allan Hancock Foundation, and these phases were supported by a grant from the National Science Foundation, which is providing support for continuing studies of *Vema* amphipods from other seas.

The *Vema* collections were supported by grants from the Bureau of Ships and Office of Naval Research of the U.S. Navy and the National Science Foundation.

Dr. Menzies sorted the majority of the samples to classes and orders and participated in the collection of the animals at sea. Additional preliminary sorting was done at various times by Thomas G. Dow and Michael Timker at the Lamont Geological Observatory.

ABYSSAL ADAPTATIONS

Most students of the deep sea search for unique adaptations of animals in these habitats. This search has been fruitless, for Bruun (1957) writes: "It appears impossible to point out any single character of adaptation, which could definitely be referred to the abyssal or hadal life." This is not to say that deep sea animals lack peculiar features, but does mean that each case of adaptation has been found also in animals of other environments, such as caves.

Instead of looking for special peculiarities of abyssal animals, it is time to assess the prominence of certain common features within each group of abyssal animals.

LIGHT

Bruun (1957) states the general rule that true abyssal animals have reduced eyes or are blind. This is the most apparent and easily assessed feature and probably applies to all abyssal benthic amphipods. On the other hand, vertically migrating bathypelagic amphipods often have eyes. Only a single oculiform species of gammaridean amphipod previously known as pelagic was found in the *Vema* South Atlantic collection. A small number of pelagic hyperiid amphipods was also found, and most of them have eyes. What is important here is that all but one of the gammaridean amphipods caught were blind, indicating that the dredge mainly fished abyssal bottoms or abyssal pelagic waters. The sparse hyperiid captures indicate that pelagic fishing was poor, leaving the residue of blind gammarideans as probable occupants of the benthos. This consideration is important, for gut content analyses have been inadequate to prove that all of the new species are benthic. It would be possible to determine habitat on the assumption that benthic or pelagic habits follow generic lines, but some genera are well adapted for both roles. In shallow waters many benthic species are trapped by plankton nets and have been shown to be good swimmers that nevertheless spend most of their lives on the bottom. In abyssal basins we have to determine how far toward the surface these animals swim and whether such swimming altitudes are great enough for passage over one sill into another basin so that epidemism results. Only a few species in the present collections, such as *Tryphosa biloba*, have broad interbasin distributions, but it is impossible to determine whether the animals are mainly abyssal-pelagic or whether they are benthic animals of good swimming altitude and thus widely dispersed. If *T. biloba* has either of these mechanisms, then why not the other Tryphosas herein and elsewhere (57 known species of which about half are blind [abyssal?]) and all other related lysianassid genera? Indeed, the ambivalence of amphipods renders them difficult subjects for endemism studies until more critical collecting techniques have been adopted.

TEMPERATURE

It is well known to amphipod students that a good correlation exists between shallow water temperatures and animal sizes, but this information is not well documented. I have had the privilege of examining subarctic amphipods in the field (Point Barrow, Alaska) and the tropics (Panama and Caribbean) and large collections in the laboratory from arctic seas and tropical islands, and have studied collections in the field and laboratory all through the mid-latitudes of Pacific North America. The facts that tropical amphipods are tiny and arctic amphipods are large are as apparent as is the fact that the same instar of a species is much larger at 42° North than at 33° North (see *Ampithoe pollex* in Barnard, 1954). This poleward size increase holds true for antarctic species also, as determined by a literature analysis (Table 3). One must remember, however, that size increase is a function within family and generic lines. For instance, the families Amphilochidae and Stenothoidae are pygmies among amphipods, but they also increase slightly in size poleward, although the final size in arctic waters is still small for amphipods.

The direction of this rule is expressed in Table 3, but the weakness of this kind of information as so assembled must be pointed out. Many maximum sizes are unknown, and some species remain undiscovered. Some faunas are better known for smaller species than others; despite the limitations, there is a marked trend to larger organisms in polar regions.

Wolff (1956a) shows that the genus *Apseudes* increases in average size with decrease in temperature, whether in high latitudes or great depths. He shows this in isopods as well (Wolff, 1956). This trend exists in many other groups.

The trend of size increase is not well shown in benthic deep sea amphipods, witness Table 3. There are not many unconfuted benthic abyssal amphipods, so the data are scanty. In the column listing the known benthic and presumed benthic amphipods

Table 3

MAXIMUM SIZE OF KNOWN AMPHIPODS IN SEVERAL FAUNAS

Based on about 80 References

The maximum known size of each species of amphipod in each fauna has been taken; these have been averaged together, and medians have been struck for the incorporated data of the table. The data have been split also into families composed of small-sized amphipods and families of large-sized amphipods, since there is some regional discrepancy in the study effort applied to the smaller animals.

Region	Total Species			Species of Small-sized Families			Species of Large-sized Families		
	Number of Species	Length (mm.) Average	Length (mm.) Median	Number of Species	Length (mm.) Average	Length (mm.) Median	Number of Species	Length (mm.) Average	Length (mm.) Median
Arctic	95	17	12	20	5	4	75	21	15
Norway	304	8	7	50	5	5	254	9	8
Mediterranean	240	6	6	32	4	4	208	7	6
Tropical Africa	126	6	5	14	4	3	112	6	5
Tropical Indo-Pacific	135	5	5	17	3	3	118	5	5
South Africa	102	9	8	9	6	3	93	9	8
Antarctic	314	13	12	37	5	4	277	14	13
Abyssal benthic (from the literature)[a]	26	9	6	—	—	—	—	—	—
Abyssal true and presumed benthic from the Vema[b]	34	4.5	4	—	—	—	—	—	—
All abyssal benthic[c]	86	8	6	10	6	5	76	8	6
Bathypelagic	76	16	12						

[a] Only firmly known benthic species are included.
[b] Both firmly and presumed benthic species are included.
[c] All benthic abyssal species, firm and presumed are included.

collected by the *Vema* the results are even more startling, the average size of the species being less than that of a tropical fauna. This might indicate that previous deep sea expeditions have caught only the larger species or that small species have not been analyzed by the specialists. Whatever the cause, it is logical to believe that the average deep sea amphipod is a small organism since food supplies in the abyssal are theoretically so much smaller than on shallow bottoms.

Bathypelagic amphipods, on the other hand, are as large as arctic and antarctic species, but I believe that many bathypelagic species have yet to be discovered, especially the smaller ones. Many bathypelagic trawls are coarse-meshed and allow organisms smaller than 5 mm. to escape. However, it is logical to assume that bathypelagic amphipods flourish in relatively rich feeding grounds, for they have the ability to rise near the surface.

As collecting techniques become more critical it will be interesting to follow these trends. It must not be forgotten, however, that the largest known gammaridean amphipods are bathypelagic or, at best, benthic facultatives (these are *Alicella scotiae* Chevreux, 140 mm. and *Eurythenes gryllus* [Lichtenstein], 90 mm.).

SUBSTRATUM

The deep sea is underlain by oozes usually less compacted than sediments in shallow waters. Abyssal benthic organisms have more difficulty with the problem of sinking into these oozes. Some deep sea isopods and crabs are provided with excessively long legs to overcome this difficulty, and Pirlot (1936) has suggested that this same adaptation is the reason for long legs in a number of amphipod genera. Some of these are *Lepechinella*, *Rhachotropis*, and *Cleonardo*, but it is difficult to apply such reasoning to all long-legged amphipods, for each of the above genera has been collected in bathypelagic tow nets, so they are not strictly benthic. In the summary of abyssal species (Tables 8–12) I have had to classify some of the above genera as bathypelagic, despite Pirlot's assertion.

FOOD OF ABYSSAL AMPHIPODS

Many, but not all, benthic amphipods in shallow water eat organic materials which settle on the sea floor (Enequist, 1949). Some of these animals ingest mud indiscriminately, while others feed selectively on organic detritus having little admixture of mineral particles. Some benthic amphipods are filter feeders, others are scavengers on debris, yet no carnivorous amphipods are known on soft bottoms, although carnivorous pelagic amphipods probably are common.

The determination that an amphipod is mainly benthic rather than pelagic is of importance in deciding whether the animal has restricted or unrestricted means of dispersal. Because dredge hauls capture both benthic and bathypelagic amphipods the habitats of the animals cannot be determined by the collecting device. At the outset of this study it was believed that some evidence on the habitat might come from examination of gut contents in those animals which are not well-known pelagic members. It would be possible to separate true benthic species by determining in dredge hauls the residual species which were absent in plankton tows taken at the same time, but this kind of information has not been systematically collected by abyssal expeditions.

Several preliminary considerations for the interpretation of gut contents in deep sea animals have to be taken into account before the study: (1) what potential foods are available to abyssal benthic animals; (2) the mud-ingesting habit of some shallow species; and (3) the gut contents of true pelagic species. These points are discussed below.

KINDS OF FOOD

Except for cases of carnivorous feeding, it is generally assumed that most foods of the deep sea are of two kinds: (1) very finely particulate materials which settle from the upper layers and which already have been attacked by plankton, nekton, and bacteria before reaching bottom, resulting in a particulate detritus; and (2) benthic bacteria forming rich slimes. Coarse detritus and chunks would come largely from the decaying bodies of animals already existing abyssally, or from materials carried by turbidity currents onto basin floors. Because filter-feeding animals are usually thought to require dense concentrations of suspended matter it might be thought that filter feeders are absent from the deep sea. This is not the case, suggesting that filter feeders are able to adjust to low concentrations of suspended matter, just as

deposit feeders adjust to low concentrations of settled matter.

MUD INGESTING

Because many shallow water amphipods ingest mud indiscriminately or scrape detritus from mud surfaces, it was believed that the presence of refractory mineral particles in gut contents might suggest that the animal was caught feeding at the bottom, and that the absence of mineral particles might indicate that it was bathypelagic. The results of my studies utilizing this approach have not been satisfactory.

In the first place, mineral particles have been sparse in gut contents, even in animals adapted for burrowing and known to be benthic (e.g., haustoriids). This suggests a marked efficiency in locating and utilizing pure detrital or bacterial deposits with the ingestion of mineral sediments accidentally. So far only one case of gross mud ingestion (*Eurythenes gryllus*) has been discovered, suggesting that the particulate organic matter is too widely dispersed for animals to survive by the indiscriminate eating of clay or other sediments.

Perhaps it is not too early to propose that much of the organic material in the guts of these amphipods is not detritus but coagulated or agglutinated bacterial slimes (resulting from preservation), and that most of the benthic amphipods forage on bacteria with such facility that sediment particles are rarely ingested (Plate 1). (See Zobell, 1956.)

FEEDING OF PLANKTERS

Probably many truly pelagic amphipods, either Gammaridea or Hyperiidea, are carnivorous. Some of these carnivores also may be facultative omnivores, eating debris or phytoplankton in the upper water layers, but it is believed that the main habit is a carnivorous one. Unfortunately, studies on gut contents of pelagic amphipods have not been made or reported upon, so that this is speculation. Some of the Gammaridea and many of the Hyperiidea are inquilinous, living as commensals or semiparasites in other animals, mainly tunicates and medusae. Some of these burrow into the jelly-like bodies of their hosts and have mouth parts adapted for penetration and sucking.

One difficulty in trying to establish principles of abyssal feeding is caused by my discovery in *Galathea* collections now being studied that the gut of one specimen of *Eurythenes gryllus* (bathypelagic) was full of silt, indicating that some pelagic amphipods feed on

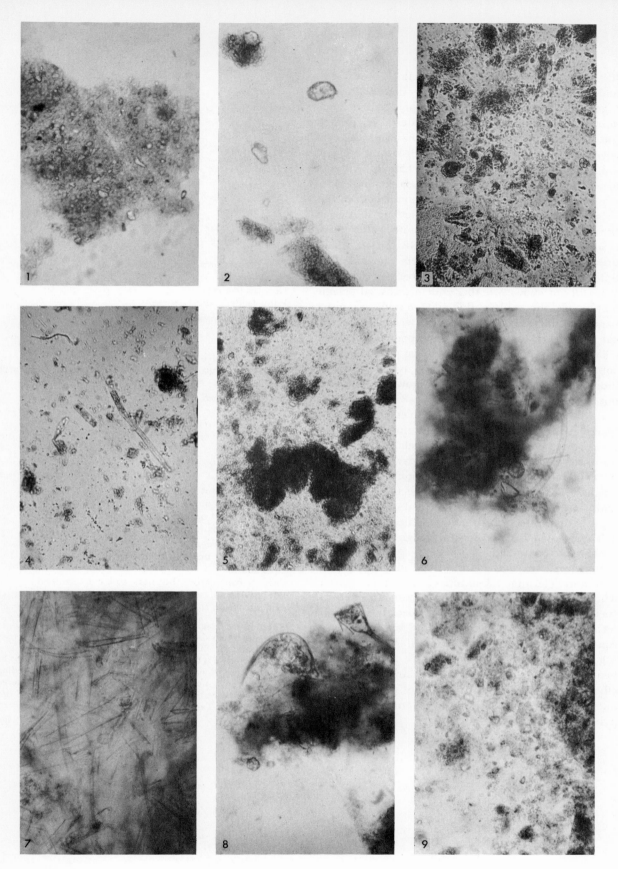

Photographic Plate 1. Gut contents of abyssal amphipods—photomicrographs of stomach-content smears of representative analyses. 1: *Pseudotiron golens*, mineral and organic matter; 2: *Carcangolia mandibularis*, mineral and organic matter; 3: *Ampelisca byblisoides*, few forams, minerals, largely organic matter—ampeliscids are semi-filter feeders; 4: *Elimedon cristatus*, plant debris and minerals; 5: *Chironesimus adversicola*, few minerals, largely organic matter; 6: *Harpinia laevis capensis*, minerals, discoaster, copepod setae; 7: *Cyphocaris richardi*, pelagic, containing copepod setae; 8: *Harpinia laevis capensis*, benthic, remains of copepod; 9: *Lepechinella pangola*, numerous mineral particles and organic matter.

the bottom. This is a small reversal of Zenkevich's and Birstein's (1956) idea of the descendance of organic matter to the bottom through bathypelagic animals, for in this case bottom material is elevated into the pelagic. *Eurythenes gryllus* has vestigial eyes covering the head, like other well-known pelagic animals, and has an oily body. The difficulty of identifying any presumed abyssal pelagic amphipods which lack eyes but which may feed on the bottom and so contain sediments or finely particulate matter in the stomach has not been solved. Another alternative is suggested: most pelagic amphipods contain quantities of oil which aid them in their buoyancy, an indication that they may eat diatoms or oily copepods. It is still not known whether endemic abyssal pelagic amphipods also contain this oil, for such organisms would not migrate into upper layers where they would eat diatoms. None of these amphipods in the *Vema* collections, except for the well-known pelagic genera, contained visible oil globules, but again this is no indication that some species of unknown habitat may not be abyssally pelagic.

Additional evidence on the problem of demersal species is the presence of occasional mineral particles (one or two per stomach) in known pelagic amphipods, not as strong a case as in *E. gryllus* above. These might be explained as accidental ingestion of suspended particles or those carried down by feces of other animals, but bottom feeding is not ruled out.

All of these interesting phases have been summarized in Table 4, which offers food for thought on the several problems to be studied.

It is apparent that more critical methods are required to determine the nature of the organic matter, whether in the form of bacteria or colloidal detritus (peloglea). This will involve special shipboard techniques in the preservation and analysis of gut contents in freshly collected animals. What has been suggested, however, is important: that deep sea benthic amphipods show a remarkable feeding efficiency by an apparent absence of the indiscriminate and wasteful feeding found in amphipods occupying food-rich shallow bottoms.

Table 4

MORPHOLOGICAL AND FEEDING CONDITIONS IN AMPHIPODS

Littoral benthic amphipods
  Body not oily
  Eyes present 95 percent
  Scavengers
  Detritus feeders
  Filter feeders
  Mud eaters

Bathyal benthic amphipods
  Body not oily
  Eyes present or absent
  Scavengers
  Detritus feeders
  Filter feeders (mud eaters?)

Abyssobenthic amphipods
  Body not oily
  Eyes absent
  Particulate detritus feeders
  (Filter feeder groups are present, but may actually seek out detritus?)

Epipelagic amphipods
  Oily body[a]
  Eyes present, well developed
  Usually carnivorous, but may feed on diatoms (none known)

Mesopelagic amphipods[b] *with great vertical migration*
  Oily body
  Eyes distinct but poorly developed
  Often carnivorous
  Some also feed on bottom
  In upper layers may also feed on diatoms

Abyssopelagic amphipods
  Body may not be oily (unknown)
  Eyes absent
  Possibly carnivorous, but none so far determined
  Potential ones, so far, all eat finely particulate matter evidently from the bottom

[a] The oil of pelagic amphipods may be secondary in origin from eating copepods which have foraged on diatoms, or it may be specifically manufactured.
[b] Included here is the potential class of feeders which might be called demersal or epibenthic, which combine benthic feeding with some pelagic morphology and swimming power to undergo wide or narrow vertical migration. Potential members of this group are seen in Tables 9 and 10.

ENDEMISM IN THE DEEP SEA

Because the deep sea offers so little variability in environment, ecologists have commonly asserted that abyssal faunas are cosmopolitan or pandemic. This point of view is aptly summarized by Bruun (1957, p. 664). Very little well-documented evidence to support this assertion has appeared, most of the positive assertions having to do with eurybathic species. In addition, the number of animals recovered from great depths is painfully inadequate, and these specimens come from stations widely scattered through the many ocean basins. Even the cumulative total of dredgings from the several expeditions is inadequate. However, an acceleration in this cumulative total from recent deep sea expeditions will begin to shed light on the problem, at least as far as amphipods are concerned. Vinogradova (1959), analyzing past records of deep sea bottom animals in several phylogenetic groups (not amphipods, however), has shown at least a one-ocean endemism of about 84 percent and pointed out that eurybathic species have wider horizontal distributions than abyssal stenobathic species. A very interesting figure in her paper (no. 2) shows the effect of macro-relief (undersea ridges) in separating endemic faunas below 2000 meters depth, the barrier being the Mid-Atlantic ridge between the North American and North African basins. This is strong evidence against pandemism as a principle.

It has been pointed out by Ekman (1953) that abyssal animals with pelagic larvae would have broader abyssal distributions than those without, although Bruun (1957) contests this by pointing out Fage's (1951) work on a pycnogonid (non-larval) proved to exist in both the North Atlantic and the South Pacific, thus demonstrating a cosmopolitan character in non-larval animals. (Perhaps this is an eurybathic species.)

Both Wolff (1956) and Zenkevich et al. (1954) have shown that hadal faunas are highly endemic, although some cosmopolitan eurybathic species occupy hadal depths. One must consider several factors in such problems of speciation. If Birstein and Wolff prove to be correct in believing that each hadal fauna (fauna of trenches or deeps below 6000 meters) is endemic as far as its stenobathic species are concerned and Vinogradova's brief résumé of two abyssal basins (2000 to 6000 meters) with high percentages of endemism proves to apply to other basins, then one of the principal conclusions must be that undersea macro-relief acts as isolative barriers between the faunas. Wolff has shown in several instances that the hadal species in each trench have their closest relatives in the shallower nearby basins. There is reason to believe that if isolation occurs in trenches it should also occur in the abyssal basins. Interpretations must be guarded from the possibility that some trenches are younger than others and that insufficient time has passed for endemic faunas to have evolved. The same reasoning might apply to basins, since not all macro-relief is of the same age. The lack of endemism in some basins and trenches may indicate youthful origins of the isolative barriers. For this reason, it is vitally important that critical systematic work be one goal for deep sea studies.

Both isopods and amphipods are important and diversified components of deep sea faunas. Both groups incubate their eggs in brood pouches, so that no larvae are distributed through the lower water masses. Obligatorily benthic members of these groups swim through the lower water masses, but probably not far. Potentially, such Crustacea are among the more restricted of deep sea animals in their dispersal mechanisms and offer possibilities as endemic abyssal-basin members.

It will require a great number of bottom samples in all abyssal areas to outline the distributional perimeters of all species. However, a shortcut through the difficulty would be provided if the complete faunas of a small number of abyssal basins could be documented and the percentage of endemism, if any, determined. The material presented in this paper is a step toward this goal, utilizing materials from the East Scotia, Angola, Valdivia, Cape, and Argentine basins of the South Atlantic Ocean.

RESULTS OF THE *VEMA* STUDY CONCERNING ENDEMISM

The benthic trawl samples are a mixture of species, some of definite benthic habitat (40 percent of the specimens), some of known pelagic habitat (20 percent), and the remainder of unknown habitat (40 percent), some of which are probably inquilinous, such as *Figorella tanidea*, n. gen. In both earlier and later sections there are discussions of the various analytical problems concerning the ways in which the habitats of amphipods are determined. The present discussion concerns endemism.

The several South Atlantic basins and their known benthic species are summarized in Table 5. In Table 6 the basins and their probable benthic species are listed.

Table 5

KNOWN BENTHIC AMPHIPODS COLLECTED BY THE *VEMA*

CAPE BASIN SLOPE
(1861 meters)
Harpinia excavata[a]
Harpinia cinca
Carangolia mandibularis
Urothoe rotundifrons
Ampelisca byblisoides

EAST SCOTIA BASIN
Photis coecus

VALDIVIA BASIN
Harpinia wandichia
Urothoe vemae[a]

ANGOLA BASIN
Harpinia excavata, var.[a]
Urothoe simplignathia
Bonnierella angolae

CAPE BASIN
Harpinia laevis capensis
Harpinia excavata[a]
Harpinia cinca
Urothoe rotundifrons
Leptophoxoides molaris
Carangolia mandibularis
Urothoe vemae[a]
Liljeborgia zarica
Lembos lobata
Podoceropsis lapisi
Bogenfelsia incisa
Neoxenodiceca prellinoides

[a] Interbasin species.

Within a single basin, separate samples of the bottom may differ as greatly in their species as separate samples from two basins, as may be seen in Table 2 (the station list). Within Cape Basin, however, several of the samples contain a repetition of species. It is apparent that not all of the fauna has been collected, since the diversity is greater than the number of samples taken, indicating the need for additional collecting until uniformity appears.

Table 6

POSSIBLE BENTHIC AMPHIPODS COLLECTED BY THE *VEMA*

CAPE BASIN SLOPE
(1861 meters)
Chironesimus rotundatus
Tryphosa quadrata
Uristes antennibrevis
Lepidepecreum clypodentatum
Tryphosa caecoides
Uristes typhlops mediator[a]
Jeddo simplisyrrhis[b]
Kindia sorpresa[b]

ARGENTINE BASIN
Clepidecrella cabinda[b]

EAST SCOTIA BASIN
Necochea pardella

VALDIVIA BASIN
Uristes typhlops mediator[a]

ANGOLA BASIN
Uristes typhlops mediator[a]
Elimedon cristatus

CAPE BASIN
Chironesimus adversicola
Chironesimus rotundatus
Tryphosites coxalis
Syrrhoites torpens[b]
Kindia lorida[b]
Bruzelia diodon[b]
Tryphosa triplans
Lysianella mimica
Pseudotiron golens
Bruzelia cuspidata[b]
Tryphosa biloba
Atylus aberrantis[b]

[a] Interbasin species.
[b] Most certainly benthic species.

What appears to be significant, however, is the scarcity of interbasin species, suggesting high endemism. A particular note of importance in the *Vema* collection concerns the very small average size of the animals. This indicates the care with which the samples were preserved and sorted, but may also indicate that the small oblong trawl in use captures smaller organisms efficiently. The absence of large species probably indicates not that the South Atlantic is peculiar in lacking such, but simply that the trawl fishes a small area of bottom while large trawls fished for long distances capture only rarer large animals—which is what most deep sea expeditions have captured.

The several cases of interbasin pandemism indicated in Tables 5 and 6 appear to concern eurybathic and possibly pelagic species. In some cases these species may have their optimum foci on the slopes above basins and descend into the basin floors from above. This has been shown to occur in the small, shallow basins (1000 to 2500 meters) off the coast of California by Hartman and Barnard (1958). In these basins many slope species and some from the coastal shelf occupy the basin floors in diminished numbers and, in some cases, as vegetative and otherwise aberrant individuals.

The evidence from the *Vema* samples indicates that an endemic fauna tends to develop in each basin of the South Atlantic. Each basin has a separate *Urothoe*. Each has an *Harpinia*, although the interbasin differences of this genus are not as sharp as those of *Urothoe*.

The data about species of presumed benthic habitat are scanty (Table 6), but Cape Basin has a very diversified fauna of new genera and species not heretofore reported, which suggests a considerable degree of endemism.

Table 7A

PELAGIC AND BATHYPELAGIC AMPHIPODS
COLLECTED BY THE *VEMA*

Andaniexis australis[a]
Cyphocaris challengeri
Cyphocaris richardi
Harpinioidella fissicauda
Lepechinella echinata[a]
Lepechinella pangola[a]
Phippsiella nipoma
Stegocephalodies katalia
Stenopleura atlantica

[a] Occasional mineral gut contents.

Table 7B

OTHER POSSIBLE BATHYPELAGIC AMPHIPODS
COLLECTED BY THE *VEMA*, SOME OF WHICH
FEED ON THE BOTTOM
(Some Duplication from Table 6)

Species	Evidence Suggesting Bathypelagic Habits
Chironesimus adversicola[a]	Poorly developed eyes
Chironesimus rotundatus	Distribution pattern of related species
Lysianella mimica	Morphological adaptations similar to other bathypelagic species
Tryphosa biloba	Morphological adaptations similar to other bathypelagic species; widespread interbasin distribution
Tryphosa kerguelini restricted	Possibly widespread interbasin distribution
Tryphosa quadrata	Morphological adaptations similar to other bathypelagic species
Tryphosa triplans	Morphological adaptations similar to other bathypelagic species
Uristes typhlops mediator	Distribution pattern of related species

[a] Evidence of benthic feeding.

SUMMARY OF WORLD ABYSSAL AMPHIPODS

Tables (8–12) are a survey of the literature on abyssal records of amphipods (2000 meters or more). This material is brought together for the first time, although Schellenberg (1955) assembled the species known from depths greater than 3000 meters. Very little precision is possible in these tables, for many of the species have been caught in an apparatus which also fished pelagic waters shallower than 2000 meters as the samples were recovered from greater depths. The known benthic species are well enough established as to depth, but the bulk of abyssally recorded amphipod species is pelagic or belongs to families where the ecology is so poorly known and where the morphology gives so few clues that I hesitate to assign them definitely either to a pelagic or to a benthic existence.

In general, the Ampeliscidae, Phoxocephalidae (except *Joubinella*), Haustoriidae, Liljeborgiidae, Aoridae, Photidae, Corophiidae, and Podoceridae are obligatorily benthic, although male Phoxocephalidae assume a pelagic phase, at least in shallow water. These surely benthic species are listed in Table 8. The well-known bathypelagic species, recovered only in tow nets which did not fish the benthos, are listed in Table 10. Many of these may actually live shallower than 2000 meters in depth but were caught in tows hauled from depths greater than 2000 meters to the surface.[1] Some of the records are obviously exaggerated, as noted in the table, and others where closing nets restricted the fishing are cited within the limits of the open phase. Tables 9, 11, and 12 list possible benthic, possible bathypelagic, and possible inquilinous species. In Table 9 it is probable that the Tironidae are truly benthic, but the numerous Lysianassidae pose the greater problem, for the family has both bottom and pelagic representatives. Morphology holds few clues to this problem. I suspect, however, that most of those listed in Table 8 actually are benthic, for they have not been caught in strictly pelagic tows, although wide-ranging distribution records in some cases infer that bathypelagic habits occur.

It is probable that many amphipods actually are demersal: feeding on the bottom, moving from place to place, occasionally swimming up into the upper pelagic. These species are difficult to detect until more critical sampling has been effected.

[1] Depth is not invariably an abyssal criterion, as temperature too plays a significant role. Thus, polar depths much shallower than 2000 meters where the temperature is 4° C. or less are essentially abyssal.

Table 8

BENTHIC ABYSSAL AMPHIPODS OF THE WORLD, BASED ON THE LITERATURE

Species	Maximum Depth (meters)	Minimum Depth (meters)	Basin or Region
Ampelisca abyssicola	3975	714	N. American
Ampelisca byblisoides	1861	1281	Cape
Ampelisca gibba	3200	60	W. European
Bathyceradocus stephenseni	7290	1165	Indo-Pacific
Bogenfelsia incisa, n. sp.	4893	—	Cape
Bonnierella angolae, n. sp.	3015	—	Angola
Byblis serrata	1910	659	N. Atlantic
Camacho bathyplous	2011	86	S. Pacific-Atlantic
Carangolia mandibularis, n. sp.	2972	1861	Cape
Dulichia abyssi	3229	1096	Arctic-Atlantic
Dulichia nordlandica	2258	200	Arctic-Atlantic
Eurystheus thomsoni[a]	2000(?)	100	S. Pacific
Haploops abyssorum	1900	—	Azores
Haploops setosa	2702	50	Arctic-Atlantic
Haploops similis	2702	105	Arctic-Atlantic
Haploops vallifera	1960	913	N. Atlantic
Harpinia abyssi	2702	552	N. Atlantic
Harpinia amundseni	2800	40	Arctic
Harpinia brevirostris	1919	1495	W. European
Harpinia cinca, n. sp.	2972	1861	Cape
Harpinia curtipes	3521	—	Labrador
Harpinia excavata and var.	5110	425	E. Atlantic
Harpinia laevis capensis, n. ssp.	4961	4893	Cape
Harpinia spaercki Dahl, 1959	7270	6580	Banda
Harpinia pacifica	2300	1800	N. Pacific
Harpinia wandichia, n. sp.	2747	—	Valdivia
Ischyrocerus tenuicornis	2090	—	Norwegian
Ischyrocerus tuberculatus (*I. hoeki*)	2071	125	Norwegian, S. Pacific
Lembos lobata, n. sp.	4893	—	Cape
Leptophoxoides molaris, n. sp.	4961	—	Cape
Leptophoxus falcatus	2258	60	Arctic-N. Atlantic
Liljeborgia caeca Birstein and Vinogradova, 1960	5207–6156	—	N. Pacific
Liljeborgia fissicornis	2500	10	Arctic-Atlantic
Liljeborgia zarica, n. sp.	4893	—	Cape

Table 8 (continued)

Species	Maximum Depth (meters)	Minimum Depth (meters)	Basin or Region
Melita abyssorum	2258	—	SW Greenland
Melita pallida	2510	800	Greenland
Melita richardi	2258	1287	N. Atlantic
Mesopleustes abyssorum	3013	694	Atlantic-Indonesia
Metaceradocoides vitjazi Birstein and Vinogradova, 1960	7230–7210	—	N. Pacific
Metaphoxus typicus	1910	950	W. European
Neohela monstrosa	2288	70	Arctic-Atlantic
Neoxenodice caprellinoides	4893	3397	Cape-Antarctic
Oediceroides zanzabaricus	2900	—	Zanzibar
Onesimoides carinatus	2560	—	Coral Sea
Onesimoides cavimanus	6650	1158	Banda
Onesimoides chelatus	2053	1264	Indo-Pacific
Paradryope orguion	4200	—	N. Pacific
Paronesimoides lignivorus	2053	—	Celebes Sea
Photis coecus, n. sp.	3725	—	E. Scotia
Podoceropsis lapisi, n. sp.	4893	—	Cape
Unciola laticornis	2448	120	Arctic-Atlantic
Unciola petalocera	2000	600	Arctic
Urothoe elegans	3100	5	Arctic-Atlantic
Urothoe rotundifrons, n. sp.	2972	1861	Cape
Urothoe simplignathia, n. sp.	3015	—	Angola
Urothoe vemae, n. sp.	4893	2747	Valdivia-Cape
Westwoodilla abyssalis	2900	—	Bering
Bruzelia cuspidata, n. sp.	4050	—	Cape
Bruzelia dentata	1996	1090	Norwegian
Bruzelia diodon	2972	1189	Cape
Bruzeliopsis alberti	4380	—	W. European
Chironesimus adversicola	4961	564	Cape
Chironesimus rotundatus	4050	1188	Cape
Cleippides bicuspis	2150	1318	Iceland
Cleippides quadricuspis	2000	28	Arctic
Clepidecrella cabinda, n. sp.	5041	—	Argentine
Elimedon cristatus, n. sp.	3916	—	Angola
Halirages gorbunovi	2500	—	Arctic
Halirages quadridentatus	2000	547	Arctic
Haliragoides abyssi	2450	1140	Arctic
Hippomedon bidentatus	2500	133	Mediterranean-Atlantic
Hippomedon holbolli	2222	15	Arctic-Atlantic
Hippomedon longimanus	2215	78	Atlantic
Hippomedon serratipes	2150	1900	N. Atlantic
Jeddo simplisyrrhis, n. sp.	1861	—	Cape
Kindia lorida, n. sp.	3045	—	Cape
Kindia sorpresa, n. sp.	1861	—	Cape
Lepechinella echinata	4380	4050	Atlantic
Lepechinella pangola,[a] n. sp.	4893	—	Cape
Lepechinella ultraabyssalis Birstein and Vinogradova, 1960	6571–6475	—	N. Pacific
Lepechinella wolffi Dahl, 1959	6770–6660	—	Kermadec
Lepidepecreum clypodentatum, n. sp.	1861	—	Cape
Lysianella mimica, n. sp.	4050	2972	Cape
Necochea pardella, n. sp.	3725	—	E. Scotia
Onisimus turgidus	3310	408	Arctic
Orchomene oxystoma	2258	—	SW Greenland
Orchomenella abyssalis	2258	—	SW Greenland
Orchomenella abyssorum sensu Dahl, 1959	8300	8210	Kermadec
Orchomenella chevreuxi	4360	3970	Cape Verde
Orchomenella dilatata	2500	2276	Mediterranean
Pardaliscella boecki	2258	188	Arctic-Atlantic
Pardaliscoides longicaudatus Dahl, 1959	10000	5180	Kermadec-Philippine
Princaxelia abyssalis Dahl, 1959	8300	6620	Kermadec
Pseudonesimus abyssi	4380	—	W. European
Pseudotiron golens, n. sp.	4893	4050	Cape
Schisturella galatheae Dahl, 1959	7000	6960	Kermadec
Sympleustes megacheir	2448	1022	Arctic-Atlantic
Syrrhoites septentrionalis	2702	885	Arctic
Syrrhoites serratus	2000	300	Arctic-Atlantic
Syrrhoites torpens, n. sp.	3045	2972	Cape
Tmetonyx cicada	3230	0	Arctic-Atlantic
Tmetonyx orchomenoides	3230	80	Arctic
Tryphosa abyssalis	2465	—	Norwegian
Tryphosa barentsi	2460	—	Arctic

References to all species may be found in Barnard's (1958) *Index to the Gammaridean Amphipoda* except where authors and dates of later published species are specifically included or where new species are so denoted.

[a] Has eyes.

Table 9

PROBABLE BENTHIC ABYSSAL AMPHIPODS OF THE WORLD, BASED ON THE LITERATURE

Species	Maximum Depth (meters)	Minimum Depth (meters)	Basin or Region
Amathillopsis atlantica	1919	1600	N. Atlantic
Amathillopsis australis	2560	1264	Indonesia
Amathillopsis pacifica	2850	—	Okhotsk
Amathillopsis spinigera	1996	66	Arctic
Andaniotes corpulentus	2012	0	Antiboreal
Anonyx ampulloides	1919	—	N. Pacific
Arrhis phyllonyx	2258	10	Arctic-Atlantic
Astyroides carinatus Birstein and Vinogradova, 1960	7230–7210	—	N. Pacific
Atylus aberrantis, n. sp.	4893	—	Cape
Bathypanoploea australis	2790	2675	Antarctic
Bathyschraderia magnifica Dahl, 1959	7000–6960	—	Kermadec

Species	Maximum Depth (meters)	Minimum Depth (meters)	Basin or Region
Tryphosa biloba	2972	1861	Arctic-Atlantic
Tryphosa bruuni Dahl, 1959	6770	6660	Kermadec
Tryphosa caecoides, n. sp.	1861	—	Cape
Tryphosa kergueleni	3015	10	Antiboreal
Tryphosa quadrata, n. sp.	4893	—	Cape
Tryphosa triplans, n. sp.	2972	—	Cape
Tryphosites coxalis, n. sp.	3045	—	Cape
Uristes antennibrevis, n. sp.	1861	—	Cape
Uristes typhlops mediator, n. sp.	3015	1861	S. Atlantic
Valettia coheres	3612	—	Antarctic
Valettiopsis macrodactyla	2600	1692	N. Atlantic

References to all species may be found in Barnard's (1958) *Index to the Gammaridean Amphipoda* except where authors and dates of later published species are specifically included or where new species are so denoted.

[a] Bottom feeder.

Table 10

ABYSSAL PELAGIC AMPHIPODS OF THE WORLD, BASED ON THE LITERATURE

Species	Maximum Depth (meters)	Minimum Depth (meters)	Area or Basin
Andaniexis abyssi	2700	378	Atlantic
Andaniexis australis[a]	4893	1000	Cape
Andaniexis spinescens	3646	—	Bengal
Andaniexis stylifer Birstein and Vinogradov, 1960	8500–0[b]	—	Pacific
Andaniexis subabyssi	9000–6400	—	Kurile-Kamchatka
Astyra bogorovi	4000–3000	2000	Kurile-Kamchatka
Astyra zenkevichi	8000[b]	2000	Kurile-Kamchatka
Bathycallisoma pacifica Dahl, 1959	7000–6960	—	Kermadec
Bathystegocephalus globosus	2500	408	Cosmopolitan
Chevreuxiella metopoides[c]	4000	—	W. European
Cleonardo appendiculatus	3354	1880	Norwegian
Cleonardo biscayensis	4330	—	W. European
Cleonardo longipes	3244	1500	S. Pacific-Atlantic
Cleonardo longirostris	9120–0[b]	1500	Atlantic-Pacific
Cleonardo macrocephala	8050–4190	1500	Kurile-Kamchatka
Cleonardo microdactylus	3500	1096	N. Atlantic
Cleonardo neuvillei	5285	—	Canaries
Cleonardo spinicornis	3975	3000	Azores
Crybelocephalus crassipes Birstein and Vinogradov, 1960	6300[b]	—	Pacific
Crybelocephalus megalurus	7250[b]	1096	Pacific-Atlantic
Cyclocaris guilelmi	8000[b]	130	Arctic

Species	Maximum Depth (meters)	Minimum Depth (meters)	Area or Basin
Cyphocaris anonyx	6580[b]	475	Cosmopolitan
Cyphocaris bouvieri	4990–4440	887	Pacific-Atlantic
Cyphocaris challengeri	6000[b]	25	Cosmopolitan
Cyphocaris faurei	2800	175	Cosmopolitan
Cyphocaris polaris	4200	2460	Arctic
Cyphocaris richardi	7800–4200	76	Cosmopolitan
Epimeria pelagica Birstein and Vinogradov, 1958	8000–0[b]	—	Kurile-Kamchatka
Euandania gigantea	3430	1281	Cosmopolitan
Eurythenes gryllus[a]	6500	180	Cosmopolitan
Eurythenes obesus	3410	500	Cosmopolitan
Eusirella elegans	3000	1000	Atlantic
Eusirella longisetosa Birstein and Vinogradov, 1960	8500–0[b]	—	Pacific
Eusirella multicalceola	8000[b]	1000	N. Pacific
Eusirogenes homocarpus	2000	—	Kurile-Kamchatka
Eusiropsis riisei	6050[b]	0	Cosmopolitan
Eusirus bathybius	7900–7625	—	Atlantic-Pacific
Eusirus fragilis Birstein and Vinogradov, 1960	9120–0[b]	—	Pacific
Eusirus perdentatus	2000	70	Antarctic
Halice abyssi	2465	188	Atlantic-Arctic
Halice aculeata	8050–4190	1985–1000	Atlantic-Pacific
Halice quarta	9000–6400	—	Pacific
Halice rotundata Birstein and Vinogradov, 1960	6080–4050	—	Pacific
Halice subquarta Birstein and Vinogradov, 1960	10500–0[b]	—	Pacific
Harpinioidella fissicauda	4893	385	Atlantic-Antarctic
Hirondellea antarctica	5500[b]	366	Pacific-Antarctic
Hirondellea brevicaudata	5940	—	Azores
Hirondellea dubia Dahl, 1959	7960–6170	—	Kermadec
Hirondellea gigas	9000–6400	—	Pacific
Hyperiopsis anomala Birstein and Vinogradov, 1960	6900–0[b]	—	Tonga
Hyperiopsis laticarpa	9000–6400	—	Kurile-Kamchatka
Hyperiopsis tridentata	3000	500–300	Atlantic-Pacific
Hyperiopsis vitjazi Birstein and Vinogradov, 1958	6050–0[b]	—	Pacific
Hyperiopsis voringi	2480	393	Pacific-Atlantic
Ichnopus pelagicus	2400	—	NW Wharton
Ichnopus taurus	2620	0	Cosmopolitan
Koroga megalops	4400–2200	1150–550	Cosmopolitan

Table 10 (continued)

Species	Maximum Depth (meters)	Minimum Depth (meters)	Area or Basin
Mesocyphocaris longi-caudatus Birstein and Vinogradov, 1960	3500–0[b]	—	Pacific
Metacyclocaris polycheles	6200–0[b]	—	Kurile-Kamchatka
Metacyphocaris helgae	5700[b]	500	Cosmopolitan
Metandania islandica	7900[b]	1318	N. American
Meteusiroides curvidactyla	3500	2500	N. Atlantic
Meteusiroides plumipes	4500–3500	—	Kurile-Kamchatka
Orchomenella abyssorum	3578	0	Cosmopolitan
Orchomenella affinis	6000[b]	2000	Kurile-Kamchatka
Orchomenella distincta Birstein and Vinogradov, 1960	2000–0	—	Pacific
Orchomenella pelagica Birstein and Vinogradov, 1960	4300–2020	—	Pacific
Paracallisoma alberti	4400–2200	550	Cosmopolitan
Paracyphocaris brevicornis	7700[b]	2000	Pacific
Paracyphocaris predator	4800	600	Pacific-Atlantic
Paralicella microps (see Birstein and Vinogradov, 1960)	8480[b]	6580	Pacific
Paralicella similis Birstein and Vinogradov, 1960	3000–0[b]	—	Pacific
Paralicella tenuipes	7300[b]	1414	Pacific-Atlantic
Parandania boecki	6030–4100[b]	300	Cosmopolitan
Parandaniexis mirabilis	3715–0	—	Pacific
Parargissa affinis Birstein and Vinogradov, 1960	8500–0[b]	—	Bougainville
Parargissa arcuata	8050–4190	—	Kurile-Kamchatka
Parargissa curticornis Birstein and Vinogradov, 1960	8000–0[b]	—	New Hebrides
Parargissa longipes Birstein and Vinogradov, 1960	8500–0[b]	—	Bougainville
Parargissa nasuta	1919	1300	N. Atlantic
Pareusirogenes carinatus	3000	—	Kurile-Kamchatka
Phippsiella minima	2380	130	Arctic-Atlantic
Phippsiella nipoma, n. sp.	2972	1861	Cape
Phippsiella similis	2375	200	N. Atlantic
Rhachotropis anoculata, n. sp.	3725	—	E. Scotia
Rhachotropis distincta	7000–0[b]	378	Atlantic-Pacific
Rhachotropis flemmingi Dahl, 1959	7160[b]	—	Sunda
Rhachotropis grimaldi	2850	460	Atlantic-Pacific
Rhachotropis natator	7000[b]	818	Pacific
Rhachotropis proxima	4380	—	W. European
Scopelocheiropsis abyssalis	3000	—	Atlantic

Species	Maximum Depth (meters)	Minimum Depth (meters)	Area or Basin
Scopelocheirus hopei	2500	60	N. Atlantic
Scopelocheirus schellenbergi Birstein and Vinogradov, 1958	8000[b]	6580	Atlantic-Pacific
Socarnes longicornis Birstein and Vinogradov, 1960	8000[b]	61	Pacific
Stegocephaloides katalia, n. sp.	4050	—	Cape
Stegocephalus inflatus	2000	19	Atlantic-Pacific
Stenopleura atlantica[c]	7485[b]	200	Cosmopolitan
Synopia ultramarina[c]	3000[b]	0	Cosmopolitan
Synopioides macronyx	3000	0	Cosmopolitan
Synopioides secundus	10,190[b]	3000	Cosmopolitan
Synopioides shoemakeri	7000[b]	183	Atlantic-Pacific
Thoriella islandica	2800	1646	Atlantic-Indian
Vitjaziana gurjanovae	7800–4200	—	Kurile-Kamchatka

References to all species may be found in Barnard's (1958) *Index to the Gammaridean Amphipoda* except where authors and dates of later published species are specifically included or where new species are so denoted.

Some species are entered here erroneously because they were caught in open tows from depths greater than 2000 meters below the surface and probably were caught in depths shallower than 2000 meters. The minimum depths are based on the maximum depth of the shallowest tow recorded for the species.

[a] Bottom feeder.

[b] Maximum depth record is probably too extreme. I consider that distribution of the species at the depth cited is unproved because the trawl was open for long vertical distances during fishing. *Stenopleura atlantica* and *Synopia ultramarina* I consider definitely not abyssal but epipelagic.

[c] Has eyes.

Table 11

PROBABLE PELAGIC ABYSSAL AMPHIPODS, BASED ON THE LITERATURE

Species	Maximum Depth (meters)	Minimum Depth (meters)	Basin or Region
Alicella gigantea	5285	—	N. Atlantic
Alicella scotiae	4870	—	S. Atlantic
Pardaliscoides tenellus	3246	1505(?)	N. Atlantic S. Pacific
Pardaliscopsis tenuipalpa	4380	—	N. Atlantic
Uristes calcaratus	2260	1203	Arctic
Uristes typhlops and subsp.	4680	2000	Arctic-S. Atlantic

References to all species may be found in Barnard's (1958) *Index to the Gammaridean Amphipoda* except where authors and dates of later published species are specifically included or where new species are so denoted.

Many of the bathypelagic species in Table 10 may actually be oriented to the benthos more than to the pelagic, but have been caught in tows. As mentioned before, a *Eurythenes gryllus* specimen in the

Galathea collections has sediment in its gut but has an oily body and diffused pelagic eyes. Morphologically, the species is more pelagic than benthic, but obviously feeds on the bottom.

Inquilinous amphipods are semiparasitic on other organisms, principally medusae and tunicates or fixed coelenterates and ascidians. Those in Table 12 are so poorly known that it is not established whether they are benthic or pelagic, although I have indicated genera normally recovered from fixed benthic hosts.

Table 12

PROBABLE INQUILINOUS ABYSSAL AMPHIPODS, BASED ON THE LITERATURE

Species	Maximum Depth (meters)	Minimum Depth (meters)	Basin or Region
Amphilochopsis hamatus	2702	360	Arctic, N. Atlantic
Bathyamaryllis haswelli	1919	120	W. European
Bathyamaryllis rostrata	2320	—	W. European
Danaella mimonectes	3000	—	Newfoundland

Species	Maximum Depth (meters)	Minimum Depth (meters)	Basin or Region
Figorella tanidea, n. sp.	3770	—	E. Scotia
Leucothoe rostrata	1919	1360	Azores
Leucothoe tridens	2000	0?	New Zealand, Pacific?
Leucothoe uschakovi	3000	—	Greenland
Metopa mirifica	2300	—	Kurile
Metopa robusta	3521	62	Arctic, N. Atlantic
Metopella pacifica	2000	1430	N. Pacific
Normanion abyssi	2368	—	Mediterranean
Proboloides aequalis, n. sp.	4986	—	Cape
Stenothoe dactylipotens	1919	170	Azores, Mediterranean
Trischizostoma longirostre	3655	—	Cape Verde

Habitats, whether on pelagic or benthic animals, are unknown, although *Leucothoe* is a well-known infestor of benthic tunicates and coelenterates in the littoral; *Metopa* has been found in both benthic and pelagic; and *Trischizostoma* has the oily body and eyes of a pelagic species.

References to all species may be found in Barnard's (1958) *Index to the Gammaridean Amphipoda* except where authors and dates of later published species are specifically included or where new species are so denoted.

COMPOSITION OF THE ABYSSAL FAUNA AND ITS RELATIONSHIP TO SHALLOW WATER

Because contemporary thinking suggests that the "cradle of evolution" is the shallow sea, it is necessary to trace abyssal faunas to a shallow water origin. There is nothing illogical in this thinking, for nearly all major phylogenetic lines are vastly better represented in shallow water. This does not discount the fact that some families and genera of animal groups are strictly abyssal. Yet, in terms of the pressure of diversity, the direction of population settlement and evolution is from shallow water to deep.

Among gammaridean Amphipoda, not many genera and families are restricted to abyssal depths, as in echinoderms and isopods. Only the pelagic family Vitjaziidae, recently described by Birstein and Vinogradov (1955), appears to be strictly abyssal.

Table 13

ABYSSAL ENDEMIC GENERA WITH SPECIES RESTRICTED TO DEPTHS OF MORE THAN 2000 METERS

Alicella	*Mesocyphocaris* Birstein and
Astyroides Birstein and	Vinogradov, 1960
Vinogradova, 1960	*Metaceradocoides* Birstein and
Bathycallisoma	Vinogradova, 1960
Bathypanoploea	*Necochea*, n. gen.
Bathyschraderia	*Neoxenodice* (1800 meters)
Bruzeliopsis	*Paradryope*
Carangolia, n. gen. (1861	*Parandaniexis*
meters)	*Pardaliscoides*
Chevreuxiella	*Pardaliscopsis*
Clepidecrella, n. gen.	*Pareusirogenes*
Danaella	*Paronesimoides*
Elimedon, n. gen.	*Pseudonesimus*
Figorella, n. gen.	*Scopelocheiropsis*
Jeddo, n. gen. (1861 meters)	*Valettia*
Kindia, n. gen.	*Vitjaziana*
Leptophoxoides, n. gen.	

References to the genera are in J. L. Barnard (1958). All are monotypic except *Alicella* and *Kindia*.

A list of the 28 amphipod genera known only from abyssal depths is presented in Table 13. All of these are monotypic, except two genera (*Alicella* and *Kindia*) with two species each.

About 20 percent of the genera which have abyssal representatives are endemic to abyssal depths, while the remaining 80 percent of the genera also have representatives in bathyal and littoral depths. Only 5 percent of all marine amphipod genera are abyssally endemic. Table 17 gives other facts concerning species and genera. A list of genera restricted to bathyal or greater depths (200 + meters) is given in Table 14. The genera restricted to abyssal depths are not included in that table.

Table 14

BATHYAL GENERA WITH SPECIES RESTRICTED TO DEPTHS OF MORE THAN 200 METERS

Genus	Number of Species
Actinacanthus	1
Alexandrella	1
Amathillopleustes	1
Amathillopsis[a,b]	6
Amphilochopsis[a]	1
Andaniexis[a]	5
Anoediceros	1
Austropleustes	2
Bathyamaryllis[a]	4
Bathyceradocus	1
Bathyphotis	1
Bathystegocephalus[a]	1
Bonnierella[a]	3
Bouvierella	1
Cacao	2
Chevreuxius	1
Clarencia	1
Cleonardo[a]	8
Cleonardopsis	1
Crybelocephalus[a]	2
Crybelocyphocaris	1
Eclysis	1
Euandania[a]	1
Eusirella[a]	3
Eusirogenes[a]	4
Gainella	1
Halice[a]	8
Hansenella	1
Harpinioides	1
Hirondellea[a]	6
Joubinella[b]	4
Koroga[a]	1
Lepechinella[a]	9
Mesopleustes[a]	1
Metacyclocaris[a]	1
Metacyphocaris[a]	1
Metambasia	1
Metandania[a]	1
Meteusiroides[a]	3
Oedicerina	1
Oediceropsoides	1
Onesimoides[a]	3

Genus	Number of Species
Paracallisoma[a]	1
Paracyphocaris[a]	1
Paralepechinella	1
Paralicella[a]	3
Parandania[a]	1
Parargissa[a]	2
Pontogeneoides?	2
Princaxelia[a]	2
Pseudepimeria	1
Pseudericthonius	1
Shackletonia	1
Stegocephalina	1
Stilipes	1
Thoriella[a]	1
Uschakoviella	1
Valettiopsis[a]	2

Endemic abyssal genera are not included in this table. References to the genera are in J. L. Barnard (1958).

[a] Has abyssal species.

[b] One species is recorded from depths shallower than 200 meters.

Table 15

PARTITION OF GENERA WITH ABYSSAL SPECIES INTO DEPTH-RESTRICTED GROUPS

	Number of Genera	Percent
Littoral-bathyal-abyssal genera	75	57
Bathyal-abyssal genera	29	22
Endemic abyssal genera	28	21
	132	100

This table is designed to show the high number of genera with ranges from the littoral to the deep sea and the low number of endemic genera in the deep sea.

Table 16

GENERIC DIVERSITY: RATIO OF SPECIES TO GENERA IN VARIOUS HABITAT GROUPS OF AMPHIPODS, ACCORDING TO DEPTH

Generic Qualifications	Number of Species per Genus
Genera of littoral to abyssal depths, less genera restricted to depths below 200 meters	5.3
Restricted to 200+ meters, less abyssal endemics	2.0
Restricted to 2000+ meters	1.1

The purpose of these various summaries is to show that the deep sea is largely populated with species belonging to genera successful in shallower waters and that abyssal generic endemism is quite low.

It would be of considerable interest to make an attempt, on the basis of morphology, to relate each deep sea species to its closest relative. In cases where the deep sea species belongs to a monotypic genus, it would be necessary to relate the genus to a closely related species in another genus. However, genera usually are very distinctly and distantly defined, so that this is impractical at the present. Many deep sea

Table 17

FACTS AND FIGURES CONCERNING GAMMARIDEAN AMPHIPODA

Total marine species, all depths	2451
Total marine genera, all depths	516
Total marine monotypic genera, all depths	202
Total genera with abyssal representatives	132
Total genera abyssally endemic	28
Total monotypic genera abyssally endemic	26
Total benthic genera abyssally endemic	6
Total endemic abyssal genera with more than one species	2
Total unrestricted abyssal species	248
Total endemic abyssal species of the above 248	133
Total genera confined to bathyal or greater depths, less endemic abyssal genera	58
Total of above 58 genera with bathyal species only	30
Total benthic and presumed benthic abyssal species	126
Total endemic abyssal benthic and presumed benthic species	70
Total benthic and presumed benthic genera with abyssal species	72
Total endemic abyssal benthic and presumed benthic genera	21
Ratio of all marine species to all marine genera	4.7:1
Ratio of all world species to all monotypic genera	12:1
Ratio of all abyssal species to monotypic abyssal genera	10:1
Ratio of endemic abyssal species to monotypic abyssal genera	5:1
Ratio of all abyssal species to all abyssal genera	2:1
Percent of monotypism in endemic abyssal genera	92%
Percent of monotypism in all marine genera	39%

Table 18

IMPORTANT ABYSSAL BENTHIC AMPHIPOD FAMILIES AND THEIR DIVERSITY IN OTHER FAUNAS
(in Percent that Each Family Constitutes in Each Fauna)

	Abyssal Benthic	Arctic Shelf	Antarctic Shelf	Norwegian	France-Mediterranean	Tropical Pacific	Total Marine World
Lysianassidae	31	43	27	18	17	5	26
Phoxocephalidae	11	6	5	4	3	2	4
Tironidae	9	2	2	2	0	1	1
Ampeliscidae	8	9	4	6	6	9	5
Haustoriidae	5	3	1	4	4	3	2
Photidae	3	4	7	4	8	4	6
Oedicerotidae	3	16	7	11	4	16	6
Gammaridae	3	11	2	5	11	11	7
Aoridae	1	2	2	2	5	2	2

species belong to genera with large numbers of species, such as *Ampelisca, Harpinia, Urothoe,* etc., and many of the shallow water species in these genera are poorly known. For instance, in a forthcoming paper on Phoxocephalidae I am more than quadrupling the shallow water fauna of southern California. Thus, amphipod systematists are not ready to state the relationships of individual deep sea species, as has been done by Wolff for isopods (1956).

Because shallow water amphipod faunas are still inadequately described it is possible only to summarize faunas on a familial basis (Table 18). The Lysianassidae are a striking part of abyssal faunas, but their percentage in these faunas is scarcely larger than their percentage in the world total, although Lysianassidae are mainly polar in shallow waters and are sparsely represented in the tropics. This might be construed as evidence of the origin of abyssal faunas from cold polar waters, but is contradicted by other figures in the table, such as the Oedicerotidae, which are well concentrated in the arctic but are poor in the deep sea. The information in Table 18 is still inadequately assembled, and it is hoped in forthcoming parts of the series to show relationships of faunas by different methods than percentages.

SYSTEMATICS

Synonymies, references, and diagnoses to families and genera have been omitted, except where some original contribution or alteration has been made. References to these may be found in my Index (J. L. Barnard, 1958).

Because of the difficult circumstances under which amphipods are dredged from great depths, many are returned in mutilated condition. In Table 2 a number of specimens are listed which have not been described herein. I have failed to describe these only because their incompleteness or mutilation renders them nearly indistinguishable as specific entities. It would not serve amphipod systematics to name and describe these. However, every effort has been made to include each species possible. Painstaking reconstruction has been carried out on several animals, as seen by some of the figures of broken parts. It is hoped that further dredging planned by the *Vema* in South Atlantic waters will recover unbroken members of unreported animals, so that identification and recording can be undertaken later.

Because each species is figured as completely as possible the diagnoses and descriptions have been made brief; in each case the diagnosis restricts each species from its relatives.

Family: LYSIANASSIDAE

Genus: CHIRONESIMUS Sars

Chironesimus adversicola (K. H. Barnard)
Figure 2

Synonyms: *Lakota adversicola* K. H. Barnard, 1925, pp. 327–329. *Chironesimus adversicola*, Schellenberg, 1926, pp. 219–220, Fig. 13.

Identification: The peculiar shape of the third pleonal epimeron was instrumental in the present identification. Schellenberg notes some difference of his material from that of K. H. Barnard, and several differences are evident in the present specimens. These are the slightly oblique, not transverse palm of the first gnathopod (it appears transverse while still attached to the animal), the less cleft telson, and probably the less developed upper lip.

The material differs from Schellenberg's by the slight pseudocarina of pleon segment 4. The eyes are not visible.

Food: The stomach of the 4.5 mm. specimen contained finely particulate organic matter, one foraminifer test, and a few mineral particles.

The parts not specifically figured herein are like those figured for *Chironesimus rotundatus*.

Material examined: *Vema* Stations 52 (2.5 mm.), 53 (4.5 mm., female 4.25 mm., 4.0 mm., 2.5 mm.).

Distribution: Previously reported from the Cape Agulhas slope area, 564 meters (Schellenberg) and 1021–1280 meters (K. H. Barnard). Reported here from the Cape Basin, 4961 meters and 4893 meters. This semipelagic species apparently feeds on the bottom and thus shows a eurybathic range.

Chironesimus rotundatus (K. H. Barnard)
Figure 3

Synonyms: *Lakota rotundatus* K. H. Barnard, 1925, pp. 329–330.

Diagnosis: Eyes absent; coxa 1 shorter than and partially covered by coxa 2, subtriangular; article 6 of gnathopod 1 not narrower than article 5; third pleonal epimeron with straight posterior edge, lower corner slightly prolonged and rounded.

Remarks: This species differs from others in the genus by the first coxa. Although this character is of possible generic value, I have discussed the intergrading of it in *Tmetonyx* and *Tryphosa* under the latter heading.

I am indebted to Dr. K. H. Barnard for the loan of comparative specimens of this species. The chitin of the *Vema* specimens was opaque, but Dr. Barnard's material was transparent, so that considerable cellular material of the head was visible, the position of which suggests its sensitivity to light (similar to *Eurythenes*); however, this material was not organized into ommatidea. It is possible that this species and others in the genus are pelagic and bathypelagic, although the shape of the upper lip is similar to other genera such as *Aruga* and *Lysianassa*, which are benthic.

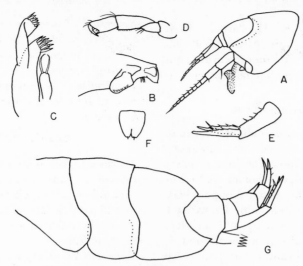

Figure 2. *Chironesimus adversicola* (K. H. Barnard). Sex?, 4.5 mm., *Vema* Sta. 53.   A:
head;   B: mandible;   C: maxilla 1;   D:
gnathopod 1;   E: uropod 2;   F: telson;   G:
pleon.

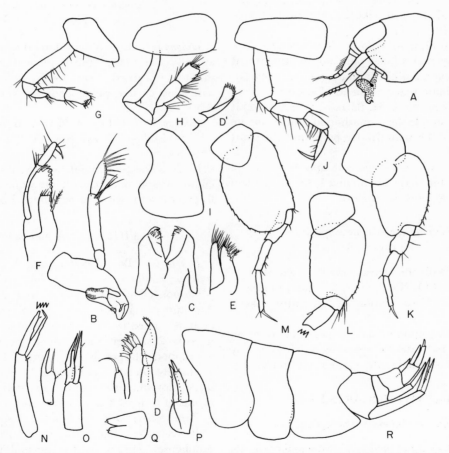

Figure 3. *Chironesimus rotundatus* (K. H. Barnard). Sex?, 3.5 mm., *Vema* Sta. 54. A: head;
B: mandible; C: lower lip; D, E: maxillae 1, 2; D': palp of maxilla 1; F: maxilliped;
G, H: gnathopods 1, 2; I: coxa 4; J, K, L, M: peraeopods 1, 3, 4, 5; N, O, P: uropods
1, 2, 3; Q: telson; R: pleon.

Material examined: *Vema* Stations 18 (2.5 mm.), 54 (3.5 mm.).

Distribution: Recorded by K. H. Barnard from northeast of Cape Point, South Africa, 650–700 fathoms (1188–1281 meters); present records from Cape Basin, 4050 meters, and slope, 1861 meters.

CLEPIDECRELLA, new genus

Diagnosis: Article 1 of antenna 1 slightly carinate dorsally, and overlapping article 2; accessory flagellum well developed, composed of three articles; mandible with poorly developed molar; palp immense and attached over molar, article 2 of palp very elongate; maxillae 1 and 2 short, palp of maxilla 1 biarticulate; maxillipedal palp long and slender; gnathopod 1 simple and smaller than gnathopod 2; gnathopod 2 subchelate; inner ramus of uropod 3 very short, scale-like; telson poorly cleft, short, slightly emarginate.

Type species: *Clepidecrella cabinda*, n. sp.
Relationship: This genus differs from *Lepidepecreum* Bate and Westwood by the attachment position of the mandibular palp, the long maxillipedal palp, the short telson, and the scale-like inner ramus of uropod 3.

It differs from *Lepidepecreella* Schellenberg (1926, p. 281) by the large mandibular palp and its attachment position, the long maxillipedal palp (or short plates), and the emarginate telson (instead of entire).

From *Lepidepecreoides* K. H. Barnard (1932, p. 62) it differs by the simple first gnathopod, the elongate second article of the mandibular palp, and the short fifth coxa.

This genus has the lepidepecreoid appearance more by its head and the shape of antenna 1, less by the fact that its body segments are smooth.

Clepidecrella cabinda, new species
Figures 4, 5

Diagnosis: With the characters of the genus.
Holotype: L.G.O. No. 5, sex?, 3.5 mm., unique.
Type locality: *Vema* Station 12, Argentine Basin, 5041 meters.
Remarks: Peraeopod 5 has a compensation ridge on article 2 which indicates that peraeopod 5 is folded by the animal to hook below the epimeron of pleon segment 1.

Genus: CYPHOCARIS Boeck

Cyphocaris challengeri (Stebbing)

Synonyms: *Cyphocaris challengeri*, Shoemaker, 1945, p. 187, Fig. 1c and references.
Material examined: *Vema* Station 18 (one, 4 mm.).
Distribution: Bathypelagic cosmopolitan. Recorded here from Cape Basin, bottom haul, 0–4050 meters.

Cyphocaris richardi Chevreux

Synonyms: *Cyphocaris richardi* Chevreux, J. L. Barnard, 1954, p. 53, pls. 2, 3, and references.
Food: The stomach was filled with copepod setae.
Material examined: *Vema* Station 53 (male, 15 mm.).
Distribution: A cosmopolitan bathypelagic species. Reported here from Cape Basin in a bottom haul at 4893 meters.

ELIMEDON, new genus

Diagnosis: Epistome and upper lip small and inconspicuous; antenna 2 scarcely longer than antenna 1; mandible with well-developed molar, palp long, article 3 very short; gnathopod 1 like *Hippomedon*, article 6 shorter than 5 and ovate, subchelate; telson cleft to middle.

Type species: *Elimedon cristatus*, new species.
Relationship: This genus differs from *Hippomedon* Boeck only by the short third palp article of the mandible and the short second antenna. The gills are too poorly preserved for analysis.

Elimedon cristatus, new species
Figure 6

Diagnosis: Eyes absent, lateral head lobes narrow, apically rounded; third pleonal epimeron with slightly upturned long tooth; pleon segment 4 with acute carina; peraeopods 3–5 well developed, not short.

Holotype: L.G.O. No. 8, sex?, 6 mm., unique.
Type locality: *Vema* Station 23, Angola Basin, 3916 meters.
Food: The gut contents were a mass of finely particulate organic matter, with a few questionable diatom fragments and two or three mineral particles.

FIGORELLA, new genus

Diagnosis: Body slender, turgid, similar to *Pachychelium* Stephensen (1925) but differing by the possession of normal maxillae and a short accessory flagellum; mandible lacks molar, cutting edge not dentate; maxilla 1 with uniarticulate palp; plates of maxilla 2 slender, inner much shorter than outer; gnathopod 1 larger than 2, article 6 large, subchelate or slightly chelate; gnathopod 2 subchelate; coxa 1 large, not hidden; telson apparently entire; inner ramus of uropod 3 small, scale-like.

Type species: *Figorella tanidea*, n. sp.
Relationship: The genus differs from *Pachychelium* Stephensen (1925) by the normal maxillae; from *Koroga* Holmes (1908) and *Pseudokoroga* Schellenberg (1931) by the simple palp of maxilla 1, the short accessory flagellum, and a number of other minor features.

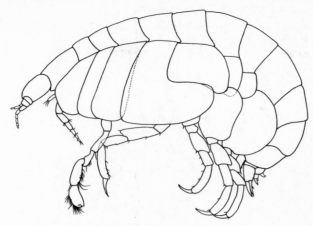

Figure 4. *Clepidecrella cabinda*, n. gen., n. sp. Sex?, 3.5 mm., *Vema* Sta. 12. Lateral view of animal.

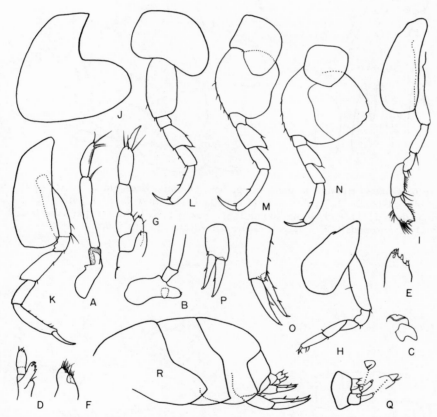

Figure 5. *Clepidecrella cabinda*, n. gen., n. sp. Sex?, 3.5 mm., *Vema* Sta. 12. A, B: mandibles; C: upper lip and one half of lower lip; D, F: maxillae 1, 2; E: maxilla 1, outer plate; G: maxilliped; H, I: gnathopods 1, 2; J: coxa 4; K, L, M, N: peraeopods 1, 3, 4, 5; O, P: uropods 1, 2; Q: pleon segment 6, telson, and uropod 3; R: pleon.

Figorella tanidea, new species

Figures 7, 8

Diagnosis: With the characters of the genus.

Holotype: L.G.O. No. 9, sex?, 3.5 mm., unique.

Type locality: *Vema* Station 47, East Scotia Basin, 3770 meters.

Remarks: The upper lip, lower lip, and telson were irreparably damaged during dissection, so that they cannot be figured accurately.

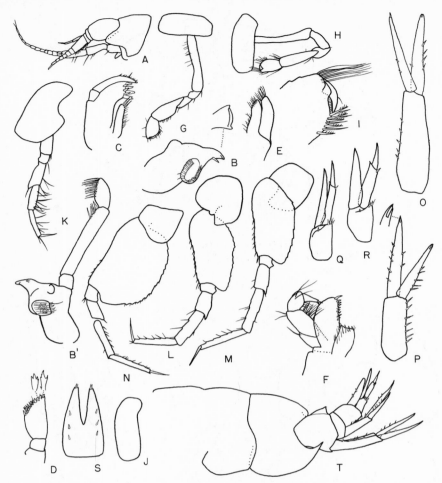

Figure 6. *Elimedon cristatus*, n. gen., n. sp. Sex?, 6 mm., *Vema* Sta. 23. A: head; B, B′: mandibles; C: maxilla 1; D: palp of maxilla 1; E: maxilla 2; F: maxilliped; G, H: gnathopods 1, 2; I: end of gnathopod 2; J: coxa 3; K, L, M, N: peraeopods 2, 3, 4, 5; O, P, Q, R: uropods 1, 2, 3, 3; S: telson; T: pleon segments 2–6.

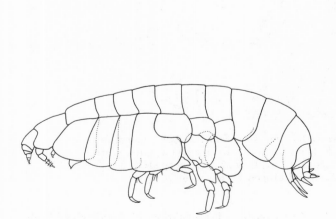

Figure 7. *Figorella tanidea*, n. gen., n. sp. Sex,? 3.5 mm., *Vema* Sta. 47. Lateral view of animal.

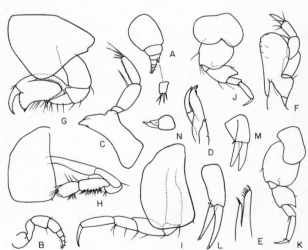

Figure 8. *Figorella tanidea*, n. gen., n. sp. Sex?, 3.5 mm., *Vema* Sta. 47. A, B: antennae 1, 2; C: mandible; D, E: maxillae 1, 2; F: maxilliped; G, H: gnathopods 1, 2; I, J, K: peraeopods 1, 3, 4; L, M, N: uropods 1, 2, 3.

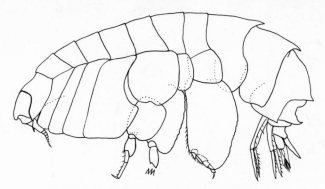

Figure 9. *Lepidepecreum clypodentatum,* n. sp. Male, 5.5 mm., *Vema* Sta. 54. Lateral view of animal.

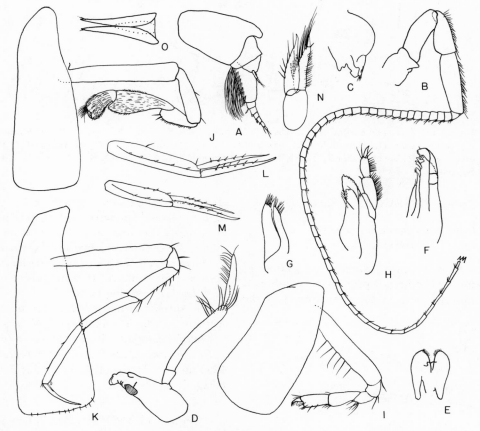

Figure 10. *Lepidepecreum clypodentatum,* n. sp. Male, 5.5 mm., *Vema* Sta. 54. A, B: antennae 1, 2; C: upper lip and epistome, lateral; D: mandible; E: lower lip; F, G: maxillae 1, 2; H: maxilliped; I, J: gnathopods 1, 2; K: peraeopod 1; L, M, N: uropods 1, 2, 3; O: telson.

Genus: LEPIDEPECREUM Bate and Westwood

Lepidepecreum clypodentatum, new species
Figures 9, 10

Diagnosis: Article 2 of peraeopod 5 produced downward strongly; the rest of the appendage is very short so that article 2 extends down to the end of article 5 (similar to *L. clypeatum* Chevreux, see Chevreux, 1900, p. 28, Pl. 4, Fig. 2); dorsal carinae of pleon segments 1–3 ending in teeth; pleon segment 4 with an erect, acute process; eyes not visible; inner rami of uropods 1–2 subequal to outer rami.

Holotype: L.G.O. No. 10, male, 5.5 mm., unique.

Type locality: *Vema* Station 54, Cape Basin, 1861 meters.

Relationship: This species and *L. clypeatum* are the only members of the genus with the peculiar configuration of peraeopod 5. The new species differs from *L. clypeatum* principally by the teeth on pleon segments 1–2.

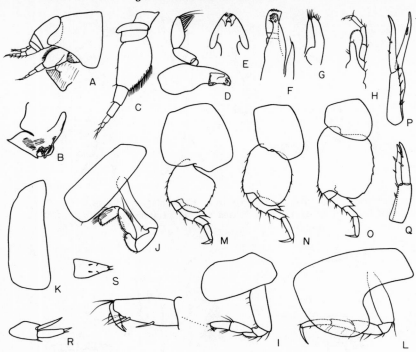

Figure 11. *Lysianella mimica*, n. sp. Male, 3.75 mm., *Vema* Sta. 16. A: head; B: epistome; C: antenna 2; D: mandible; E: lower lip; F, G: maxillae 1, 2; H: maxilliped; I, J: gnathopods 1, 2; K: coxa 3; L, M, N, O: peraeopods 2, 3, 4, 5; P, Q, R: uropods 1, 2, 3; S: telson.

Genus: LYSIANELLA Sars

Lysianella mimica, new species
Figures 11, 12

Diagnosis: Eyes absent; anterior projection of upper lip acute, epistome not produced; gnathopod 1 lacks the minute palm of the type species of the

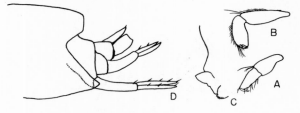

Figure 12. *Lysianella mimica*, n. sp. Female, 4 mm., *Vema* Sta. 16. A, B: gnathopods 1, 2; C: epistome; D: pleon segments 3–6.

genus; peraeopods 3–5 are quite short; pleon segment 3 dorsally and posteriorly produced to a quadrate process; third pleonal epimeron attenuated behind, lower corner acute; pleon segment 4 not elevated; telson triangular, minutely cleft between the two apical spines.

Holotype: L.G.O. No. 11, female?, 3 mm.

Type locality: *Vema* Station 18, Cape Basin, 4050 meters.

Relationship: This species differs from the type species *L. petalocera* Sars (see Sars, 1895, pl. 18) by the

lack of eyes, the shape of gnathopod 1, pleon segment 3, third pleonal epimeron and the telson. The shorter peraeopods 3–5 and lack of a palm on gnathopod 1 might be considered generic differences and will be useful as such if the genus becomes larger. The diagnosis is quite sufficient to distinguish the species from *L. dellavallei* Stebbing (1906).

The specific name refers to the mimicry of pleon segment 3, which resembles *Tryphosa quadrata*, n. sp.

Material examined: *Vema* Stations 16 (one), 18 (two).

Distribution: Cape Basin, bottom hauls of 2972 and 4050 meters. It is probable that this species is abyssal pelagic.

Genus: TRYPHOSA Boeck, new synonymy

Synonyms: *Tryphosa* Boeck, Stebbing, 1906, p. 68. *Tmetonyx* Stebbing, 1906, p. 73.

Discussion: The differences between *Tryphosa* and *Tmetonyx* are minor. Using the type species of each genus, *Tryphosa horingi* Boeck and *Tmetonyx cicada* (Fabricius), in each case figured by Sars (1895), the differences are quite obscure indeed. Stebbing (1906) in his key to the Lysianassidae used the short inner plate of the second maxilla of *Tmetonyx* to distinguish it from *Tryphosa* and other genera. However, one of the species Stebbing assigned to *Tmetonyx* showed second maxillae with equal plates (*T. miersi* Stebbing, 1888), and the maxillary differences between the type species of both genera are scarcely significant. Undoubtedly the extreme short-ness as exhibited by *T. cicadoides* Stebbing (1888), if typical of all *Tmetonyx*, and apposed to the second maxillae of *T. miersi* (above), if typical of all *Tryphosa*, would be a valid distinguishing feature. However, among the many species assigned to both genera is a plethora of intergradation in this regard. There is no justification for dividing this intergradation into two generic groups.

Unfortunately, the combination of these two genera supplies a single genus with 57 species, an unwieldy assemblage. In most cases, the differences among the many species are quite minor. Most of the species are poorly described and poorly figured. The writer has made an attempt at a key to the genus, based mainly on four characters: (1) presence or absence of eyes; (2) acuteness or obtuseness of lateral head lobes; (3) presence or absence of a tooth on the third pleonal epimeron; (4) the presence or absence of a discrete dorsal process on pleonal segment 4. The use of these criteria in amphipod systematics is at best an artificial approximation of relationships and is little better than pigeon-holing. Until each species can be adequately figured and described, this is the best that can be done.

In the following key there may be some difficulty in deciding on the structure of the fourth pleonal pro-cess, which I consider to be either a distinct carina or boss, or a dorsal hump which ends abruptly above the fifth pleonal segment. Most species which lack a dorsal process do have a dorsal hump on segment 4, which is smooth and does not end abruptly above segment 5.

Dotted lines indicate that no distinguishing characters are available in the literature.

The species marked "Tm." were originally in the genus *Tmetonyx*, the remainder in *Tryphosa*. *Tryphosa leucophthalmus* is cited twice. *Tryphosa grandimana* is a synonym of *T. sarsi*.

The following species are not included:

Tmetonyx carinata (Schellenberg, 1931) should be removed from this group of species because of the strongly produced epistome which appears to be a fusion of the upper lip and epistome. No genus for its reception can be suggested.

Tmetonyx gulosus (Krøyer), see Shoemaker (1930). Stebbing (1906) fused this with *T. cicada*. Shoemaker revived the species, but did not indicate the specific criteria.

Tmetonyx nobilis (Stimpson), see Shoemaker (1930). This species bears an enlarged and produced upper lip, for which the species should be transferred to *Chironesimus*. The first gnathopod also indicates that this species is a chironesimid.

Tryphosa adarei Walker (1903) has article 6 of gnatho-pod 1 distinctly longer than article 5 and should be transferred to the genus *Tryphosella*.

Tryphosa murrayi Walker (1903) is a synonym of *T. adarei*, according to Walker (1907). K. H. Barnard (1930) questioned the advisability of fusing the two species, and Nicholls (1938) concurs, with evidence. Walker's original figure on Plate 9 shows article 6 of gnathopod 1 definitely longer than article 5, but Nicholls's Figure 12 does not. Confusion still reigns! The species keys out to couplet 51.

Tryphosa nugax Holmes (1904) has the first gnathopod of *Tryphosella*, but the epistome has not been described, so that no genus may be suggested for its reception.

Tryphosa onconotus Stebbing (1908) has the first gnathopod of *Hippomedon* and branchial vesicles with accessory lobes, so that it must be transferred to *Hippomedon*. In addition, its head is similar to other blind Hippomedons.

I have resurrected *Tryphosa camelus* Stebbing (1910), which was submerged in *T. sarsi* by Chilton (1921). *T. camelus* obviously is quite distinct from *T. sarsi* by the large process of pleon segment 4. Chilton (1921) noted intergradation of pleon segment 4, which I believe may have been due to mixture of several species, a facile occurrence in *Tryphosa*.

If this generic fusion is acceptable to other amphi-pod systematists, *Tmetonyx serratus* Schellenberg (1931) becomes a homonym to *Tryphosa serrata* Schellenberg (1931) and will require a new name.

Tryphosa biloba (Stephensen)
Figure 13

Synonyms: *Lepidepecreopsis biloba* Stephensen, 1925, pp. 119–121, Figs. 33–34. *Tryphosa biloba*, Gurjanova, 1951, pp. 260–261, Fig. 130.

Diagnosis: Head with broadly rounded lateral lobes, eyes absent; third pleon segment with rounded pellucid dorsal process, pleon segment 4 with upright

Figure 13. *Tryphosa biloba* (Stephensen). Fe-male, 4 mm., *Vema* Sta. 16. Pleon segments 3–6.

rounded pellucid keel; third pleonal epimeron with straight posterior edge, not prolonged, lower corner quadrate; telson bears two dorsal spines on each lobe; gnathopod 1 with distinct palm.

Material examined: *Vema* Stations 16 (two), 54 (two).

Distribution: This species was described from the North Atlantic near Greenland at a depth of 2702

KEY TO TRYPHOSA AND TMETONYX

1. Third pleonal epimeron serrate behind 2
1. Third pleonal epimeron not serrate behind . . . 6
2. Pleon segment 4 with dorsal process . . . . *analogica*
2. Pleon segment 4 lacks dorsal process 3
3. Third pleonal epimeron, serrations quadrate *castellata*
3. Third pleonal epimeron, serrations pointed . . . 4
4. Epistome is a subconical lobe . . . . . *Tm. serratus*
4. Epistome scarcely overhanging upper lip 5
5. Pleon segment 4 with dorsal cryptic notch *Tm. paramoi*
5. Pleon segment 4 with dorsal broad
depression . . . . *Tryp. serrata*
6. Third pleonal epimeron with tooth at lower
corner 7
6. Third pleonal epimeron lacks tooth at lower
corner 38
7. Eyes present 8
7. Eyes absent 22
8. Pleon segment 4 lacks dorsal process 9
8. Pleon segment 4 with dorsal process 18
9. Head lobes acute 10
9. Head lobes rounded 17
10. Eyes white . . . . *Tm. leucophthalmus*
10. Eyes dark 11
11. Gnathopod 1, articles 5–6 very long . . *Tm. longichela*
11. Gnathopod 1, articles 5–6 not very long . . 12
12. Epistome strongly projecting . . . *Tm. orchomenoides*
12. Epistome not strongly projecting 13
13. Head lobes strongly projecting 14
13. Head lobes not strongly projecting 15
14. Coxa 4 narrow . . . . *triangula*
14. Coxa 4 broad . . . . *Tm. acutus*
15. Coxa 4, posterior lobe narrow, nearly
acute . . . . *Tm. cicada*
15. Coxa 4, posterior lobe broad 16
16. Uropod 3 twice as long as telson . . . . *Tm. similis*
16. Uropod 3 about 1.5 times as long as
telson . . . . *Tm. gracilipes*
17. Gnathopod 1, article 7 has anterior
tooth . . . . *Tm. trionyx*
17. Gnathopod 1, article 7 lacks anterior
tooth . . . . *Tm. rotundatus*
18. Head lobes acute 19
18. Head lobes rounded 20
19. Third pleonal epimeron tooth short . . *groenlandica*
19. Third pleonal epimeron tooth very long . . *rusanovi*
20. Pleon segment 4, carina angulate
behind . . . . *spitzbergensis*
20. Pleon segment 4, carina rounded behind . . . 21
21. Epistome not overhanging upper lip . . . . *schneideri*
21. Epistome overhangs upper lip . . . . . . *nanoides*
22. Pleon segment 4 with dorsal process 23
22. Pleon segment 4 lacks dorsal process 29
23. Head lobes acute 24
23. Head lobes rounded 27
24. Pleon segment 4, carina erect, acute 25
24. Pleon segment 4, carina rounded 26
25. Pleon segment 3 with acute dorsal
process . . . . *triplans*, n. sp.
25. Pleon segment 3 lacks acute dorsal process . *trigonica*
26. Epistome broadly produced . . . . . . *intermedia*
26. Epistome flush with upper lip . . . . . *Tm. caeculus*
27. Peraeopods 3–5 well developed, peraeopod 3
twice as long as its coxa . . . . *propinqua*
27. Peraeopods 3–5 feeble, peraeopod 3 1.5 times as
long as its coxa 28
28. Pleon segment 4, carina acute behind . . *macropareia*
28. Pleon segment 4, carina rounded behind . . *abyssalis*

29. Head lobes rounded 30
29. Head lobes acute 32
30. Third pleonal epimeron, tooth very short . . *oxystoma*
30. Third pleonal epimeron, tooth very long 31
31. Third pleonal epimeron, tooth stout . . *Tm. cicadoides*
31. Third pleonal epimeron, tooth slender . *Tm. barentsi*
32. Third pleonal epimeron, tooth very long 33
32. Third pleonal epimeron, tooth short 34
33. Epistome produced in flat lamina . . . . . . *major*
33. Epistome not produced in flat lamina . . *kerguelini*
34. Third pleonal epimeron, tooth scarcely distinct. 35
34. Third pleonal epimeron, tooth distinct but short . 37
35. Gnathopod 1, articles 5–6 short . . . . *Tm. cicadopsis*
35. Gnathopod 1, articles 5–6 long 36
36. Head lobes projecting, telson long, epistome is a
flat lamina . . . . *caecoides*, n. sp.
36. Head lobes poorly projecting, telson short, epistome
broadly rounded . . . . *leucophthalmus*
37. . . . . *Tm. bruuni*
37. . . . . *africana*
37. . . . . *coeca*
38. Eyes present 39
38. Eyes absent 46
39. Pleon segment 4 with dorsal process 40
39. Pleon segment 4 lacks dorsal process 44
40. Head lobes rounded 41
40. Head lobes acute 43
41. Pleon segment 4, carina bidentate . . . . . *compressa*
41. Pleon segment 4, carina not bidentate 42
42. Pleon segment 4, carina angular . . . . . *horingi*
42. Pleon segment 4, carina rounded, very long . . *minima*
43. Antenna 1, article 1 not overlapping article 2 . *angulata*
43. Antenna 1, article 1 overlaps article 2 . . . *cucullata*
44. Head lobes rounded 45
44. Head lobes acute . . . . *Tm. albidus*
45. Maxilla 2, inner plate very short . . . . *Tm. exiguus*
45. Maxilla 2, inner plate subequal to
outer . . . . *grandimana* and *sarsi*
46. Pleon segment 4 with dorsal process 47
46. Pleon segment 4 lacks dorsal process 52
47. Head lobes rounded 48
47. Head lobes acute 50
48. Pleon segment 3 with large posterior process . *biloba*
48. Pleon segment 3 lacks large posterior process . 49
49. Process of pleon segment 4 small, angular . . *pusilla*
49. Process of pleon segment 4 very large,
rounded . . . . *camelus*
50. Pleon segment 3 with quadrate dorsal
process . . . . *quadrata*, n. sp.
50. Pleon segment 3 lacks dorsal process 51
51. Epistome broadly rounded . . . . *rotundata*
51. Epistome slightly pointed . . . . . . *triangularis*
52. Pleon segment 4 not dorsally humped . . . *insignis*
52. Pleon segment 4 is dorsally humped 53
53. Coxa 5 bears a lateral crest . . . . . *Tm. mucronatus*
53. Coxa 5 probably does not bear a lateral crest . . 54
54. Third pleonal epimeron slightly prolonged
behind . . . . *insignioides*
54. Third pleonal epimeron not prolonged behind . 55
55. Telson short 56
55. Telson long 57
56. . . . . *normalis*
56. . . . . *Tm. miersi*
57. Epistome slightly more produced than next
species . . . . *bispinosa*
57. Epistome slightly less produced than above
species . . . . *Tm. longitelson*

meters. The present records are in Cape Basin and slope from bottom hauls of depths of 2972 and 1861 meters. It is possible that this species is bathypelagic, hence the wide geographic range.

Tryphosa caecoides, new species
Figure 14

Diagnosis: Eyes absent, head lobes projecting, acute; epistome is a flat lamina in front; articles 5 and 6 of gnathopod 1 long, palm nearly obsolete,

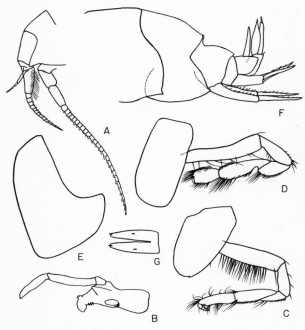

Figure 14. *Tryphosa caecoides*, n. sp. Sex?, 10 mm., *Vema* Sta. 54. A: head; B: mandible; C, D: gnathopods 1, 2; E: coxa 4; F: pleon segments 2–6; G: telson.

article 7 bears an inner tooth; third pleonal epimeron with a very small tooth at lower posterior corner; pleon segment 4 dorsally convex, lacking any distinct carinal process; telson long.

Holotype: L.G.O. No. 14, male, 10 mm.

Type locality: *Vema* Station 54, Cape Basin, 1861 meters.

Relationship: This species is closely related to *Tmetonyx leucophthalmus* Sars (1895, Pl. 34) especially by the elongated articles of gnathopod 1, but differs from that species by the projecting head lobes, the lack of white eyes, the long telson, the smaller tooth of the third pleonal epimeron, and the flat epistome.

The species is also related to *Tmetonyx longitelson* K. H. Barnard (1932), but differs by the slighter tooth of the third pleonal epimeron and by the projecting head lobes. Because K. H. Barnard (1932) relates *T. longitelson* to *Tmetonyx cicadopsis* Schellenberg (1926) it is probable that articles 5–6 of gnathopod 1 are

short on *T. longitelson* and thus different from *T. caecoides*, n. sp.

Food: The 5 mm. male was dissected; the stomach contained a small amount of finely particulate organic matter.

Material examined: *Vema* 54 (the holotype and a 5-mm. male).

Tryphosa kergueleni (Miers) *sensu* Schellenberg 1926
Figure 15

Synonyms: *Tryphosa kergueleni*, Schellenberg, 1926, pp. 266–267, Fig. 15.

Remarks: The third pleonal epimeron is like that figured for *T. kergueleni* by Schellenberg (1926), while Stebbing (1888, Pl. 8) shows a much longer and more slender tooth for this species. K. H. Barnard (1932) implies by his description and Fig. 14 (*T. major*) that in his material of *T. kergueleni* the tooth is as long as figured by Stebbing (1888). I doubt that such a considerable latitude between these two forms can be accepted, and I suspect that the present material and Schellenberg's should be designated as a new species. However, variation in this character has not been well studied, and the final decision must be left to a worker with extensive material.

The upper lip and epistome are similar to K. H. Barnard (1932, Fig. 13a).

Material examined: *Vema* Station 22 (female, 6 mm.).

Distribution: Schellenberg's material came from Kerguelen Island and Gauss Station, Antarctica, shallow water. The present record is from Angola Basin, 3015 meters, probably caught in shallower waters.

Tryphosa quadrata, new species
Figures 16, 17

Diagnosis: Head with acute but broad lateral lobes, eyes absent; third pleon segment with bulky quadrate process, thinning posteriorly to form a thick keel; pleon segment 4 with a strongly developed dorsal hump; third pleonal epimeron with straight posterior edge, slightly prolonged, smooth, lower corner acute but not produced; telson lacks dorsal spines; no definite palm on gnathopod 1.

Holotype: L.G.O. No. 16, female, 6.5 mm., unique.

Type locality: *Vema* Station 53, Cape Basin, 4893 meters.

Relationship: This single specimen is larger than *T. biloba* (Stephensen), but resembles it considerably, especially by the configuration of the dorsal process on pleon segment 3. However, the processes on pleon segments 3 and 4 are solid, not pellucid as on *T. biloba*, and the first gnathopod lacks a definite palm as on *T. biloba*.

The new species resembles *Tryphosa triplans*, n. sp., but differs by the quadrate, not acute dorsal process of

Figure 15. *Tryphosa kergueleni* (Miers), *sensu* Schellenberg (1926). Female, 6 mm., *Vema* Sta. 22. A: head; B: antenna 1; C: upper lip; D: mandible; E: lower lip; F, G: maxillae 1, 2; H: maxilliped; I: palp article 4 of maxilliped; J, K: gnathopods 1, 2; L, M, N, O: peraeopods 1, 3, 4, 5; P, Q, R: uropods 1, 2, 3; S: pleon; T: telson.

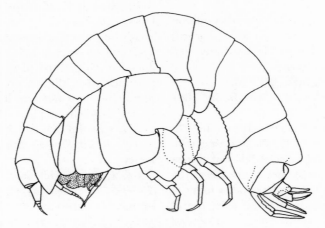

Figure 16. *Tryphosa quadrata*, n. sp. Female, 6.5 mm., *Vema* Sta. 53. Lateral view of animal.

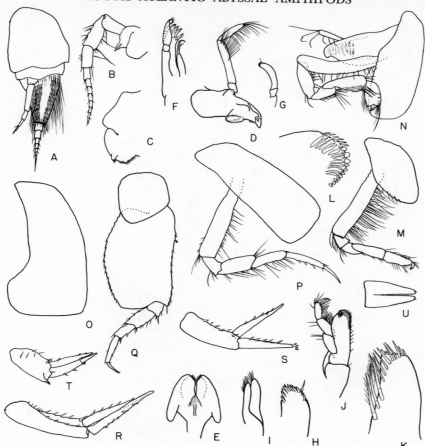

Figure 17. *Tryphosa quadrata*, n. sp. Female, 6.5 mm., *Vema* Sta. 53. A, B: antennae 1, 2; C: upper lip and epistome, lateral; D: mandible; E: lower lip; F, G: maxilla 1; H: maxilla 1, end of palp; I: maxilla 2; J: maxilliped; K: inner plate of maxilliped; L: outer plate of maxilliped; M, N: gnathopods 1, 2; O: coxa 4; P, Q: peraeopods 1, 5; R, S, T: uropods 1, 2, 3; U: telson.

pleon segment 3 and the unproduced lower corner of the third pleonal epimeron.

Tryphosa triplans, new species
Figure 18

Diagnosis: Eyes absent, head lobes projecting and acute; epistome rounded in front, flush with upper lip; articles 5 and 6 of gnathopod 1 short; pleon segment 3 with an acute postero-dorsal process; pleon segment 4 with a triangular dorsal carina, varying from slightly taller to slightly shorter than figured; third pleonal epimeron prolonged behind into a very small upturned tooth at the lower posterior corner. The second maxilla has subequal lobes.

Holotype: L.G.O. No. 17, female, 4.5 mm.

Type locality: *Vema* Station 16, Cape Basin, 2972 meters.

Relationship: This species differs from the closely related *T. trigonica* (Stebbing, 1888, Pl. 9) by the process of pleon segment 3. It is also related to and easily confused with *T. quadrata*, n. sp., but differs by the prolonged and weakly produced third pleonal epimeron, as well as the characteristic dorsal process of pleon segment 3.

Material examined: *Vema* Station 16 (the holotype, figured 4 mm. female, and seven smaller specimens, 2.5 to 3.5 mm.).

Distribution: Cape Basin, 2972 meters. It is possible that this species is abyssal pelagic.

Genus: TRYPHOSITES Sars

Tryphosites (?) *coxalis*, new species
Figures 19, 20

Diagnosis: Epistome slightly produced conically beyond upper lip; coxa 1 about one-half as long as coxa 2, partly hidden by coxa 2; eyes absent; lateral head lobes large, conical, apices rounded; articles 5–6 of gnathopod 1 subequal, article 6 slender, scarcely subchelate; pleon segment 3 with large postero-dorsal oblique conical process; pleon segment 4 with elevated subacute process; third pleonal epimeron slightly concave behind, lower corner subacute.

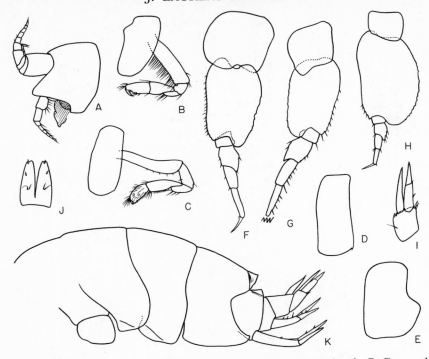

Figure 18. *Tryphosa triplans*, n. sp. Female, 4 mm., *Vema* Sta. 16. A: head; B, C: gnathopods 1, 2; D, E: coxae 3, 4; F, G, H: peraeopods 3, 4, 5; I: uropod 3; J: telson; K: pleon.

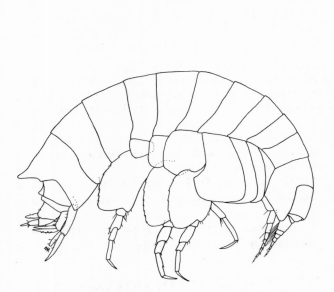

Figure 19. *Tryphosites coxalis*, n. sp. Sex?, 3.5 mm., *Vema* Sta. 14. Lateral view of animal.

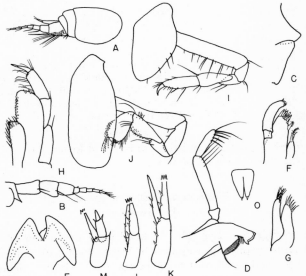

Figure 20. *Tryphosites coxalis*, n. sp. Sex?, 3.5 mm., *Vema* Sta. 14. A, B: antennae 1, 2; C: epistome and upper lip; D: mandible; E: lower lip, damaged; F, G: maxillae 1, 2; H: maxilliped; I, J: gnathopods 1, 2; K, L, M: uropods 1, 2, 3; O: telson.

Holotype: L.G.O. No. 18, sex?, 3.5 mm., unique.

Type locality: Vema Station 14, Cape Basin, 3045 meters.

Relationship: Except for the type species, *T. longipes* (Bate and Westwood) (see Sars, 1895, Pls. 28, 29), the other three species of this genus are not well described, but the present species differs from all others by the large process on pleon segment 3.

From the type species, *T. coxalis* differs in characters of possible generic value, hence the questionable assignment. These characters are the poorly sub-chelate first gnathopod and the short first coxa as well as the less produced epistome. However, it is believed better to refer this species to *Tryphosites* until a realignment of Lysianassidae can be undertaken to assess the generic limits of gnathopod 1, coxa 1, and the epistome.

This species also bears considerable resemblance to genera which are allied to the *Ambasia* group—for instance, *Ambasiopsis* K. H. Barnard (Barnard, 1932). This resemblance concerns the small and partially hidden first coxa. The present species differs from *Ambasiopsis* by the produced epistome.

Genus: URISTES Dana, new synonymy

Synonyms: *Uristes* Dana, Stebbing, 1906, pp. 63–64. *Tryphosella* Bonnier, Stebbing, 1906, pp. 67–68. *Uristoides* Schellenberg, 1931, p. 27. *Tryphosoides* Schellenberg, 1931, p. 38.

Diagnosis: Epistome and upper lip small and inconspicuous; mandible with ridged molar; article 6 of gnathopod 1 distinctly longer than article 5, ranging from a transverse subchelate palm to non-subchelate; telson deeply cleft.

Type species: *Uristes gigas* Dana.

Discussion: A list of the species which I include in this new synonymy is to be found in Table 19, along with the condition of the first gnathopod. It may

Table 19

REVISED SPECIES LIST OF *URISTES*, ACCORDING TO THE PALMAR CONDITION OF GNATHOPOD 2

Tryphosella barbatipes	X
Tryphosella albina	X
Tryphosella georgiana	XO
Uristes antennibrevis, n. sp.	XO
Uristes gigas[a]	XO
Uristes natalensis	OX
Uristes umbonatus	OX
Tryphosoides falcatus	OX
Uristoides subchelatus	OX
Centromedon typhlops	OX
Uristes serratus	O
Centromedon calcaratus	O
Centromedon productus	O

X = palm transverse, fully subchelate
XO, OX = intergrading states of oblique well-defined palms and oblique poorly defined palms
O = palm absent, not subchelate
See J. L. Barnard (1958) for references to the species.
[a] Gnathopod palm according to K. H. Barnard (1932).

appear presumptuous to include under a single genus such widely diverging gnathopod types as those of *Tryphosella barbatipes* (Stebbing, 1888, Pl. 7) and *Centromedon productus* (Goës) (see Gurjanova, 1951, p. 245), but, as is shown by Table 19, all intergrades between the two extremes have been described. There is no justification for arbitrarily breaking this sequence somewhere in the middle.

It appears that several contradictions in the literature have caused the promulgation of generic

separation in the several species groups combined here. Some of these are explained below.

In the first place, Stebbing (1906) used the closely packed first four coxae of *Uristes* in his lysianassid key to separate *Uristes* from *Centromedon*. He must have been relying on this condition in *Uristes umbonatus* as figured by Sars (1895, Pl. 29, Fig. 2), but this condition apparently is not present in the type species, *U. gigas* Dana, or in any of the other species assigned to *Uristes* since. Thus, *U. umbonatus* is unique in this regard. The other species of *Uristes* might be assigned to *Centromedon* or, on the other hand, *Centromedon* might be fused to *Uristes*, except for the fact that *Centromedon pumilus* (Liljeborg) (see Sars, 1895, Pl. 34, Fig. 2), the type species, has a distinctive laminar, unridged molar and is generically valid. However, the other three species of *Centromedon* have a ridged blunt molar and must be removed to *Uristes*, leaving *Centromedon* conditionally monotypic. In addition, *C. pumilus* has distinct first gnathopods, articles 5 and 6 being subequal in length.

In Stebbing's (1906) key to the lysianassids, *Tryphosella* was segregated from *Uristes* and *Centromedon* by the perfect subchelae of gnathopod 1, while the latter two genera bear imperfect subchelae. At that time this was a logical separation, but since then both *Tryphosella* and *Uristes* have had species described within their limits which intergradate this qualitative feature, as shown by Table 19. The new species described below is one of these. To maintain an arbitrary break between these extremes is quite difficult unless it is substantiated by other generic characters, which I have not been able to detect from the literature. Naturally it will be prudent to examine all of the included species with greater care for such features when all of the types can be brought together.

Schellenberg (1931) distinguished *Tryphosoides* from *Tryphosella* in part by descriptive words on the mandibular molar, but figures of the two type species are similar. *Tryphosoides* also has broader third uropodal rami and a "one-jointed outer ramus" which may be accidental. This distinction has quantitative value only, at best specific. The "rudimentary" accessory flagellum is two-jointed, just one joint less than the following described species. Despite Schellenberg's words to the contrary, the shapes of the third mandibular palp articles are scarcely distinctive, perhaps the result of mounting or cover-glass pressure.

Schellenberg (1931) distinguished *Uristoides* from *Uristes* by the longer second antenna. It is always difficult in amphipods to decide the generic merits of quantitative differences in the lengths of antennae, and I believe that firmer differences should be present in the Lysianassidae than this single character. Another quantitative feature is the slightly longer outer plate of the maxilliped. Maxilla 2 is like *Tmetonyx*, meaning a short inner plate. This brings to bear the problem that several species assigned to *Tmetonyx* have long inner plates on the maxillae (see *T. miersi* in Stebbing, 1888, Pl. 10) and only a few species are as short as in *T. cicadoides* (Stebbing, 1888, Pl. 4). In fact, the type species, *Tmetonyx cicada* (Sars, 1895, Pl. 32), is intermediate in this condition, and by way of fact is scarcely different from *Uristes umbonatus* (Sars, 1895, Pl. 29), which Schellenberg logically would have used for comparative value, since *U. gigas*, the type species, is not figured in this respect. Schellenberg (1931, p. 27) continues by saying that the first five coxae are normal (presumably to distinguish from *Uristes*, erroneously because the type species, *U. gigas*, is also normal) and not closely packed as stated by Stebbing (1906, p. 64). Furthermore, Schellenberg described his *Uristes serratus*, n. sp., just ahead of *Uristoides* and claimed normal coxae for it!

Thus, there has been a plethora of confusion in these genera, mainly for the lack of clarity in the type species of each or failure to refer to type species instead of better-figured representatives assigned to each later It is unfortunate that the family Lysianassidae is ridden with just this kind of confusion, and considerable revision is in order. Because the family contains more than 100 genera and more than 600 species, such a revision will be a monumental task.

There is variation in the first coxa of the revised species list of *Uristes* which suggests that Gurjanova (1951) segregated *Tryphosa* from *Tmetonyx* (and other genera) by the tryphosid coxa, narrowed distally and occasionally prolonged anteriorly. Unfortunately, some species of *Tmetonyx* do show this tryphosid coxa and probably should be transferred to *Tryphosa*, although *Tryphosa* is supposed also to differ by the subequal plates of maxilla 2. Parenthetically, the evidence is mounting that *Tmetonyx* and *Tryphosa* are not presently distinct, especially because each genus has so many species and so much intergradation between formerly qualitative criteria has been described (see under *Tryphosa*). Because first coxal differences in *Uristes* cannot be correlated with other generic criteria (at the moment) it is my belief that these differences have only specific value or at best subgeneric value.

The following species probably are not valid members of the *Uristes* complex:

Tryphosella abyssi Norman (1900, p. 205) was assigned to that genus by Norman when it was his belief that *Tryphosella* was a synonym of *Tryphosa*. On that basis *T. abyssi* should be removed provisionally to *Tryphosa*, but Norman's description of the epistome indicates that it may be a *Tryphosites* or some other genus.

Uristes induratus K. H. Barnard (1925, p. 333) has an exceptionally small first coxa hidden by coxa 2 and obviously is not a *Uristes*. No other genus for its reception can be suggested.

Uristes serratus Schellenberg (1931, p. 26) probably belongs to some other genus (unsuggested) because the expanded sixth article of the first gnathopod is unique, although the configuration is scarcely remarkable from *Tryphosella* (= *Uristes*) *albina* K. H. Barnard (1932).

Uristes antennibrevis, new species
Figures 21, 22

Diagnosis: Eyes absent, lateral lobes of head narrow, acute; antennae short, accessory flagellum of antenna 1 triarticulate; epistome and upper lip both rounded in front, the complex small; coxa 1 tapering distally; gnathopod 1 subchelate, palm slightly oblique, article 6 not inflated, about 1.25 times as long as article 5; third pleonal epimeron broadly convex behind; pleon segment 4 with a slight dorsal hump; inner ramus of uropod 3 shorter than article 1 of outer ramus.

Holotype: L.G.O. No. 19, sex?, 4 mm.

Type locality: Vema Station 54, Cape Basin, 1861 meters.

Relationship: This species is related to *Uristoides subchelatus* (= *Uristes*) Schellenberg (1931), but differs by the equal-sized plates of maxilla 2, the shorter inner ramus of uropod 3, the slightly stouter first gnathopod, the shorter second antenna, the longer hind lobe of coxa 4, and the shorter telson.

It differs from *Tryphosella georgiana* Schellenberg (1931) and *Tryphosoides falcata* Schellenberg (1931) (both = *Uristes*) by the broadly rounded third pleonal epimeron.

Material examined: Vema Station 54 (two).

Distribution: Cape Basin, 1861 meters.

Uristes typhlops mediator, new subspecies
Figure 23

Diagnosis: Differing from *Uristes typhlops* (Sars, 1885, p. 145) of the subarctic regions by the slightly longer tooth of the third pleonal epimeron, the slightly more projecting palmar corner of gnathopod two, and the slightly shorter telson. The observed differences may be only circumstantial in technical and drawing procedures.

Holotype: L.G.O. No. 20, sex?, 5 mm.

Type locality: Vema Station 54, Cape Basin Slope, 1861 meters.

Material examined: Stations 22 (female, 6 mm.), 49 (sex? 3 mm.), 54 (five specimens, including holotype, sexes unknown, probably males, 5, 4.5, 4, 3, 3 mm.).

Distribution: Angola Basin, 3015 meters; Cape Basin, 1861 meters; Valdivia Basin, 2747 meters. It is believed that this species is abyssal pelagic.

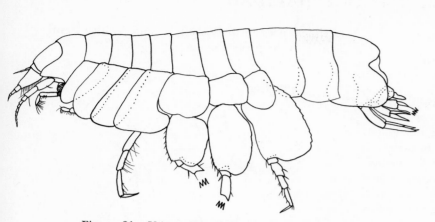

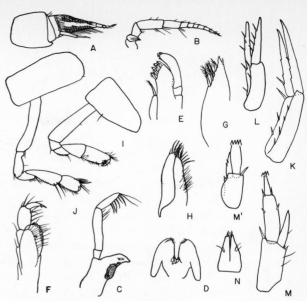

Figure 21. *Uristes antennibrevis*, n. sp. Sex?, 4 mm., *Vema* Sta. 54. Lateral view of animal.

Figure 22. *Uristes antennibrevis*, n. sp. Sex?, 4 mm, *Vema* Sta. 54. A,B: antennae 1, 2; C: mandible; D: lower lip; E, H: maxillae 1, 2; F: maxilliped; G: inner plate of maxilliped; I, J: gnathopods 1, 2; K, L, M, M': uropods 1, 2, 3, 3; N: telson.

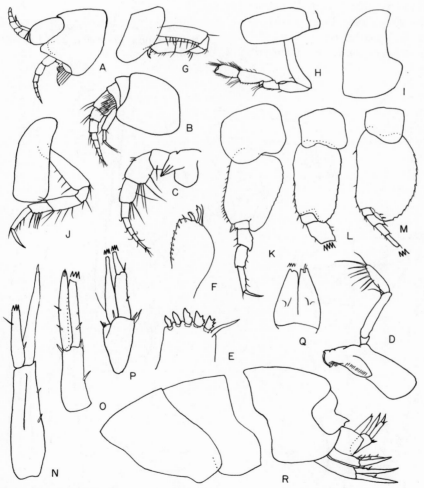

Figure 23. *Uristes typhlops mediator*, n. ssp. Sex?, 4.5 mm., *Vema* Sta. 54. A: head; B, C: antennae 1, 2; D: mandible; E: maxilla 1, end of palp; F: outer plate of maxilliped; G, H: gnathopods 1, 2; I: coxa 4; J, K, L, M: peraeopods 1, 3, 4, 5; N, O, P: uropods 1, 2, 3; Q: telson; R: pleon.

Family : STEGOCEPHALIDAE

Genus: ANDANIEXIS Stebbing

Andaniexis australis (?) K. H. Barnard
Figures 24, 25

Synonyms : Andaniexis australis K. H. Barnard, 1932, pp. 76–77, Fig. 34.

Diagnosis : Article 6 of gnathopod 2 moderately stout, posterior edge straight, subequal to article 5; article 2 of peraeopod 4 slender; article 2 of peraeopod 5 with posterior edge sparsely serrated; coxa 4 rather slender; third pleonal epimeron with lower posterior corner pointed, slightly produced; telson triangular.

Remarks : This species differs from *A. abyssi* (Boeck), in Sars (1895, Pls. 71–72), by the stouter second gnathopod. It differs from *A. subabyssi* Birstein and Vinogradov (1955, p. 240, Fig. 16) by the pointed third pleonal epimeron and the shape of peraeopod 5, article 2, which is symmetrical in *A. australis*. From *A. spongicola* Pirlot (1933, p. 148, Figs. 51–53) it differs by the stouter second gnathopod.

A number of minor features on K. H. Barnard's

specimens need further description for positive identification of the present material.

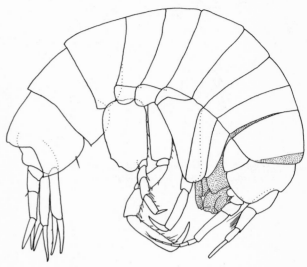

Figure 24. *Andaniexis australis* K. H. Barnard. Sex?, 9 mm, *Vema* Sta. 53. Lateral view of animal.

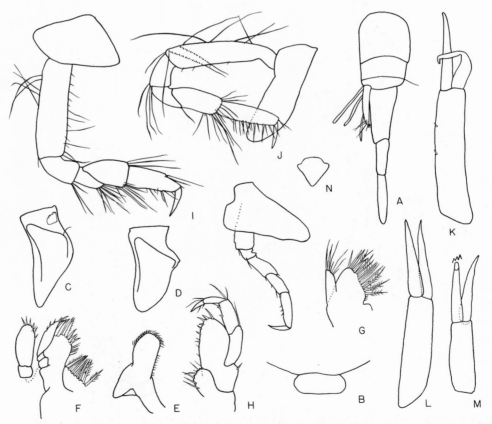

Figure 25. *Andaniexis australis* K. H. Barnard. Sex?, 9 mm., *Vema* Sta. 53. A: antenna 1; B: upper lip; C, D: mandibles; E: one half of lower lip; F, G: maxillae 1, 2; H: maxilliped; I, J: gnathopods 1, 2; K, L, M: uropods 1, 2, 3; N: telson.

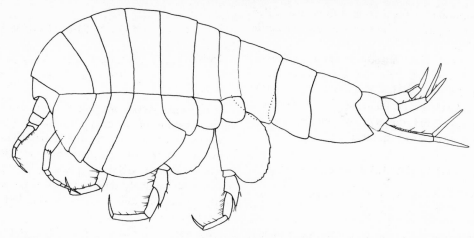

Figure 26. *Phippsiella nipoma* J. L. Barnard. Sex?, 4.5 mm., *Vema* Sta. 16. Lateral view of animal.

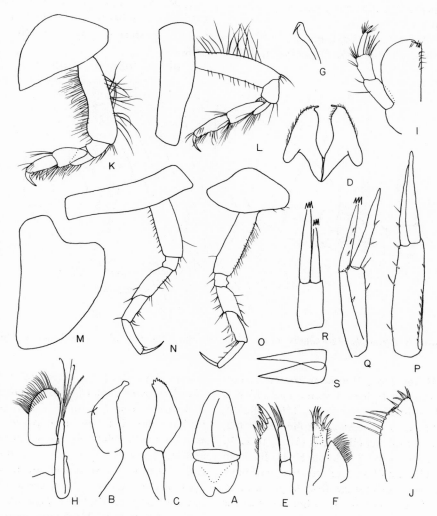

Figure 27. *Phippsiella nipoma* J. L. Barnard. Sex?, 4.5 mm., *Vema* Sta. 16. A: upper lip;
B, C: mandibles; D: lower lip; E, F: maxilla 1; G: spine of maxilla 2, outer plate;
H: maxilla 2; I: maxilliped; J: inner plate of maxilliped, enlarged; K, L: gnathopods
1, 2; M: coxa 4; N, O: peraeopods 1, 3; P, Q, R: uropods 1, 2, 3; S: telson.

Food: The stomach of the 4-mm. animal was filled with particulate organic matter and a few refractile mineral particles.

Material examined: *Vema* Station 53 (five specimens, 9.0, 5.5, 4.0, 2.0, and 1.5 mm., sexes unknown).

Distribution: In two vertical pelagic tows, 0–1000 meters in Cape Basin (K. H. Barnard); recorded here from Cape Basin, 4893 meters. A pelagic species, possibly feeding on bottom materials.

Genus: PHIPPSIELLA Schellenberg

Phippsiella nipoma J. L. Barnard
Figures 26, 27

Synonym: *Phippsiella nipoma* J. L. Barnard, 1961, p. 58, Fig. 28.

Diagnosis: Rostrum poorly developed; third pleonal epimeron with a prolonged posterior edge, lower posterior corner angular, not produced, lacking evidence of a notch.

Holotype: L.G.O. No. 24, sex?, 2 mm.

Type locality: *Vema* Station 54, Cape Basin, 1861 meters.

Genus: STEGOCEPHALOIDES Sars

Stegocephaloides katalia, new species
Figures 28, 29

Diagnosis: Accessory flagellum of antenna 1 as long as first article of primary flagellum; upper lip symmetrically incised; front edge of article 2 of peraeopod 5 longer than rest of appendage, article 2 reaching slightly beyond article 3, lower edge rounded, posterior edge sparsely serrated; third pleonal epimeron with posterior lower corner rounded, protruding slightly.

Holotype: L.G.O. No. 26, male, 4 mm., unique.

Type locality: *Vema* Station 18, Cape Basin, 4050 meters.

Relationship: This species differs from *Stegocephaloides vanhöffeni* Schellenberg (1926, p. 299) by the smooth posterior edge of the third pleonal epimeron.

It differs from *S. christianiensis* (Boeck) and *S.*

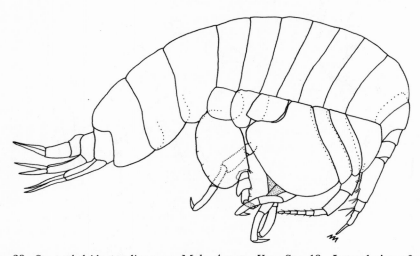

Figure 28. *Stegocephaloides katalia,* n. sp. Male, 4 mm., *Vema* Sta. 18. Lateral view of animal.

Relationship: Differs from the other known species by the shape of the third pleonal epimeron, which is neither serrated as in *P. similis* (Sars, 1895, Pl. 70, Fig. 1) nor notched as in *P. minima* Stephensen (1925, p. 131) and *P. kergueleni* Schellenberg (1926, p. 220). The rostrum is small, unlike *P. rostrata* K. H. Barnard (1932, p. 76). The small size of the two available specimens indicates a possibility that large animals might have an epimeral notch. In other respects the species is close to *P. kergueleni.*

Material examined: *Vema* Stations 16 (one), 54 (one).

Distribution: Cape Basin, 2972 and 1861 meters. It is probable that this species is abyssal pelagic.

auratus Sars (both in Sars, 1895, Pl. 70) by the rounded lower edge of article 2 on peraeopod 5.

It differs from *S. australis* K. H. Barnard (1916, p. 129) by the distinctive fifth peraeopod, which in *S. australis* has a relatively longer portion composed of articles 3–7 and has article 2 produced down to the end of article 4. Moreover, in *S. australis* the upper lip is asymmetrical; the accessory flagellum is only half as long as the first primary flagellar article; the rami of uropod 1 are equal; and there are other distinctive features.

It differs from *S. attingens* K. H. Barnard (1916, p. 131) by the fifth peraeopod in the same way as *S. australis.*

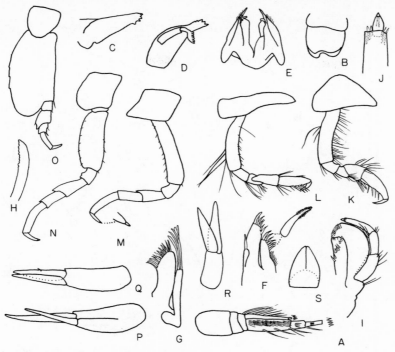

Figure 29. *Stegocephaloides katalia*, n. sp. Male, 4 mm., *Vema* Sta. 18. A: antenna 1; B: upper lip; C, D: mandibles; E: lower lip; F, G: maxillae 1, 2; H: maxilla 2, spine of outer plate; I: maxilliped; J: palp articles 3–4 of maxilliped; K, L: gnathopods 1, 2; M, N, O: peraeopods 3, 4, 5; P, Q, R: uropods 1, 2, 3; S: telson.

Family: HAUSTORIIDAE

Genus: CARANGOLIA J. L. Barnard

Synonym: Carangolia J. L. Barnard 1961, p. 73.

Diagnosis: Mandible very large, bulky; the mandibular triturating surface is large and smooth and lies apically at the cutting edge rather than in the normal molar position, mandibular palp small in relation to body of mandible but triarticulate; antenna 1 not geniculate; peraeopods 3–5 slender; coxae 1–4 subequal; uropod 3 small, short, stubby.

Type species: Carangolia mandibularis J. L. Barnard 1961.

Relationship: Except for the structure of the mandibles and third uropods, this genus resembles *Urothoe* Dana closely.

Carangolia mandibularis J. L. Barnard
Figure 30

Synonym: Carangolia mandibularis J. L. Barnard, 1961, p. 73.

Descriptive features: Accessory flagellum vestigial; maxilla 1 with biarticulate palp; posterior edge of article 2 on third peraeopod is castellate; palm of gnathopod 2 with a small projection as figured. Otherwise, with the characters of the genus.

The body is very short and flattened, twice as broad as tall, resembling an harpacticoid copepod.

Holotype: L.G.O. No. 27, sex?, 2.25 mm.

Type locality: Vema Station 54, Cape Basin, 1861 meters.

Food: The gut contents of the holotype consisted of clumps of finely particulate organic matter, mineral particles, and coccoliths.

Material examined: Vema Station 16 (one), 54 (one).

Distribution: Cape Basin, 2972 and 1861 meters. Benthic.

Genus: UROTHOE Dana

Notes: The generic limits of the genus are difficult to define, because many of the species are rather poorly known.

Principal groups in the genus which are strikingly separated by the gnathopodal configurations and which probably are worthy of at least *subgeneric* appellations are as follows:

(1) The *elegans* group consists of species with both gnathopods similar, article 6 short, stout, and expanded into a poorly defined palm. Includes *brevicornis, dentata?, denticulata, elegans, marina, pulchella, ruber, spinidigitus, varvarini,* and *vemae,* n. sp. *U. abbreviata* is closest to the *elegans* group. Probably *U. irrostrata* belongs here, as well as *U. poucheti.*

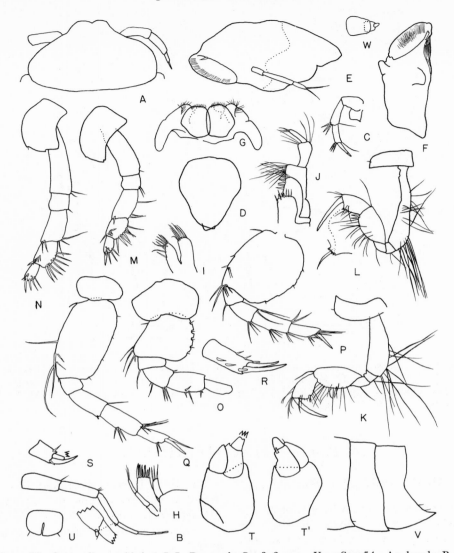

Figure 30. *Carangolia mandibularis* J. L. Barnard. Sex?, 3 mm., *Vema* Sta. 54. A: head; B, C: antennae 1, 2; D: upper lip; E, F: mandibles; G: lower lip; H, I: maxillae 1, 2; J: maxilliped; K, L: gnathopods 1, 2; M, N, O, P, Q: peraeopods 1, 2, 3, 4, 5; R, S, T, T', W: uropods 1, 2, 3, 3, 3; U: telson; V: pleon segments 1–3.

(2) The *grimaldii* group consists of species with both gnathopods similar, article 6 elongated, slender, with a short blunt palmar surface. Includes *grimaldii*, *leone*, and *pestai*.

(3) The *falcata* group includes species with the gnathopods dissimilar. Gnathopod 1 is simple, article 6 elongated, slender, bearing no palm. Gnathopod 2 has a suboval or slightly expanding sixth article with a distinct, rounded palm. Includes *falcata*, *orientalis*, and *rotundifrons*, n. sp.

(4) The *simplignathia* group is composed of the single new species, with both gnathopods similar, simple, lacking palms.

The gnathopods of *U. pinnata* and *U. serrulidactylus* are not described or are unclear.

The genus *Urothoides* Stebbing was distinguished by Stebbing (1906) for the downward-produced second article of peraeopod 5. K. H. Barnard (1932) added a species lacking this character and defined the genus by the medially curving first coxae and the fourth coxal configuration. I am doubtful that these criteria suffice for the separation, but advise more detailed study of this problem. Both species of *Urothoides* fall into the *elegans* group in terms of gnathopods.

It must be pointed out that considerable variation of the accessory flagellum is present in *Urothoe*, ranging from a vestigial single article to seven well-developed articles, but there seems to be no correlation with other features such as gnathopods.

Indeed, *Urothoe* is exceedingly variable!

Strangely, the type species, *U. irrostratus* Dana (1853), is obscure specifically. See Stebbing and Robertson (1891) for comments.

Another peculiarity exists. Bate (1857) described *U. marina*, without figure. In 1862 he figured *U. marina* (Pl. 19) and on the same plate figured a new species, *U. bairdi*. Stebbing (1891, p. 7) dismissed *U. bairdi* as a synonym of *U. marina*. Yet gnathopods 1 and 2 are very distinct, those of *U. bairdi* being more slender, especially article 5. Stebbing's own figure (1891, Pl. 2) of *U. marina* is more like *U. bairdi*. Then in 1906 Stebbing listed *U. bairdi* as a dubious species in his monograph (not as a synonym of *U. marina*). These events need clarification by European workers.

Urothoe rotundifrons, new species
Figures 31, 32

Diagnosis: Eyes absent, a pair of red ganglia situated on top of head; palp of maxilla 1 uniarticulate (unique); accessory flagellum rudimentary; gnathopod 1 simple, article 6 slender, article 7 long; gnathopod 2 slightly subchelate, article 6 suboval; third pleonal epimeron slightly prolonged, conical, corner angular; peraeopods 3–5 very slender.

Holotype: L.G.O. No. 29, sex?, 4 mm.

Type locality: Vema Station 16, Cape Basin, 2972 meters.

Relationship: The species is related to *U. falcata* Schellenberg (1931, p. 61) and *U. orientalis* Gurjanova

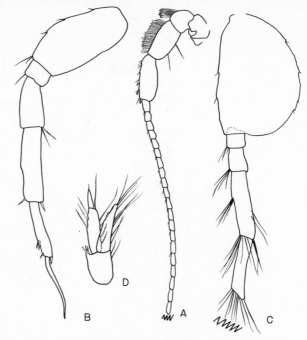

Figure 31. *Urothoe rotundifrons*, n. sp. Male, 4 mm., *Vema* Sta. 16. A: antenna 2; B, C: peraeopods 4, 5; D: uropod 3.

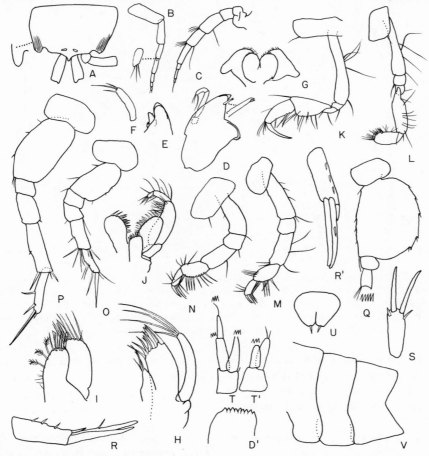

Figure 32. *Urothoe rotundifrons*, n. sp. Female, 3 mm., *Vema* Sta. 16. A: head—to left is lateral view of head lobe; B, C: antennae 1, 2; D, E: mandibles; D': mandible molar; F: palp article 3 of mandible; G: lower lip; H, I: maxillae 1, 2; J: maxilliped; K, L: gnathopods 1, 2; M, N, O, P, Q: peraeopods 1, 2, 3, 4, 5; R, R', S, T, T': uropods 1, 1, 2, 3, 3; U: telson; V: pleon segments 1–3.

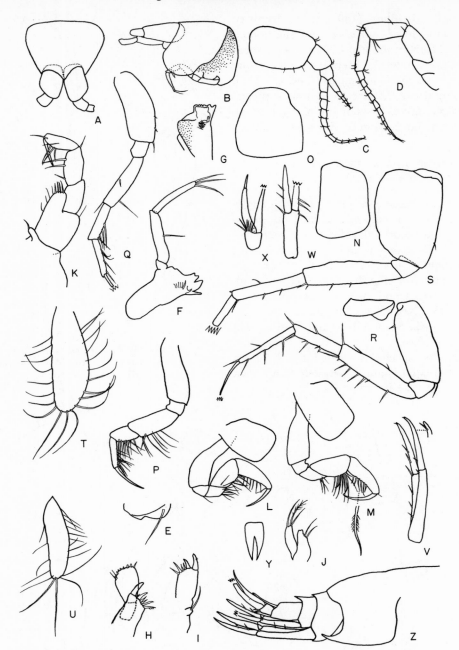

Figure 33. *Urothoe simplignathia*, n. sp. Female, 3.75 mm., *Vema* Sta. 22. A, B: head, dorsal and lateral; C, D: antennae 1, 2; E: upper lip; F, G: mandible; H, I: maxilla 1, inner lobe shown at right; J: maxilla 2; K: maxilliped; L, M: gnathopods 1, 2; N, O: coxae 3, 4; P, Q, R, S: peraeopods 1, 3, 4, 5; T, U: gills of peraeopod 1 and gnathopod 2; V, W, X: uropods 1, 2, 3; Y: telson; Z: pleon segments 6–3.

(1951, p. 354) by the configuration of its gnathopods, but differs from both species by the lateral head prolongation being rounded instead of acute, by the slender third peraeopods, and by the lack of a tooth on pleon segment 3.

Material examined: Stations 16 (eight specimens, males and females), 54 (four).

Food: Two specimens were dissected. Gut contents included large clumps of organic particles and mineral grains, plus many coccoliths.

Distribution: Cape Basin, 2972 and 1861 meters. Benthic.

Urothoe simplignathia, new species
Figure 33

Diagnosis: Eyes absent; palp of maxilla 1 biarticulate; accessory flagellum well developed; gnathopods 1 and 2 similar, both simple; third pleonal epimeron with a long acute tooth, peraeopods 3–5 slender.

Figure 34. *Urothoe vemae*, n. sp. Female, 3.5 mm., *Vema* Sta. 49. A: dorsal anterior edge of head, slightly damaged; B, C: antennae 1, 2; D: anterior view of mandibles and upper lip; E, F: mandible bodies—arrow indicates palp attachment point; G: mandibular palp; H: lower lip; I, J: maxillae 1, 2; K: maxilliped; L, M: gnathopods 1, 2; N, O: coxae 3, 2; P, Q, R: peraeopods 2, 3, 4; S, T, U: uropods 1, 2, 3; V: telson; W: lower posterior corner of third pleonal epimeron.

Holotype: L.G.O. No. 30, female, 3.75 mm., unique.

Type locality: *Vema* Station 22, Angola Basin, 3015 meters. Benthic.

Relationship: This species is unique in the genus, for both pairs of gnathopods are simple. See the remarks under the generic heading.

Other peculiarities include the minute inner plate of maxilla 1, the very slender and acute telsonic lobes, and the small inner plate of the maxilliped.

Urothoe vemae, new species

Figure 34

Diagnosis: Eyes absent; palp of maxilla 1 biarticulate; accessory flagellum well developed; gnathopods 1 and 2 similar, of the *elegans* type, subchelate; third pleonal epimeron with small tooth; peraeopods 3–5 slender.

Notes from the holotype, not figured: Article 2 of

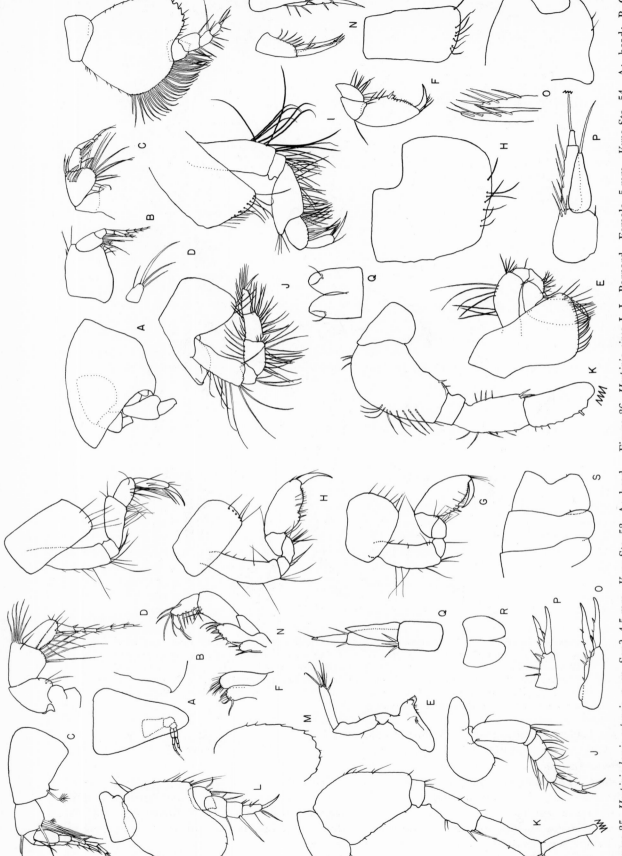

Figure 35. *Harpinia laevis capensis*, n. sp. Sex?, 4.5 mm., *Vema* Sta. 53. A: head, dorsal; B: lower lateral anterior corner of head; C, D: antennae 1, 2; E: mandible; F: maxilla 2; G, H: gnathopods 1, 2; I, J, K, L: peraeopods 1, 3, 4, 5; M: peraeopod 5, article 2 of left side; N: maxilliped; O, P, Q: uropods 1, 2, 3; R: telson; S: pleon segments 1–3.

Figure 36. *Harpinia cinca* J. L. Barnard. Female, 5 mm, *Vema* Sta. 54. A: head; B, C: antennae 1, 2; D: maxillipedal palp article 4; E, F: gnathopods 1, 2; G, H: coxae 2, 4; I, J, K, L: peraeopods 1, 3, 4, 5; M, N, P: uropods 1, 2, 3; O: uropod 2, ends of rami; Q: telson; R: pleon segment 3.

peraeopod 5 is 1.3 times as wide as article 2 of peraeopod 4; in addition, the same article is shorter on peraeopod 5; article 6 of peraeopod 5 extends down to article 5 of peraeopod 4 (as the peraeopods are fixed to the animal); articles 3–7 more slender than on peraeopod 4. Antenna 1, flagellum has five articles; antenna 2, flagellum has three articles.

Holotype: L.G.O. No. 31, female, 3.5 mm.

Type locality: *Vema* Station 53, Cape Basin, 4893 meters.

Relationship: The slender peraeopods 3–5, lack of eyes, and the tooth of the third pleonal epimeron are distinctive among the species assigned to the *elegans* group. The species is closest to *U. denticulata* Gurjanova (1951), but differs by the lack of eyes, the shorter tooth of the third pleonal epimeron, the stouter third peraeopod, and the more slender fifth peraeopod.

Material examined: Stations 49 (one female, 3.5 mm.), 53 (one).

Distribution: Slope of South Sandwich Trench, 2747 meters, and Cape Basin, 4893 meters. Probably a eurybathic species with wide geographic range. Benthic.

Family: PHOXOCEPHALIDAE

Genus: HARPINIA Boeck

Harpinia laevis capensis, new subspecies
Figure 35

Diagnosis: Head with lower corner produced to a minute point; epistome not produced; peraeopod 5, article 2 produced down to the end of article 4, posterior edge with three to nine small teeth; third pleonal epimeron straight behind, lower corner rounded but protruding slightly beyond posterior margin.

Male: Unknown.

Holotype: L.G.O. No. 33, sex unknown, 3.5 mm.

Type locality: *Vema* Station 53, Cape Basin, 4893 meters.

Material examined: Stations 52 (one, sex unknown, 8 mm.), 53 (holotype and figured specimen, sex unknown, 4.5 mm.).

Relationship: This subspecies differs from *Harpinia laevis* Sars (1895, Pl. 56) only by the slightly different configuration of the third pleonal epimeron. The lower corner of the head is slightly produced, unknown in the typical subspecies.

The large 8-mm. specimen of Station 52 is identical to the holotype except for the greater setosity of the animal and the greater number (nine) of teeth on the posterior edge of article 2 of peraeopod 5. Uropod 2 has seven peduncular setae.

Food: The stomach of the figured specimen contained the usual finely particulate matter with remains of harpacticoid copepods, coccoliths, discoasters, and unknown setae. The large specimen of Station 52 was dissected and the stomach contained only the usual finely particulate matter.

Distribution: Cape Basin, 4893 and 4961 meters. Benthic. The typical subspecies is known in western European waters, 40–1505 meters.

Harpinia cinca J. L. Barnard
Figure 36

Synonym: *Harpinia cinca* J. L. Barnard, 1961, p. 70.

Diagnosis: Head with medium-sized process at lower corner; epistome not produced; peraeopod 5, article 2 produced down to the end of article 3, posterior edge with three small serrations, below which is a large posteriorly directed tooth followed by a smaller one; lower edge with about five serrations; distal anterior edge of article 2 quite expanded and armed with up to 25 large plumose setae; rest of appendage rather short; third pleonal epimeron bears a medium-sized, slightly upturned tooth at the lower corner.

Male: Unknown.

Holotype: L.G.O. No. 35, female, 5.5 mm.

Type locality: *Vema* Station 54, Cape Basin, 1861 meters.

Material examined: Stations 16 (3.5 and 3.0 mm., unknown sex), 54 (18 specimens, 3.0 to 5.5 mm., all females or juveniles).

Relationship: This species resembles *Harpinia latipes* Norman (1900, p. 338) in the produced tooth of the third pleonal segment and the expanded setal row of peraeopod 5, but differs by the fact that the teeth of peraeopod 5 are on the posterior edge of article 2, while they are on the ventral edge in *H. latipes*.

Food: Two specimens of Station 54 were dissected. The stomach contents consisted only of finely particulate organic matter.

Distribution: Cape Basin, 1861 and 2972 meters.

Harpinia excavata Chevreux
Figures 37, 38

Synonyms: *Harpinia excavata* Chevreux, 1888, pp. 3–5; Chevreux, 1900, pp. 37–38, Pl. 6, Fig. 1; Stebbing, 1906, pp. 142–143; K. H. Barnard, 1925, pp. 340–341.

Diagnosis: Head with a small process at lower corner; epistome not produced; peraeopod 5, article 2 produced down to the end of article 3; posterior edge smooth, lower oblique edge with about ten small serrations; distal anterior edge of article 2

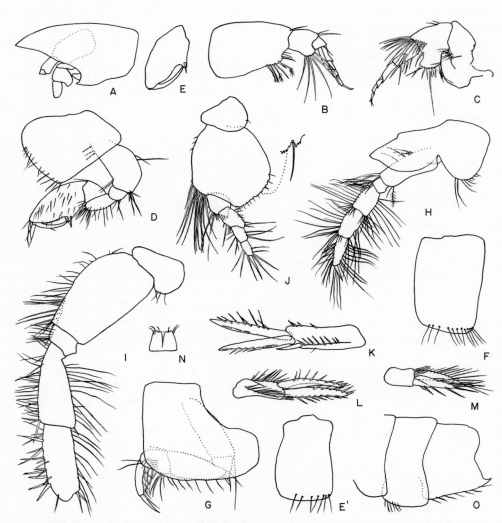

Figure 37. *Harpinia excavata* Chevreux. Female, 8 mm., *Vema* Sta. 54. A: head; B, C: antennae 1, 2; D, E: gnathopods 1, 2; E': coxa 2; F: coxa 3; G, H, I, J: peraeopods 2, 3, 4, 5; K, L, M: uropods 1, 2, 3; N: telson; O: pleon segments 1–3.

Figure 38. *Harpinia* cf. *excavata* Chevreux. Female, 7 mm., *Vema* Sta. 22. A, B: head, both sides; C, D: antennae 1, 2; E: gnathopod 1; F: coxa 2; G: gnathopod 2, articles 6–7; H: coxa 4; I, J, K, L: peraeopods 1, 3, 4, 5: M, N, O: uropods 1, 2, 3; P: telson; Q: pleon segment 3.

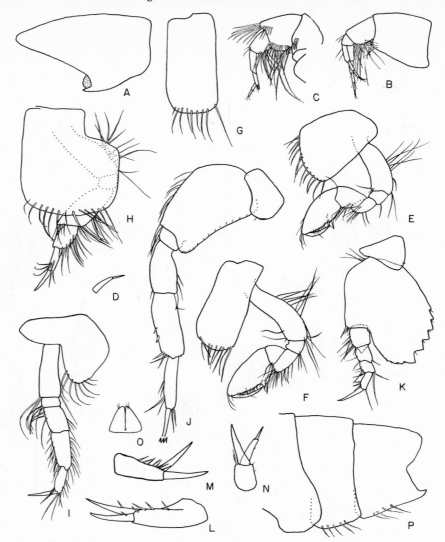

Figure 39. *Harpinia wandichia*, n. sp. Female, 4.25 mm., *Vema* Sta. 49. A: head; B, C: antennae 1, 2; D: maxillipedal palp article 4; E, F: gnathopods 1, 2; G: coxa 3; H, I, J, K: peraeopods 2, 3, 4, 5; L, M, N: uropods 1, 2, 3; O: telson; P: pleon segments 1–3.

expanded and bearing about 12 large plumose setae; third pleonal epimeron with a small tooth at lower posterior corner.

Male: Unknown.

Material examined: Stations 16 (three females?, 5–7 mm.), 54 (three females?, 5, 5, and 8 mm.).

Varietal form: Differs by the longer tooth of the third pleonal epimeron.

Material examined: Station 22 (two females, 4 and 7 mm., and a juvenile, 2.5 mm.).

Remarks: The very spinose uropods 1 and 2 are relatively rare in this genus.

Food: The stomach of a juvenile, 2.5 mm., station 22, contained only finely particulate matter.

Distribution: The normal form lives in Cape Basin, 2972 and 1861 meters, and the variety in Angola Basin, 3015 meters. Benthic. Previously recorded from Western European Basin 363–510 meters, and Cape Basin slopes, 448 and 1280 meters.

Harpinia wandichia, new species
Figure 39

Diagnosis: Head with a small process at the lower corner; epistome not produced; peraeopod 5, article 2 produced down to the end of article 4, distal posterior edge oblique, bearing four large broad, shallow teeth, above which are two smaller ones, six teeth in all; lower edge with two serrations; third pleonal epimeron with a short tooth at lower posterior corner.

Male: Unknown.

Holotype: L.G.O. No. 40, female, 4.25 mm., unique.

Type locality: Vema Station 49, slope of South Sandwich Trench, 2747 meters. Benthic.

Relationship: This species is closely related to *Harpinia tarasovi* Bulycheva (1936, p. 248), but differs by the shallower posterior teeth of peraeopod 5.

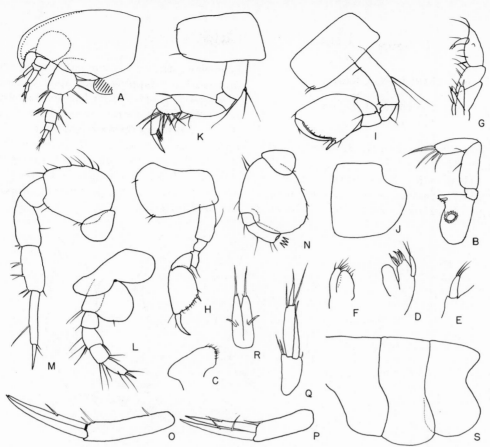

Figure 40. *Leptophoxoides molaris*, n. gen. n. sp. Sex?, 3 mm., *Vema* Sta. 52. A: head; B: mandible; C: half of lower lip; D: maxilla 1; E: palp of maxilla 1; F: maxilla 2; G: maxilliped; H, I: gnathopods 1, 2; J: coxa 4; K, L, M, N: peraeopods 1, 3, 4, 5; O, P, Q: uropods 1, 2, 3; R: telson; S: pleon segments 1–3.

LEPTOPHOXOIDES, new genus

Diagnosis: Rostrum sharp and deflexed; mandible with well-developed and slightly ridged molar; inner plate of maxilla 1 as large as outer plate; apex of maxillipedal palp article 3 produced.

Type species: Leptophoxoides molaris, n. sp.

Relationship: This genus is very closely related to *Leptophoxus* Sars, but differs by the large slightly ridged molar and the large inner plate of the first maxilla.

The well-developed molar, which rarely occurs in phoxocephalids, I consider to be a primitive character in this particular amphipod family, where the progressive evanescence of the feature is common. In other respects the following species is scarcely distinguishable from *Leptophoxus falcatus* Sars. Perhaps it stretches systematic splitting to entertain this new genus, but precisely this same difference has been used

to separate *Phoxocephalus* Stebbing and *Metaphoxus* Bonnier, where cross comparison of some species pairs between the two genera reveals scarcely any specific differences, merely generic differences.

Leptophoxoides molaris, new species
Figure 40

Diagnosis: With the characters of the genus.

Descriptive features differentiating this species from *Leptophoxus falcatus:* the lower posterior corner of the third pleonal epimeron is rounded, the lower edge quite convex; inner ramus of uropod 3 is nearly as long as article 1 of outer ramus.

Holotype: L.G.O. No. 41, female, 3 mm., unique.

Type locality: Vema Station 52, Cape Basin, 4961 meters. Benthic.

Family: AMPELISCIDAE

Genus: AMPELISCA Krøyer

Ampelisca byblisoides K. H. Barnard
Figure 41

Synonyms: Ampelisca byblisoides K. H. Barnard, 1916, pp. 335–336, Pl. 34, Fig. 4.

Diagnosis: Head with front broadly truncate, lower part slightly indented for reception of antenna 2, not oblique as in most ampeliscids; antennae lanceolate, slender; telson with medial edges of lobes lined with overlapping setae, apices subacute.

Remarks: K. H. Barnard wrote that the third uropodal rami of his material were foliaceous, while in the present specimens they are lanceolate. The otherwise remarkable similarity of the present specimens to *A. byblisoides* and their uniqueness among 90 species in the genus *Ampelisca* does not permit the description of a new species until the problem of uropod 3 can be explored further.

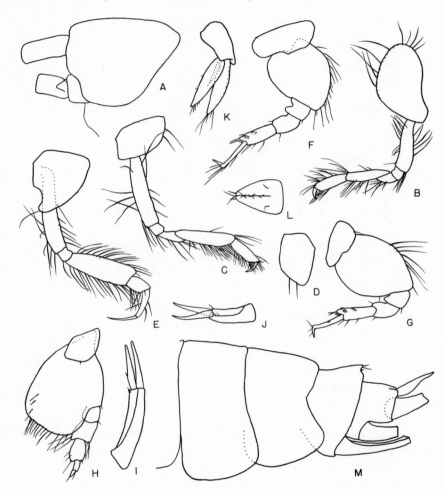

Figure 41. *Ampelisca byblisoides* K. H. Barnard. Female, 6 mm., *Vema* Sta. 54. A: head; B, C: gnathopods 1, 2; D: coxa 3; E, F, G, H: peraeopods 2, 3, 4, 5; I, J, K: uropods 1, 2, 3; L: telson; M: pleon segments 2–6 (5–6 fused).

missing; eyes and corneal lenses absent; peraeopod 5, article 4 longer than article 3, expansion of article 2 with slightly oblique setose lower edge, articles 6 and 7 very short (hence "byblisoides," relationship to *Byblis*); third pleonal epimeron rounded at lower corner; pleon segment 4 with an elevated acute process, not lamellar; uropods 1 and 2 normal, slender, reaching the same distance; uropod 3, rami

Food: The stomach of the figured specimen was filled with finely particulate material, a few mineral particles, and some globigerinid foraminifers.

Material examined: Vema Station 54 (females, 6 and 6 mm., male, 6 mm., young 3.5, 2, 2 mm.).

Distribution: Previously recorded off Cape Point, South Africa, 700 fathoms (1281 meters). Recorded here from Cape Basin, 1861 meters.

Family: STENOTHOIDAE

Genus: PROBOLOIDES Della Valle

Proboloides (Metopoides) aequalis, new species
Figure 42

Diagnosis: Belonging to the antarctic subgenus *Metopoides* by the possession of a biarticulate accessory flagellum; article 3 of antenna 1 as long as article 1; gnathopod 1 very slender, scarcely subchelate; gnathopod 2, article 6 having the palm and hind margin of equal length; article 6 twice as long as broad; peraeopod 3, article 2 widening into a postero-distal lobe; third pleonal epimeron quadrate; uropod 3 broken.

Holotype: L.G.O. No. 43, male, 2 mm., unique.

Type locality: *Vema* Station 15, Cape Basin, 4986 meters.

Relationship: This blind *Proboloides* is related to *P. dentimanus* Nicholls (1938) by the slender first gnathopod, but differs by the long third article of antenna 1, which appears to be unique in the genus. Otherwise, the palm of gnathopod 2 is remarkably similar to *P. dentimanus*. Another character verifying the distinctness of the two species is the more slender fourth article of peraeopod 5 in *P. aequalis*.

The new species also is related to *P. perlatus* K. H. Barnard (1930), but differs by the lack of eyes and the configuration of articles 5 and 6 on gnathopod 2.

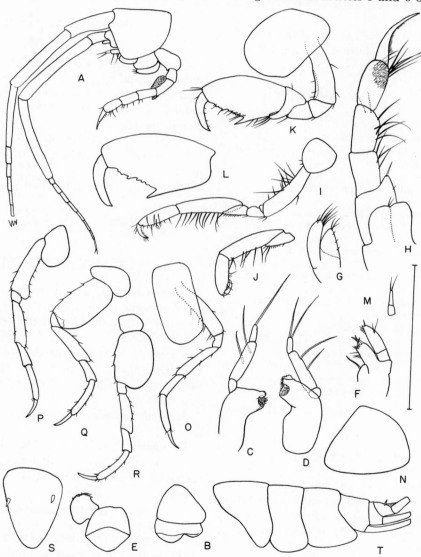

Figure 42. *Proboloides aequalis*, n. sp. Sex?, 2 mm., *Vema* Sta. 15. A: head; B: upper lip; C, D: mandibles; E: lower lip, part, with fused inner lobes; F, G: maxillae 1, 2; H: maxilliped; I, J: gnathopod 1, inside and outside; K, L: gnathopod 2; M: accessory flagellum and scale of length of article 3 of peduncle to right; N: coxa 4; O, P, Q, R: peraeopods 1, 3, 4, 5; S: telson; T: pleon segments 1–6.

Stenothoids often are inquilinous, mainly in benthic sessile organisms, but a few are in pelagic medusae, and the habitat of the present animal is unknown.

Family: TIRONIDAE

Diagnosis: Head massive, usually produced into a deflexed rostrum. Antenna 1 with normal accessory flagellum (except *Liouvillea*, where it is vestigial). Mandible with palp slight, the third article usually shortened (except *Bruzeliopsis* and *Liouvillea*). Mandible bears a well-defined molar. Inner plates of maxillipeds strongly developed. Gnathopods 1–2 feeble, slender, slightly subchelate or simple. Coxa 4 not large, often smaller than 3. Coxae long (as contrasted with Pardaliscidae). Uropods 1–2 with outer ramus shorter than inner. Telson cleft (except in *Bruzelia* and *Bruzeliopsis*).

The combination of long coxae, mandibular molar, and well-developed inner plates of the maxilliped is significant.

KEY TO THE FAMILY TIRONIDAE

1. Telson entire   2
1. Telson slightly or fully cleft   3
2. Mandibular palp article 3 very short . . . . *Bruzelia*
2. Mandibular palp article 3 long . . . . . *Bruzeliopsis*
3. Gnathopods 1–2 subchelate   4
3. Gnathopods 1–2 simple   6
4. Article 5 of gnathopods 1–2 shorter than article 6 . . . . *Liouvillea*
4. Article 5 of gnathopods 1–2 longer than article 6 .   5
5. Mandible with small spinose molar, coxa 3 larger than 4 . . . . *Syrrhoe*
5. Mandible with large smooth molar, coxa 3 not larger than 4 . . . . *Syrrhoites*[a]
6. Coxa 3 much larger than coxa 4 and expanded ventrally   7
6. Coxa 3 not or scarcely larger than coxa 4, generally smaller, not expanded ventrally   8
7. Mandibular molar ridged, head prolonged anteriorly . . . . *Pseudotiron*
7. Mandibular molar smooth, head curved down to rostrum . . . . *Jeddo*, n. gen.
8. Mandibular molar ridged, eyes present . . . . *Tiron*
8. Mandibular molar smooth, eyes absent *Kindia*, n. gen.

[a] For the purposes of the key, *Austrosyrrhoe* K. H. Barnard (1925) is included here.

Genus: BRUZELIA Boeck

Diagnosis: Eyes vestigial or absent; rostrum large; molar of mandible large and smooth; palp article 3 of mandible short; gnathopods subchelate; coxa 4 about equal in size to coxa 3; telson entire, apex minutely emarginate.

Type species: *Bruzelia typica* Boeck.

KEY TO THE GENUS BRUZELIA

1. All peraeon segments with sharp dorsal teeth . . .   2
1. Only a few peraeon segments with dorsal teeth . .   3
2. Lower lateral margins of peraeon segments with posteriorly directed teeth . . . . *dentata*
2. Lower lateral margins of peraeon segments smooth . . . . *australis*
3. All but first peraeon and all pleon segments slightly carinate and projecting dorsally . . *tuberculata*
3. Only a few segments carinate and projecting . . .   4
4. Pleon segment 3 with a dorsal tooth   5
4. Pleon segment 3 lacks a dorsal tooth . . . . . *diodon*
5. Peraeon segments 6–7 and pleon 1–2 lack teeth . *typica*
5. Peraeon segments 6–7 and pleon 1–2 bear teeth . . . . *cuspidata*, n. sp.

Bruzelia cuspidata, new species
Figure 43

Diagnosis: Eyes absent; article 1 of antenna 1 produced distally; peraeon segments 6–7 and pleon segments 1–3 bear a dorsal posterior tooth; lower posterior corner of third pleonal epimeron with a straight tooth.

Holotype: L.G.O. No. 44, sex?, 3 mm., unique.

Type locality: Vema Station 18, Cape Basin, 4050 meters.

Relationship: Shown by the key to the species.

Bruzelia diodon K. H. Barnard
Figures 44, 45

Synonyms: Bruzelia diodon K. H. Barnard, 1916, pp. 168–169.

Diagnosis: Eyes absent; peraeon segment 7 and pleon segment 1 bear a dorsal posterior tooth; lower posterior corner of third pleonal epimeron with an upturned tooth.

Remarks: K. H. Barnard did not figure this species, but the present specimen fits his very adequate description, except for slight discrepancies in the antennae.

Material examined: Vema Station 16 (one, 3 mm.).

Distribution: Reported by K. H. Barnard from a point 36 miles off Cape Point, 650 fathoms (1189 meters). Recorded here from Cape Basin, 2972 meters.

JEDDO, new genus

Diagnosis: Eyes absent; mandible very large, covering the entire ventral surface of the head and bearing a large smooth molar; gnathopods 1–2 simple; coxa 3 much larger than others; telson cleft about one-half its length.

Type species: Jeddo simplisyrrhis, n. sp.

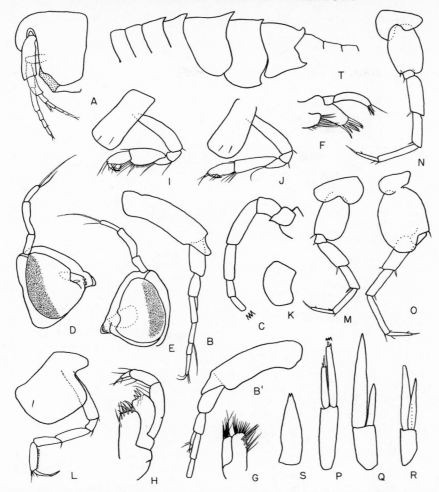

Figure 43. *Bruzelia cuspidata* n. sp. Sex?, 3 mm., *Vema* Sta. 18. A: head, B, B', C: antennae 1, 1, 2; D, E: mandibles; F, G: maxillae 1, 2; H: maxilliped; I, J: gnathopods 1, 2; K: coxa 3, damaged; L, M, N, O: peraeopods 2, 3, 4, 5; P, Q, R: uropods 1, 2, 3; S: telson; T: peraeon segments 4–7, pleon segments 1–6, left to right.

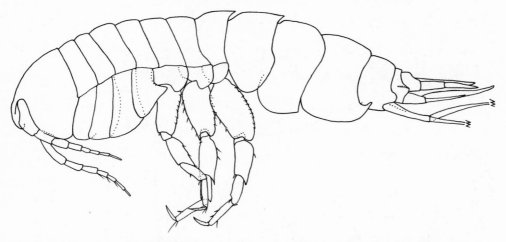

Figure 44. *Bruzelia diodon* K. H. Barnard. Sex?, 3 mm., *Vema* Sta. 16. Lateral view of animal.

Relationship: The genus is similar to *Syrrhoe* Goës in the large third coxa, but differs by the simple gnathopods. It is related to *Tiron* Liljeborg and *Pseudotiron* Chevreux by the simple gnathopods, but the mandible has a large smooth molar, not spinose and ridged as in the other two genera.

The mandibular palp is missing or absent. A very careful examination of the mandibles failed to reveal any point of attachment for palps.

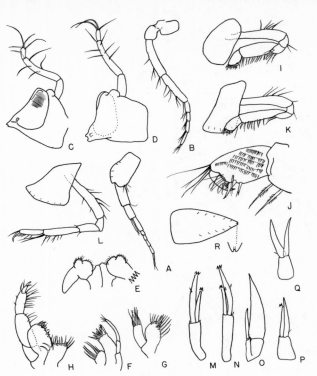

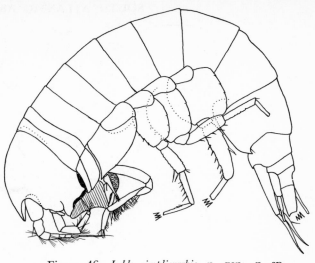

Figure 46. *Jeddo simplisyrrhis*, n. gen., n. sp. Female, 7 mm., *Vema* Sta. 54. Lateral view of animal.

Figure 45. *Bruzelia diodon* K. H. Barnard. Sex?, 3 mm., *Vema* Sta. 16. A, B: antennae 1, 2; C, D: mandibles; E: lower lip; F, G: maxillae 1, 2; H: maxilliped; I, J: gnathopod 1; K: gnathopod 2; L: peraeopod 1; M, N: uropod 1; O: uropod 2; P, Q: uropod 3; R: telson.

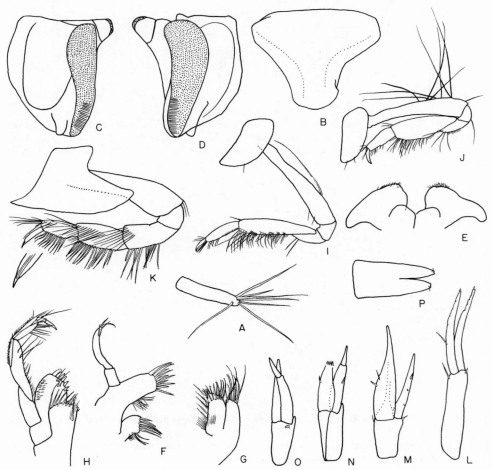

Figure 47. *Jeddo simplisyrrhis*, n. gen., n. sp. Female, 7 mm., *Vema* Sta. 54. A: accessory flagellum; B: upper lip; C, D: mandibles; E: lower lip; F, G: maxillae 1, 2; H: maxilliped; I, J: gnathopods 1, 2; K: peraeopod 1; L, M, N, O: uropods 1, 2, 3, 3; P: telson.

Jeddo simplisyrrhis, new species
Figures 46, 47

Diagnosis: With the characters of the genus.
Holotype: L.G.O. No. 46, sex?, 4 mm.
Type locality: *Vema* Station 54, Cape Basin, 1861 meters.
Material examined: *Vema* Station 54 (two).

KINDIA, new genus

Diagnosis: Head with large rostrum; mandible with large smooth molar; palp article 3 of mandible scarcely larger than article 1; gnathopods 1–2 simple; coxa 4 larger than coxa 3; telson cleft one-half its length.
Type species: *Kindia sorpresa*, n. sp.
Relationship: See the key to the Tironidae. The genus differs from *Tiron* Liljeborg and *Pseudotiron* Chevreux by its large smooth molar and from *Jeddo*, n. gen., by the small third coxa.
The mandible has the primary plate separated by a suture line in both species of the genus.

KEY TO THE GENUS KINDIA

1. Peraeon segments 5–7 bear dorsal
teeth. . . . . *sorpresa*, n. sp.
1. Peraeon segments 3–7 bear dorsal
teeth. . . . . *lorida*, n. sp.

Kindia sorpresa, new species
Figure 48

Diagnosis: Peraeon segments 5–7 and pleon segments 1–4 bear dorsal teeth.
Holotype: L.G.O. No. 47, sex?, 3.5 mm., unique.
Type locality: *Vema* Station 54, Cape Basin, 1861 meters.
Remarks: The lower lip is damaged, and uropods 1 and 3 are missing. The upper lip has an anterior carina.

Kindia lorida, new species
Figure 49

Diagnosis: Peraeon segments 3–7 and pleon segments 1–3 and 5 bear dorsal teeth (pleon segment 4 damaged dorsally).
Holotype: L.G.O. No. 48, female, 4 mm., unique.
Type locality: *Vema* Station 14, Cape Basin, 3045 meters.
Remarks: The animal is badly damaged, with coxae 3–4, gnathopod 2, peraeopods 1–5, and uropods 1–3 damaged or missing. However, it is sufficiently intact for description and assignment to this new genus.

Genus: PSEUDOTIRON Chevreux

Pseudotiron golens, new species
Figures 50, 51

Diagnosis: Head scarcely prolonged anteriorly; basal article of flagellum on antenna 1 as long as accessory flagellum; accessory flagellum has two articles and possibly a missing third; basal flagellar article of antenna 2 elongated; coxa 3 as short as coxa 2; peraeopods 3–5 short, nearly of equal length, lower posterior corners of second articles rounded; seventh articles of all peraeopods elongated, not claw-shaped; uropods 1 and 2 short, uropod 1 reaches only halfway along uropod 2; pleon segments 3 and 4 each with a slight dorsal posterior tooth.
Holotype: L.G.O. No. 49, sex unknown, 5 mm.
Type locality: *Vema* Station 53, Cape Basin, 4893 meters.
Relationship: The new species differs from *P. longicaudatus* Pirlot (1934, p. 185, Molucca Sea, 835 meters) in nearly all of the diagnostic features cited above, especially by the head, antennae, peraeopods 3–5, and uropod 1.
It differs from *P. bouvieri* Chevreux (see Stebbing, 1906, Mediterranean, 170 meters) by the less claw-like seventh articles of peraeopods 1–5.
Gut contents: Holotype—a fecal pellet contained refractory mineral particles and fine organic detritus.
Material examined: Stations 18 (? one, 6 mm., damaged), 53 (one).
Distribution: Cape Basin, 4050 and 4893 meters. Probably a bathypelagic species, feeding on bottom material.

Genus: SYRRHOITES Sars

Diagnosis: Antenna 1 with large accessory flagellum; rostrum well developed; palp article 3 of mandible very small; lower lip with slight inner lobes; gnathopods 1 and 2 slightly subchelate, article 6 shorter than 5; coxa 3 is not larger than coxa 4; telson cleft.
Type species: *Syrrhoites serratus* Sars.
Discussion: The species which have been placed in this genus exhibit an interspecific polymorphy of considerable extent, and several problems are posed in light of the species which I have at hand.
The type species of the genus has a slender fifth article of gnathopod 1. In 1925 K. H. Barnard erected the genus *Austrosyrrhoe*, which he distinguished from all related tironid genera by the stout first gnathopod (and the "simple" palms of the gnathopods). Then in 1931 Stephensen erected *Austrosyrrhoe* (?) *septentrionalis*, which also had the stout fifth article of gnathopod 1 and in other descriptive features was quite close to *Austrosyrrhoe crassipes* K. H. Barnard, the type species. However, Gurjanova (1951) transferred

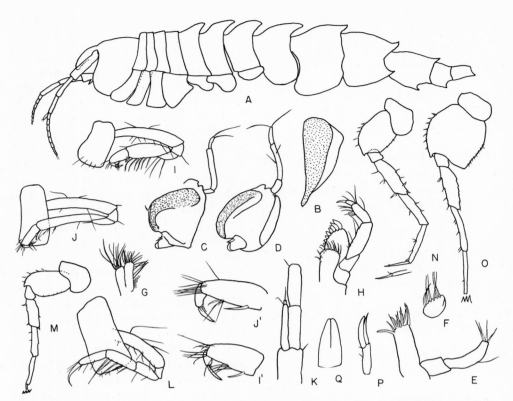

Figure 48. *Kindia sorpresa*, n. gen. n. sp. Sex?, 3.5 mm., *Vema* Sta. 54. A: body, lateral view; B: epistome, lateral, front to right; C, D: mandibles; E: maxilla 1; F: maxilla 1, inner lobe; G: maxilla 2; H: maxilliped; I, I′, J, J′: gnathopods 1, 2; K: accessory flagellum; L, M, N, O: peraeopods 1, 3, 4, 5; P: uropod 2; Q: telson.

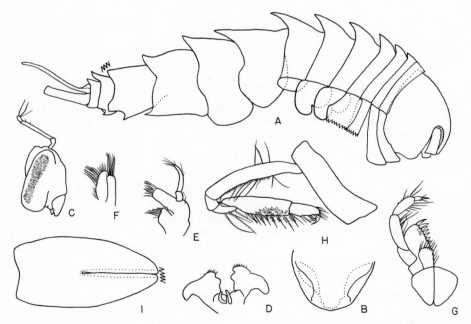

Figure 49. *Kindia lorida*, n. gen., n. sp. Female, 4 mm., *Vema* Sta. 14. A: body, lateral view; B: upper lip; C: mandible; D: lower lip; E, F: maxillae 1, 2; G: maxilliped; H: gnathopod 1; I: telson.

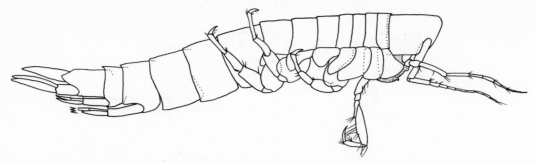

Figure 50. *Pseudotiron golens*, n. sp. Sex?, 5 mm., *Vema* Sta. 53. Lateral view of animal.

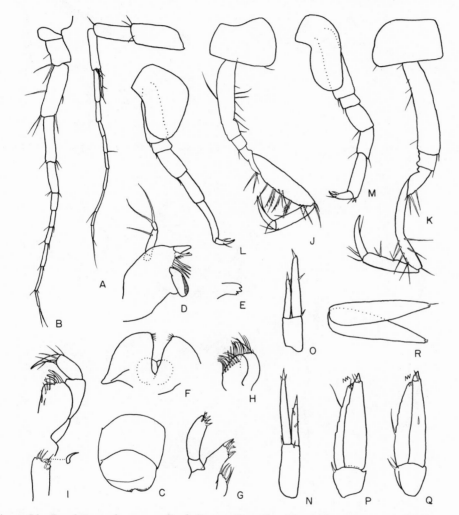

Figure 51. *Pseudotiron golens*, n. sp. Sex?, 5 mm., *Vema* Sta. 53. A, B: antennae 1, 2; C: upper lip; D: mandible; E: primary plate of other mandible; F: lower lip; G, H: maxillae 1, 2; I: maxilliped; J, K: gnathopods 1, 2; L, M: peraeopods 1, 2; N, O, P, Q: uropods 1, 2, 3, 3; R: telson.

A. septentrionalis to *Syrrhoites*, thus causing the emendation that some species of *Syrrhoites* have stout first gnathopods. This left *Austrosyrrhoe crassipes* standing alone, despite its close resemblance to *A. septentrionalis*.

In the *Vema* collections are specimens of a tironid, obviously congeneric with *S. septentrionalis* but bearing a remarkable resemblance to K. H. Barnard's description of *A. crassipes*.

I asked Dr. K. H. Barnard of the South African Museum to reexamine the unique type of *A. crassipes* in light of the present specimen, but Dr. Barnard kindly wrote that the type has since degenerated to the point of unrecognizability. One specific point of difference in the *Vema* specimens is the fact that the horizontal pleonal tooth is borne on segment 5, not 4 as described for *A. crassipes*, but so situated that in a

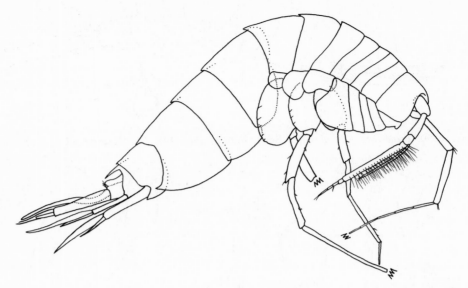

Figure 52. *Syrrhoites torpens*, n. sp. Sex?, 4 mm., *Vema* Sta. 14. Lateral view of animal.

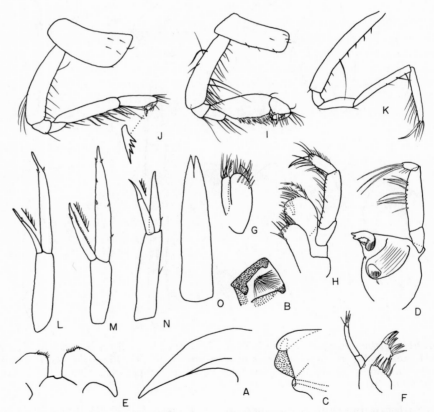

Figure 53. *Syrrhoites torpens*, n. sp. Sex?, 4 mm., *Vema* Sta. 14. A: rostrum; B: lower view of upper lip to show concavity; C: lateral view of upper lip to show hooded structure surrounding concavity; D: mandible; E: lower lip; F, G: maxillae 1, 2; H: maxilliped; I, J: gnathopods 1, 2; K: peraeopod 1; L, M, N: uropods 1, 2, 3; O: telson.

very transparent specimen it might easily be considered to arise on segment 4 and overlap segment 5, as in *A. crassipes* (see the figure herein). Another point was the need to recheck the first gnathopod, since the figure herein and K. H. Barnard's (1925) figure were not precisely identical, although fixation and mounting techniques might cause discrepancies. The next point was the fact that *A. crassipes* has a telson split about halfway, while the present one is split one-sixth. Finally, the point of the length of telson had to be considered. The present specimen has a very elongated telson, quite unlike that of *S. septentrionalis* but like *S. anaticauda* K. H. Barnard (1930). The degree of elongation in *A. crassipes* is unknown, although it was described as elongated.

In summary, the problems are these: whether the *Vema* specimen can be identified as *A. crassipes* or is a new species; whether the *Vema* specimen is actually a *Syrrhoites* and, if not *A. crassipes*, whether the latter species and its genus should be submerged in *Syrrhoites*.

Two factors have to be considered: the stoutness of the first gnathopods and the degree of telson elongation. Do these have any generic value? I incline to the view that they do not. The difference between the extremes of stoutness and slenderness of gnathopods is strictly quantitative in value, and the telson length is not correlated with the gnathopods. The gnathopods of *S. septentrionalis* and the *Vema* specimens are the same, but the telsons are quite different. On the other hand, the telsons of *S. septentrionalis* and *S. serratus*, the type species, are identical, but the first gnathopods are quite different in size.

I hesitate to submerge *Austrosyrrhoe* in *Syrrhoites* until an unquestioned specimen of *A. crassipes* is discovered, and the *Vema* specimen has too many discrepancies, as cited, including characters of the first antenna. Thus the *Vema* specimen is described as a new species in *Syrrhoites*, and the decision of submerging *Austrosyrrhoe* must be deferred until better materials are discovered.

KEY TO SYRRHOITES

1. Pleon segments 1–3 lack conspicuous dorsal carinae or teeth 2
1. Pleon segments 1–3 bear conspicuous dorsal carinae or teeth 4
2. Telson very long and split only one-sixth its length . . . . *torpens*, n. sp.
2. Telson shorter, split halfway or more 3
3. Gnathopod 1, finger short, palm bears no large spine . . . . *fimbriatus*
3. Gnathopod 1, finger long, palm bears a large spine . . . . *septentrionalis*
4. Pleon segment 3, dorsal carina bidentate . . *serratus*
4. Pleon segment 3, dorsal carina not bidentate . . . 5
5. Pleon segment 3 with small dorsal reverted tooth . 6
5. Pleon segment 3 with large straight tooth or none 7
6. Rostrum long, deflexed, third epimeron with upturned tooth . . . . *pusillus*
6. Rostrum of medium length, scarcely deflexed, third epimeron with long serrated tooth . . *anaticauda*
7. Third pleonal epimeron acutely prolonged . . . *walkeri*
7. Third pleonal epimeron quadrate . . . . . . *tenellus*

Syrrhoites torpens, new species
Figures 52, 53

Diagnosis: Peraeon segments 6–7 and pleon segments 1–4 each with a very small inconspicuous dorsal tooth; pleon segment 5 bears a long horizontal tooth; third pleonal epimeron prolonged and sweeping evenly into a sharp tooth; coxa 4 conspicuously larger than coxa 3; telson reaching as far as end of uropod 3 but split only one-sixth of its length; rostrum slender, not conspicuous.

Holotype: L.G.O. No. 51, sex?, 3 mm.

Type locality: *Vema* Station 14, Cape Basin, 3045 meters.

Material examined: *Vema* Stations 14 (two), 16 (two).

Relationship: See the key to the genus, and the discussion under *Syrrhoites*.

Distribution: Cape Basin, 3045 and 2972 meters.

Family: PARDALISCIDAE

NECOCHEA, new genus

Diagnosis: Antenna 1 slightly shorter than antenna 2; accessory flagellum present; palp article 3 of mandible as long as article 2; maxilla 1 with very small inner plate; maxilla 2 vestigial, composed of two tiny lobes each bearing a seta; maxillipedal inner plates obsolete, each outer plate broad and attached to a long article; article 5 of gnathopods 1 and 2 longer than article 6; coxa 5 larger than any anterior coxa; coxa 7 hidden by coxa 6.

Type species: *Necochea pardella*, n. sp.

Relationship: This is an aberrant genus by its evanescent second maxillae and maxillipedal inner plates and by the large fifth and sixth coxae. Otherwise it is closely related to *Pardalisca* Krøyer.

Necochea pardella, new species
Figures 54, 55

Descriptive features: Pleon segments 4–5 each bear a dorsal posterior tooth.

Holotype: L.G.O. No. 53, sex?, 2.5 mm., unique.

Type locality: *Vema* Station 46, East Scotia Basin, 3725 meters.

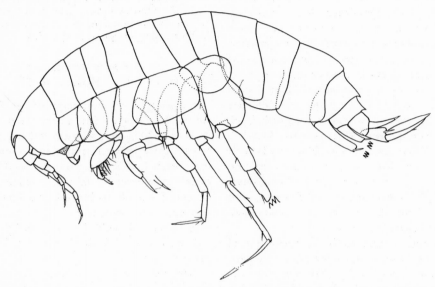

Figure 54. *Necochea pardella*, n. gen., n. sp. Sex?, 2.5 mm., *Vema* Sta. 46. Lateral view of animal.

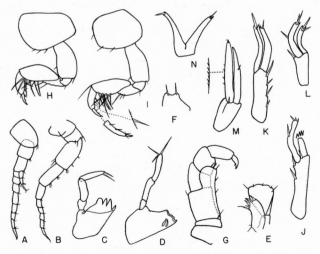

Figure 55. *Necochea pardella*, n. gen., n. sp. Sex?, 2.5 mm, *Vema* Sta. 46. A, B: antennae 1, 2; C, D: mandibles; E, F: maxillae 1, 2; G: maxilliped; H, I: gnathopods 1, 2; J, K, L, M: uropods 1, 2, 3, 3; N: telson.

Family: LEPECHINELLIDAE

Genus: LEPECHINELLA Stebbing

Lepechinella echinata (Chevreux)
Figures 56, 57

Synonyms: *Dorbanella echinata* Chevreux, 1914, pp. 1–4, Figs. 1–3. Chevreux, 1935, pp. 96–98, Pl. 13, Figs. 1, 11, 12. *Lepechinella echinata,* Schellenberg, 1955, p. 194.

Diagnosis: Rostrum long, spine-like; dorsal processes of body very long, two on peraeon segment 1, one each on peraeon segments 2–7 and pleon segments 1–4; coxa 1 not bifid, head and segments covered sparsely with stout articulated spines, which are easily broken, leaving pits; pleon segments 5–6 fused.

Mouth parts and accessory flagellum like *L. bierii* J. L. Barnard (1957).

Material examined: *Vema* Station 18 (one, 7 mm.).

Food: Very finely particulate matter, occasionally in clumps and two observed mineral particles.

Distribution: Bay of Biscay, 4380 meters (Chevreux); recorded here from Cape Basin, 4050 meters.

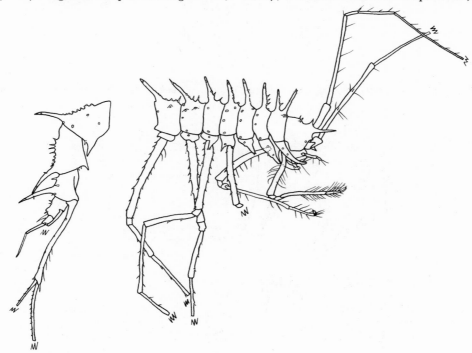

Figure 56. *Lepechinella echinata* (Chevreux). Sex?, 7 mm., *Vema* Sta. 18. Lateral view of animal, pleon segment 1 missing. Broken spines on body parts are represented by sockets.

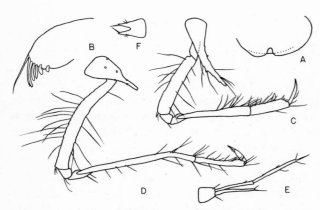

Figure 57. *Lepechinella echinata* (Chevreux). Sex?, 7 mm., *Vema* Sta. 18. A: upper lip; B: outer plate of maxilliped; C, D: gnathopods 1, 2; E: uropod 3; F: telson.

Lepechinella pangola, new species
Figures 58, 59

Diagnosis: Rostrum short; dorsal processes of body evanescent, two minute ones on peraeon segment 1, one each on peraeon segments 2–7, pleon segments 1–3 with processes increasing slightly in size, pleon segment 4 with a very acute one; coxa 1 not bifid.

Descriptive features: Antennae 1 and 2 are equal in length, and as long as segments 1–9 of body. Inner ramus of uropod 1 short. Mouth parts like *L. bierii* J. L. Barnard (1957), except that the outer plate of the maxilliped has longer setae distally and on both sides.

Holotype: L.G.O. No. 55, female, 15 mm.

Type locality: *Vema* Station 53, Cape Basin, 4893 meters.

Material examined: Station 53 (13 specimens, ranging down to 3-mm. juveniles).

Relationship: Differs from *L. cetrata* K. H. Barnard (1932, p. 186) by the short rostrum and the presence of distinct but minute processes on peraeon segments 1–7.

Food: A 10-mm. specimen contained particulate matter with a few probable mineral particles.

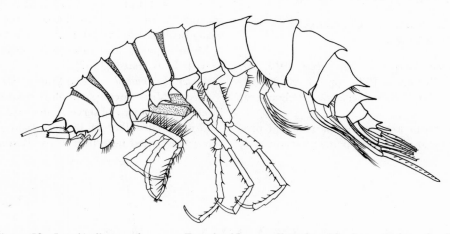

Figure 58. *Lepechinella pangola*, n. sp. Female, 15 mm., *Vema* Sta. 53. Lateral view of animal.

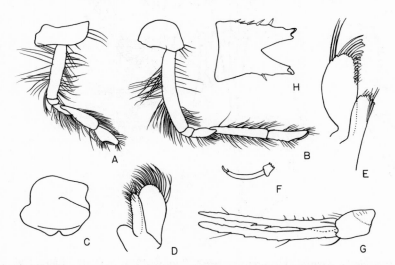

Figure 59. *Lepechinella pangola*, n. sp. Female, 15 mm., *Vema* Sta. 53. A, B: gnathopods 1, 2; C: upper lip; D: maxilla 2; E: maxilliped, minus palp; F: article 7 of peraeopod 2; G: uropod 3, H: telson.

Family : CALLIOPIIDAE

Genus: STENOPLEURA Stebbing

Stenopleura atlantica Stebbing
Figures 60, 61

Synonyms: *Stenopleura atlantica* Stebbing, 1888, p. 950, Pl. 84; Stephensen, 1915, pp. 45–46, Fig. 27.

Remarks: The telson is quite variable, as is seen in the present figures and has been noted by previous authors.

This species has eyes and has been caught in vertical and horizontal net tows, so that it is pelagic, probably upper pelagic.

Food: The female of Station 15 was dissected; the stomach contained a piece of copepod and either nematocysts or eggs and some unidentifiable objects which possibly were dinoflagellates. Only a very small amount of material was in the stomach.

Material examined: *Vema* Stations 15 (female, 6.5 mm.), 24 (males, 3.5 and 4 mm.).

Distribution: Recorded previously from North and South Atlantic to 36° N.; Antarctic; Indian Ocean. Reported here from the Cape Basin in a haul from 4986 meters, and from Angola Basin in a haul from 3951 meters. Pelagic.

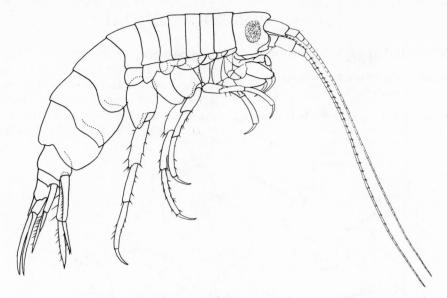

Figure 60. *Stenopleura atlantica* Stebbing. Male?, 4 mm., *Vema* Sta. 24. Lateral view of animal.

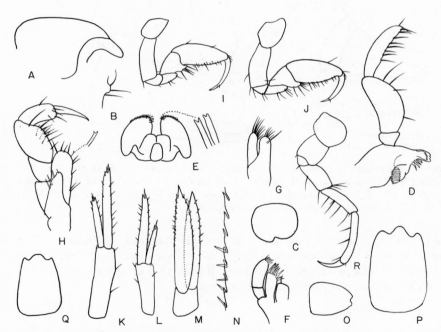

Figure 61. *Stenopleura atlantica* Stebbing. Male?, 4 mm., *Vema* Sta. 24. A: head and rostrum; B: accessory flagellum; C: upper lip; D: mandible; E: lower lip; F, G: maxillae 1, 2; H: maxilliped; I, J: gnathopods 1, 2; K, L, M: uropods 1, 2, 3; N: uropod 3, edge of inner ramus; O: telson; P: telson of male, 3.5 mm., Sta. 24; Q: telson of female, 6.5 mm., Sta. 15; R: peraeopod 5.

Family : PONTOGENEIIDAE

Genus: HARPINIOIDELLA Schellenberg

Harpinioidella fissicauda Schellenberg
Figure 62

Synonyms: *Harpinioidella fissicauda* Schellenberg, 1926, p. 357, Fig. 53.

cheir Stebbing (1888, Pl. 82). The antennae are missing on all three specimens at hand.

Material examined: *Vema* Station 53 (females, 4.5 mm., 3.25 mm., male, 4.25 mm.). The male was dissected, but no food was present in its stomach.

Distribution: Reported by Schellenberg from the

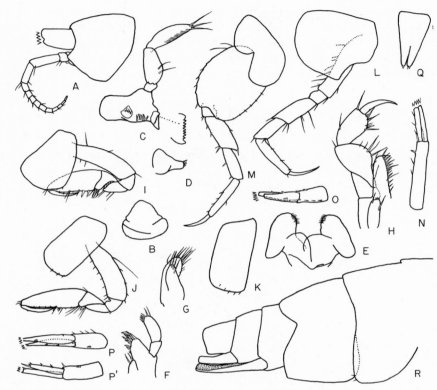

Figure 62. *Harpinioidella fissicauda* Schellenberg. Sex?, 3.25 mm., *Vema* Sta. 53. A: head; B: upper lip; C: mandible; D: molar of mandible; E: lower lip; F, G: maxillae 1, 2; H: maxilliped; I, J: gnathopods 1, 2; K: coxa 3; L, M: peraeopods 2, 3; N, O, P, P': uropods 1, 2, 3, 3; Q: telson; R: pleon segments 6–2.

Remarks: The present specimens appear identical with Schellenberg's species, although he figures only the telson, describes the mouth parts, and states that the animal is otherwise similar to *Harpinioides drepano-*

winter Antarctic ice station of the *Gauss*. Reported here from Cape Basin, 4893 meters. It is probable that this is a pelagic species, hence its wide geographic range.

Family: LILJEBORGIIDAE

Genus: LILJEBORGIA Bate

Liljeborgia zarica, new species
Figure 63

Diagnosis: Eyes absent; antennae short; head lobes rounded in front; epistome produced into a rounded lobe; article 7 of gnathopod 1 with one notch, of gnathopod 2 with three notches; pleon segments 1–5 each with one small dorsal horizontal tooth, no tooth on peraeon segment 7; third pleonal epimeron subacutely quadrate, lower corner minutely pointed; article 2 of peraeopods 3–5 ovate, not strongly serrate; telson cleft to base.

Holotype: L.G.O. No. 59, sex?, 3.5 mm.

Type locality: *Vema* Station 53, Cape Basin, 4893 meters.

Relationship: This species is closest to *L. consanguinea* Stebbing (1888, Pl. 91), but differs by the third pleonal epimeron, which is nearly quadrate, the lower tooth being scarcely evident, while in *L. consanguinea* it is produced below a sinus.

The new species is also related to *L. macronyx* Sars (1895, Pl. 188), but differs by the presence of a dorsal tooth on pleon segment 3 and the longer tooth of pleon segment 5.

Food: One 6-mm. specimen was dissected. The stomach was packed full with two large masses containing serial repetition of hooks; probably polychaetes; unfortunately, photographs did not turn out.

Material examined: *Vema* Station 53 (holotype, and specimens 6, 6, 5, 4.5, 4, 4, 3.5, 2.5 mm., none with brood plates). It is possible that this species is predaceous, although it could have fed on a dead worm. Probably benthic.

Figure 63. *Liljeborgia zarica*, n. sp. Sex?, 4.5 mm., *Vema* Sta. 53. A: head; B: antenna 1; C: upper lip; D, E, F, G: mandibles; H: lower lip; I, J: maxillae 1, 2; K: maxilliped; L, M: gnathopods 1, 2; N: coxa 3; O, P, Q: peraeopods 2, 3, 5; R, S, T: uropods 1, 2, 3; U: telson; V: pleon segments 6–1.

Family : EUSIRIDAE

Genus: RHACHOTROPIS Smith

Rhachotropis anoculata, new species
Figures 64, 65

Diagnosis: Pleon segments 1 and 2 with one posterior dorsal tooth and one postero-lateral tooth on each side; peraeon and remaining pleon segments lack teeth; eyes not visible; lateral lobes of head blunt.

Mouth parts like *R. cervus* J. L. Barnard (1957, p. 16), except where figured herein.

Holotype: L.G.O. No. 60, sex?, 10 mm., unique.

Type locality: *Vema* Station 46, East Scotia Basin, 3725 meters.

Relationship: Close to *R. inflata* Sars (see Gurjanova, 1951, p. 713, for synonymy), but lacks eyes, has a blunt lateral head lobe, and coxa 1 is shallower and broader.

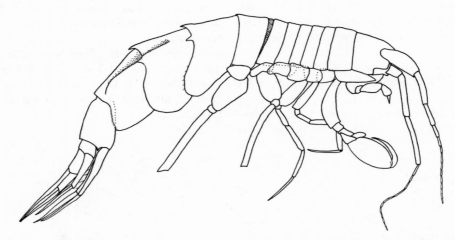

Figure 64. *Rhachotropis anoculata,* n. sp. Sex?, 10 mm., *Vema* Sta. 46. Lateral view of animal.

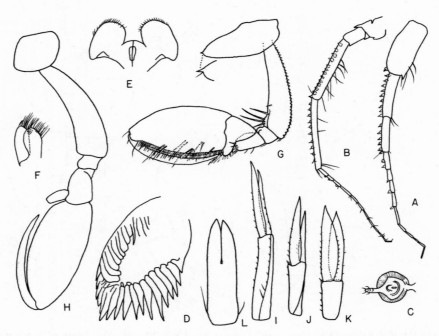

Figure 65. *Rhachotropis anoculata,* n. sp. Sex?, 10 mm., *Vema* Sta. 46. A, B: antennae 1, 2; C: statocyst of antennae; D: molar of mandible; E: lower lip; F: maxilla 2; G, H: gnathopods 1, 2; I, J, K: uropods 1, 2, 3; L: telson.

Family : ATYLIDAE

Genus: ATYLUS Leach

Atylus aberrantis, new species
Figures 66, 67

Diagnosis: Peraeon segment 7 and pleon segments 1–3 with dorsal posterior teeth, pleon segment 4 with a dorsal notch and tooth, pleon segments 5–6 (fused) with a tooth; mandibular palp article 3 short, equal to article 1 in length; peraeopods 3–5 with lower posterior corner of second article rounded and unmodified; eyes not visible; rostrum slender, straight.

Holotype: L.G.O. No. 61, sex?, 5 mm., unique.

Type locality: *Vema* Station 53, Cape Basin, 4893 meters.

Relationship: The peculiar combination of straight rostrum, lack of modification on article 2 of peraeopods 3–5, short third palp article of the mandible, and lack of eyes is characteristic.

The species is especially related to *A. homochir* Haswell (in Stebbing, 1888, p. 908, Pl. 74), but differs by the short third mandibular palp article, the lack of eyes, and the shape of the head below the rostrum.

The species is transitional to *A. reductus* (K. H. Barnard, 1930, p. 382), which lacks the third mandibular palp article.

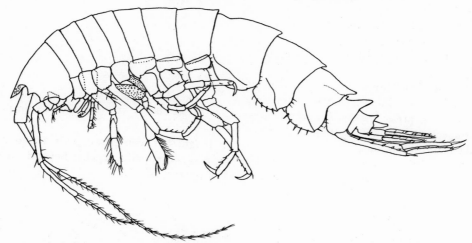

Figure 66. *Atylus aberrantis*, n. sp. Sex?, 5 mm., *Vema* Sta. 53. Lateral view of animal.

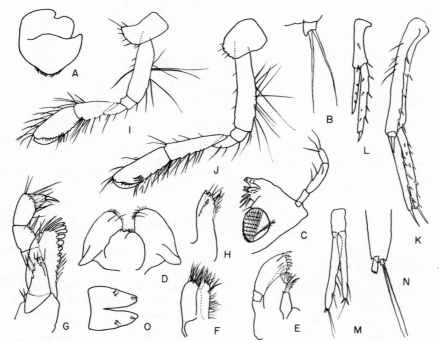

Figure 67. *Atylus aberrantis*, n. sp. Sex?, 5 mm., *Vema* Sta. 53. A: upper lip; B: accessory flagellum; C: mandible; D: lower lip; E, F: maxillae 1, 2; G: maxilliped; H: inner plate of maxilliped; I, J: gnathopods 1, 2; K, L, M: uropods 1, 2, 3; N: uropod 3, end of outer ramus; O: telson.

Family : AORIDAE

Genus: LEMBOS Bate

Lembos lobata, new species
Figures 68, 69

Diagnosis: Eyes absent, head lobes narrow, projecting; coxae very short, coxa 1 smaller than coxa 2; inner plate of maxilla 1 vestigial; palp article 3 of mandible clavate, large, nearly twice as long as article 2; gnathopod 1 only slightly larger than gnathopod 2, articles 5 and 6 subequal in size, palm occupying most of hind margin of article 6, defined by a spine; third pleonal epimeron asymmetrically quadrate; rami of uropod 3 short.

Holotype: L.G.O. No. 62, male?, 4.5 mm., unique.

Type locality: *Vema* Station 53, Cape Basin, 4893 meters.

Relationship: The only other known species of *Lembos* which lacks eyes is *L. longidigitans* (Bonnier, 1896, p. 659), and the present species is very closely related to that species, especially by the small inner plate of maxilla 1 and the coxae.

The new species differs from *L. longidigitans* by minor features: the shape of the third pleonal epimeron, which is not rounded but quadrate; the shorter mandibular lobes of the lower lip; the narrow and produced head lobes; and the greater difference

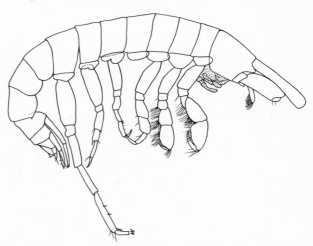

Figure 68. *Lembos lobata*, n. sp. Male, 4.5 mm., *Vema* Sta. 53. Lateral view of animal.

in length between peraeopods 4 and 5 (in *L. longidigitans* peraeopod 4 reaches beyond the end of article 5 of peraeopod 5).

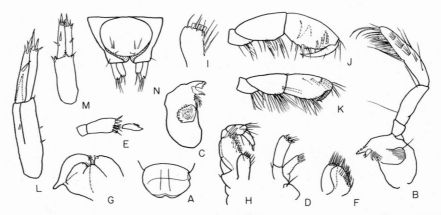

Figure 69. *Lembos lobata*, n. sp. Male, 4.5 mm., *Vema* Sta. 53. A: upper lip; B, C: mandibles; D, F: maxillae 1, 2; E: palp of maxilla 1; G: lower lip; H: maxilliped; I: inner plate of maxilliped; J, K: gnathopods 1, 2; L, M: uropods 1, 2; N: dorsal view of telson and third uropods.

Family : PHOTIDAE

Genus: BONNIERELLA Chevreux

Synonyms: *Bonnierella* Chevreux, 1900, p. 97.

Diagnosis: Third article of antenna 1 as long or longer than first article; accessory flagellum present but vestigial, composed of one long article tipped with a small terminal one; uropod 3 with two equal-sized rami; telson triangular; article 5 of gnathopod 2 short.

Type species: *Podoceropsis abyssi* Chevreux.

Remarks: As defined by Chevreux (1900), *Bonnierella* differs from *Podoceropsis* Boeck by the presence of the vestigial accessory flagellum and slender second articles of peraeopods 3–5. The type species of

Podoceropsis is *P. sophiae* Boeck, which lacks any vestige of an accessory flagellum and has broadened second articles of peraeopods 3–5. However, a number of species have been assigned to *Podoceropsis* which have the same kind of accessory flagellum as *Bonnierella*, but these species have the broadened second articles of peraeopods 3–5. In addition, another species, *Podoceropsis kermadeci* Stebbing, has a scale-like accessory flagellum. It becomes an academic question whether these small differences are valid, especially in view of *P. kermadeci*.

There are further complicating factors: the epistome of *Podoceropsis elephantis* K. H. Barnard is produced conically, and this is true for *Podoceropsis lapisi*, n. sp., but this feature has not been reported in other species and is difficult to overlook. In addition, the heads of *Bonnierella dubia*, n. sp., and *B. lapisi*, n. sp., differ considerably in the depth of insertion of antenna 2, *B. dubia* being deep and like the type species of *Bonnierella*.

In order to facilitate the understanding of this problem the various species have been arranged as follows:

1. Accessory flagellum is a scale:
    Podoceropsis kermadeci (Stebbing) (no eyes)
2. Article 2 of peraeopods 3–5 slender, accessory flagellum probably vestigial, composed of at least one long basal article; epistome unknown but believed not to be produced; insertion of antenna 2 deep:
    Bonnierella abyssi (Chevreux) (no eyes)
    Bonnierella abyssorum (Bonnier) (no eyes)
    Bonnierella angolae, n. sp. (no eyes)
3. Article 2 of peraeopods 3–5 broad, accessory flagellum vestigial, composed of at least one long basal article; epistome conically produced; insertion of antenna 2 shallow in second species:
    Podoceropsis elephantis K. H. Barnard (has eyes)
    Podoceropsis lapisi, n. sp. (no eyes)
4. Article 2 of peraeopods 3–5 broad, accessory flagellum vestigial, composed of at least one long basal article; epistome probably not produced (in no case has it been reported so); insertion of antenna 2 deep in first species:
    Podoceropsis insignis (Chilton) (has eyes)
    Podoceropsis dubia (Shoemaker) (has eyes)

5. Article 2 of peraeopods 3–5 broad, accessory flagellum apparently totally absent; epistome not described, probably not produced; insertion of antenna 2 variable; all have eyes:
    Podoceropsis angulosa (Chevreux)
    Podoceropsis lindahli (Hansen)
    Podoceropsis nitida (Stimpson)
    Podoceropsis pusilla (Chevreux)
    Podoceropsis similis (Schellenberg)
    Podoceropsis sophiae (Boeck)
    Podoceropsis inaequistylis (Shoemaker) (antenna 1 missing)

Chevreux's (1900) thesis that the slenderness of the second articles of peraeopods 3–5 is a valid generic character and that *Bonnierella* is a valid genus would not be difficult to accept if it were not for the subsequent description of species which in some ways are typical and in other ways are not typical of *Bonnierella*.

Podoceropsis kermadeci provides a neat intergradation regarding the accessory flagellum. This leaves the narrow basal articles of peraeopods 3–5 as the principal character between *Podoceropsis* and *Bonnierella*, although simultaneous inspection of all *Bonnierella* and *Podoceropsis* figures reveals subtle gnathopod differences. The first gnathopod of the *Bonnierella* species in Group 2 above is slightly larger, nearly as large as gnathopod 2, while in the other species the first gnathopod is much smaller than gnathopod 2.

In conclusion, it is my belief that the science of ecology would be better served if each of the above five groups were kept as a separate genus, especially for the study of the origin of deep sea faunas. However, I am not prepared at this time, in the absence of various type materials, to institute this segregation and provide the new names necessary.

Bonnierella angolae, new species
Figures 70, 71

Diagnosis: Eyes absent; epistome unknown; male first gnathopodal palm distinctly excavated proximal to a tooth near the hinge, palmar corner distinct but

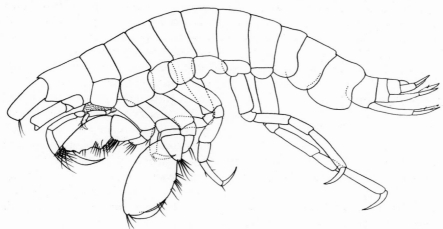

Figure 70. *Bonnierella angolae* n. sp. Male, 3 mm. *Vema* Sta. 22. Lateral view of animal.

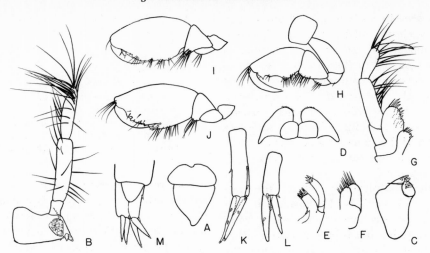

Figure 71. *Bonnierella angolae* n. sp. Male, 3 mm., *Vema* Sta. 22. A: upper lip; B, C: mandible; D: lower lip; E, F: maxillae 1, 2; G: maxilliped; H: gnathopod 1; I, J: gnathopod 2; K, L: uropods 1, 2; M: telson and third uropods.

not produced; palm of gnathopod 2 oblique, minutely sculptured as figured.

Holotype: L.G.O. No. 63, male, 3 mm., unique.

Type locality: *Vema* Station 22, Angola Basin, 3015 meters.

Relationship: This species is so closely related to *Bonnierella abyssorum* (Bonnier) that it may be identical. Unfortunately, the Photidae are noted for their polymorphic gnathopods within a species, and until each molt stage is worked out for a single species it is prudent to segregate slightly different configurations.

The principal feature of difference in *B. dubia* is the first gnathopod, which has a distinct hinge tooth and palmar excavation, not clearly drawn by Bonnier for *B. abyssorum.* Very critical appraisal of more materials and the two types will have to be made to clear up this problem.

Although antenna 1 is missing, except for article 1, the generic assignment of this species is uncertain, but it is so obviously related to *Bonnierella abyssorum* that little doubt about its status remains.

The new species is clearly distinguished from *B. abyssi* (Chevreux), which has median palmar sculpture on gnathopod 1 and distinctly produced cuspate palmar sculpture of gnathopod 2, as well as the longer dactyls of gnathopods 1 and 2.

Photids are exclusively benthic and usually tube builders.

Genus: PHOTIS Krøyer

Photis coecus, new species

Figure 72

Diagnosis: Eyes absent, head lobes poorly produced, but apices acute; gnathopod 2 lacks palm; uropods 1 and 2 with few spines.

Holotype: L.G.O. No. 64, sex?, 3.5 mm.

Type locality: *Vema* Station 46, East Scotia Basin, 3725 meters. Benthic.

Relationship: Because the present species is blind,

it is easy to diagnose. It is related to the only other blind species in the genus, *P. kurilica* Gurjanova (1955, p. 213), by the lack of a palm on gnathopod 2 and the poorly spinose uropods 1–2.

Material examined: Station 46 (four specimens).

Genus: PODOCEROPSIS Boeck

(Podoceropsis) lapisi, new species

Figures 73–75

Diagnosis: Eyes absent; antenna 1 with biarticulate accessory flagellum; epistome conically produced, with an apical cusp; male gnathopod 1 with palm slightly convex, simple; male gnathopod 2 palm slightly oblique, armed with two invaginations separated by acute teeth, one of the teeth located at the corner of the palm. Antenna 1 missing.

Holotype: L.G.O. No. 65, ovigerous female, 5 mm.

Type locality: *Vema* Station 53, Cape Basin, 4893 meters.

Relationship: Notations regarding the complexity of relationships among various groups of *Podoceropsis-Bonnierella* are located under *Bonnierella.* The present species is not a typical *Podoceropsis* because of the biarticulate accessory flagellum, and that feature plus a conical epistome relates it closely to *Podoceropsis elephantis* K. H. Barnard (1932). *P. lapisi* differs by lacking eyes, by lacking the conical process at the distal end of the second article of gnathopod 2, and by the slightly more slender peraeopods 3–5.

The species differs from the three known Bonnierella species by the configuration of gnathopods 1 and 2 in each respective case, and especially by the broader second articles of peraeopods 3–5.

Material examined: *Vema* Station 53 (the holotype, the figured 6-mm. male, the figured 6-mm. female, a 5-mm. female, and two 4-mm. specimens of unknown sex).

Food: The stomach of the figured female contained finely particulate organic materials.

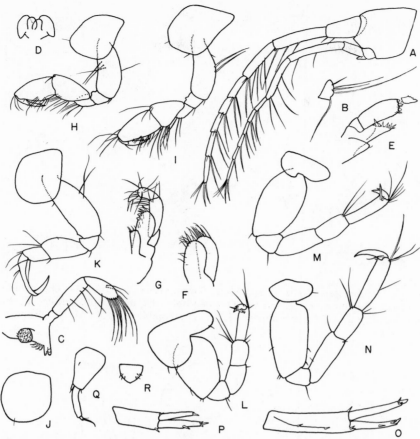

Figure 72. *Photis coecus*, n. sp. Sex?, 3.5 mm., *Vema* Sta. 46. A: head; B: accessory flagellum; C: mandible; D: lower lip; E, F: maxillae 1, 2; G: maxilliped; H, I: gnathopods 1, 2; J: coxa 4; K, L, M, N: peraeopods 1, 3, 4, 5; O, P, Q: uropods 1, 2, 3; R: telson.

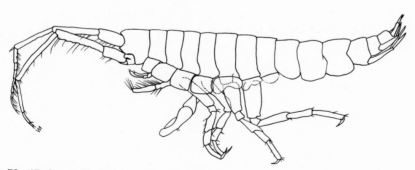

Figure 73. *(Podoceropsis) lapisi*, n. sp. Male, 6 mm., *Vema* Sta. 53. Lateral view of animal.

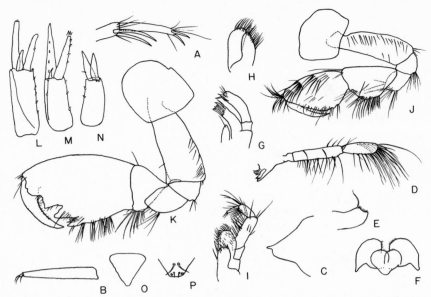

Figure 74. (*Podoceropsis*) *lapisi*, n. sp. Male, 6 mm., *Vema* Sta. 53. A: end of antenna 1; B: accessory flagellum; C: epistome; D: mandible; E: molar of mandible; F: lower lip; G, H: maxillae 1, 2; I: maxilliped; J, K: gnathopods 1, 2; L, M, N: uropods 1, 2, 3; O, P: telson.

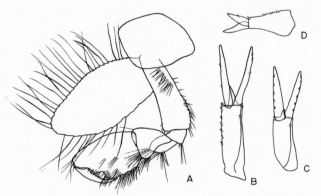

Figure 75. (*Podoceropsis*) *lapisi*, n. sp. Female, 6 mm., *Vema* Sta. 53. A: gnathopod 2; B, C, D: uropods 1, 2, 3.

Family : COROPHIIDAE

BOGENFELSIA, new genus

Diagnosis: Lower portion of head incised deeply for the reception of antenna 2; eyes absent; mandibular palp with three articles; gnathopod 2 larger than gnathopod 1; coxae not in continuity; uropods 1 and 2 each with two rami; uropod 3 with two equal-sized rami; urosome segments distinct.

Type species: *Bogenfelsia incisa,* n. sp.

Relationship: The new genus is closely related to *Camacho* Stebbing (1888) (see key to the family in Barnard, 1958), but differs by the equal-sized rami of uropod 3, the larger second gnathopod, and the shape of the head.

Bogenfelsia incisa, new species
Figures 76, 77

Diagnosis: With the characters of the genus.
Holotype: L.G.O. No. 66, female, 4.25 mm., unique.
Type locality: *Vema* Station 53, Cape Basin, 4893 meters. Benthic.

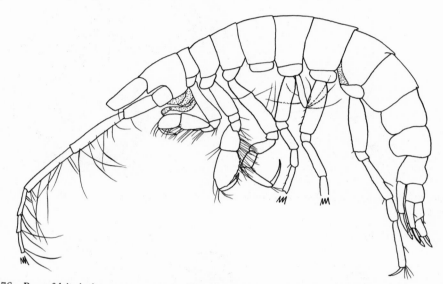

Figure 76. *Bogenfelsia incisa,* n. gen., n. sp. Female, 4.25 mm., *Vema* Sta. 53. Lateral view of animal.

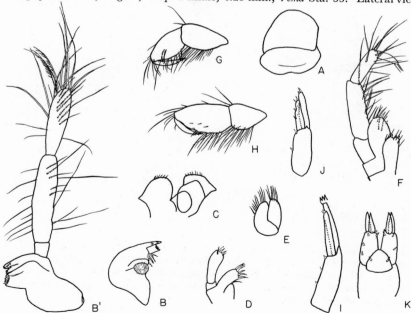

Figure 77. *Bogenfelsia incisa,* n. gen., n. sp. Female, 4.25 mm., *Vema* Sta. 53. A: upper lip; B, B′: mandibles; C: lower lip; D, E: maxillae 1, 2; F: maxilliped; G, H: gnathopods 1, 2; I, J: uropods 1, 2; K: telson and third uropods.

Family: PODOCERIDAE

Genus: NEOXENODICE Schellenberg

Neoxenodice caprellinoides Schellenberg
Figures 78, 79

Synonyms: *Neoxenodice caprellinoides* Schellenberg,
1926, pp. 474–476, Fig. 3; Schellenberg, 1955, p. 195.
Remarks: On the present specimen, in contrast to

Schellenberg's figures, the head has a dorsal ridge
and the palm of gnathopod 2 is less excavated.

Material examined: *Vema* Station 53 (one female,
11 mm., and one juvenile, 3 mm.).

Distribution: Antarctic, 65° 27′ S., 80° 33′ E., 3397
meters (Schellenberg); recorded here from Cape
Basin, 4893 meters. Probably a eurybathic wide-
ranging species.

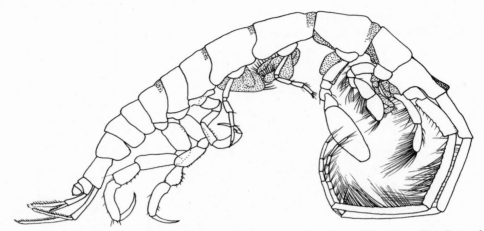

Figure 78. *Neoxenodice caprellinoides* Schellenberg. Female, 11 mm., *Vema* Sta. 53. Lateral
view of animal.

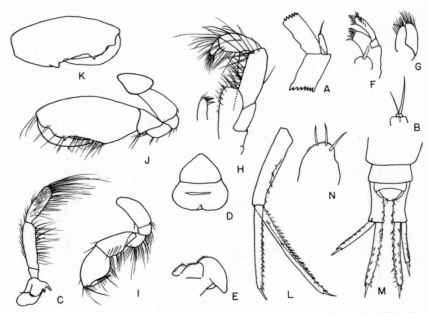

Figure 79. *Neoxenodice caprellinoides* Schellenberg. Female, 11 mm., *Vema* Sta. 53. A: accessory flagellum on antenna 1; B: apex of accessory flagellum; C: mandible; D: upper lip;
E: lower lip; F, G: maxillae 1, 2; H: maxilliped, inner lobe to left; I, J, K: gnathopods
1, 2, outside, 2 inside; L, N: uropods 1, 3; M: dorsal posterior end of pleon showing uropod
2 and telson, and hidden uropod 3.

LITERATURE CITED

Barnard, J. L. 1954. Marine Amphipoda of Oregon. Oregon State Monogs., Studies in Zool. 8: 1–103, 33 pls., 1 fig.

——— 1954a. Four species of bathypelagic Gammaridea (Amphipoda) from California. Hancock Found. Publ., Occ. Pap. 13: 52–69, Pls. 2–6.

——— 1957. New bathypelagic amphipods of the genera *Rhachotropis* and *Lepechinella* with keys to the genera. So. Calif. Acad. Sci., Bull. 56 (1): 14–20, Pls. 3–5.

——— 1958. Index to the families, genera and species of the gammaridean Amphipoda (Crustacea). Hancock Found. Publ., Occ. Pap. 19: 1–145.

——— 1958a. A remarkable new genus of corophiid amphipod from coastal marine bottoms of southern California. So. Calif. Acad. Sci., Bull. 57 (2): 85–90, Pls. 26–28.

——— 1961. Amphipoda from depths of 400 to 6000 meters. Galathea Repts., 4: 23–128, 80 figs.

Barnard, K. H. 1916. Contributions to the crustacean fauna of South Africa. 5.—The Amphipoda. So. African Mus., Ann. 15 (3): 105–302, Pls. 26–28.

——— 1925. Contributions to the crustacean fauna of South Africa. No. 8. Further additions to the list of Amphipoda. So. African Mus., Ann. 20 (5): 319–380, Pl. 34.

——— 1930. Amphipoda. British Antarctic ("Terra Nova") Exped. 1910. Nat. Hist. Repts., Zool. 8: 307–454, 63 figs.

——— 1932. Amphipoda. Discovery Repts. 5: 1–326, Pl. 1, 174 figs.

Birstein, A., and M. E. Vinogradov. 1955. Pelagicheskie gammaridy (Amphipoda-Gammaridea) Kurilo-Kamchatskoj Vpadiny. Akad. Nauk SSSR, Trudy Inst. Okean. 12: 210–287, 35 figs., 4 tables.

——— 1958. Pelagicheskie gammaridy (Amphipoda-Gammaridea) severo-zapadnoj chasti Tixogo Okeana. Akad. Nauk SSSR, Trudy Inst. Okean. 27: 219–257, 17 figs.

——— 1960. Pelagicheskie gammaridy tropicheskoi chasti Tixogo Okeana. Akad. Nauk SSSR, Trudy Inst. Okean. 34: 165–241, 34 figs.

Birstein, Ja. A., and N. G. Vinogradova. 1960. Donnye ultraabissal'nye gammaridy severo-zapadnoi chasti Tixogo Okeana. I. Semeistva Liljeborgiidae, Astyridae, Lepechinellidae, Gammaridae. Akad. Nauk SSSR, Trudy Inst. Okean. 34: 147–164, 10 figs.

Bonnier, J. 1896. Edriophthalmes. Rés. Sci. Campagne "Caudan" dans le Golfe de Gascogne. Ann. Univ. Lyon 26 (3): 527–689, Pls. 28–40.

Bruun, A. F. 1957. Deep sea and abyssal depths. Geol. Soc. Amer. Mem. 67, vol. 1: 641–672, 9 figs., 3 pls. Treatise on Marine Ecology, J. Hedgpeth, ed.

Bulycheva. A. 1936. New species of Amphipoda from the Japan Sea. Ann. Mag. Nat. Hist. (10) 18: 242–256, 35 figs.

Chevreux, E. 1888. Sur quelques crustacés amphipodes provenant d'un dragage de l'*Hirondelle* au large de Lorient. Soc. Zool. France, Bull. 13: 1–4.

——— 1900. Amphipodes provenant des campagnes de l'*Hirondelle* (1885–1888). Rés. Camp. Sci. Albert Ier, Monaco 16: i–iv, 1–195, Pls. 1–18.

——— 1914. Diagnoses d'amphipodes nouveaux provenant des campagnes de la Princesse-Alice dans l'Atlantique nord. Bull. Inst. Oceanog. 296: 1–4, 3 figs.

——— 1935. Amphipodes provenant des campagnes du Prince Albert Ier de Monaco. Rés. Camp. Sci. Albert Ier, Monaco 90: 1–214, 16 pls.

Chilton, C. 1921. Report on the amphipods obtained by the F.I.S. "Endeavour" in Australian seas. Biol. Res. Fish. Exper. F.I.S. "Endeavour," 1909–14, vol. 5 (2): 33–92, 16 figs.

Dahl, E. 1959. Amphipoda from depths exceeding 6000 meters. Galathea Repts. 1: 211–241, 20 figs.

Ekman, S. 1953. Zoogeography of the sea. 417 pp., illus., London, Sedgwick & Jackson, Ltd.

Enequist, P. 1949. Studies on the soft-bottom amphipods of the Skagerrak. Zool. Bidrag fran Uppsala 28: 297–492, 67 figs., 6 charts.

Fage, L. 1951. Sur un pycnogonide de l'expédition svédoise des grands fonds 1947–48. Rept. Swedish Deep-Sea Exped. 2 (7): 95–97, 2 figs.

Gurjanova, E. 1951. Bokoplavy morej SSSR i sopredel'nyx vod (Amphipoda-Gammaridea). Opred. po Faune SSSR, Izd. Zool. Inst. Akad. Nauk 41: 1–1031, 705 figs.

——— 1955. Novye vidy bokoplavov (Amphipoda, Gammaridea) iz severnoj chasti Tixogo Okeana. Akad. Nauk SSSR, Trudy Inst. Zool. 18: 166–218, 23 figs.

Hartman, O. and J. L. Barnard. 1958. The benthic fauna of the deep basins off southern California. Hancock Pac. Expeds. 22 (1): 1–67, chart 1, Pls. 1–2, tables.

Holmes, S. J. 1904. Amphipod crustaceans of the expedition. Harriman Alaska Exped., pp. 233–246, figs. 118–128.

——— 1908. The Amphipoda collected by the U.S. "Albatross" off the west coast of North America. . . . U.S. Nat. Mus., Proc. 35: 489–543, 46 figs.

Nicholls, G. E. 1938. Amphipoda Gammaridea. Australasian Antarctic Exped. 1911–14, Sci. Rept. C.-Zool. and Bot. 2 (4): 1–145, 67 figs.

Norman. A. M. 1900. British Amphipoda. Ann. Mag. Nat. Hist. (7) 5: 196–214, Pl. 6, and 326–346, 1 fig.

Pirlot, J. M. 1932, 1933, 1934, 1936. Les amphipodes de l'expédition du Siboga. Siboga-Exped., Mon. 33b, 33c, 33d, 33e, 57–328, figs. 12–146.

Sars, G. O. 1895. Amphipoda. An account of the Crustacea of Norway. 1: i–viii, 1–711, 240 pls., 8 suppl. pls.

Schellenberg, A. 1926. Amphipoda 3: Die Gammariden der deutschen Tiefsee-Expedition. Wiss. Ergeb. Deutschen Tiefsee-Exped. "Valdivia" 1898–1899, vol. 23: 195–243, pl. 5, 28 figs.

——— 1926a. Die Gammariden der deutschen Südpolar-Expedition 1901–1903. Deutsch Sudpolar-Exped. 18: 235–414, 68 figs.

——— 1926b. Die Caprelliden und Neoxenodice caprellinoides n. g. n. sp. der deutschen Südpolar-Expedition 1901–1903. Deutsch Südpolar-Exped. 18: 465–476, 3 figs.

——— 1931. Gammariden und Caprelliden des Magellangebietes, Südgeorgiens und der Westantarktis. Further Zool. Res. Swedish Antarctic Exped. 1901–1903, vol. 2 (6): 1–290, 1 pl., 136 figs.

1955. Amphipoda. Reps. Swedish Deep-Sea Exped. 1947–1948, vol. 2, Zool. (2) (14): 181–195, 4 figs.

Shoemaker, C. R. 1930. The Amphipoda of the Cheticamp Expedition of 1917. Canadian Biol. Fish., Contrib. 5 (10): 221–359, 54 figs.

1945. The Amphipoda of the Bermuda Oceanographic Expeditions, 1929–1931. Zoologica 30 (4): 185–266, 48 figs.

Stebbing, T. R. R. 1888. Report on the Amphipoda collected by H.M.S. *Challenger* during the years 1873–1876. Rept. Sci. Res. Voy. H.M.S. *Challenger* Zool. 29, 3 vols.

1891. On the genus *Urothoe* and a new genus *Urothoides*. Zool. Soc. London, Trans. 13: 1–30, Pls. 1–4.

1906. Amphipoda I. Gammaridea. Das Tierreich 21: 1–806, 127 figs.

1908. South African Crustacea (Part IV). So. African Mus., Ann. 6: 1–96, Pls. 1–14.

1910. Crustacea. Part 5. Amphipoda. Sci. Res. Trawling Exped. H.M.C.S. "Thetis." Australian Mus., Mem. 4, vol. 2 (12): 565–658, Pls. 47*–60*.

Stebbing, T. R. R. and D. Robertson. 1891. On four new British Amphipoda. Zool. Soc. London, Trans. 13: 31–42, Pls. 5, 6.

Stephensen, K. 1915. Isopoda, Tanaidacea, Cumacea, Amphipoda (excl. Hyperiidea). Rept. Danish Oceanog. Expeds. 1908–10, vol. 2, Biol., D, 1, 53 pp., 33 figs.

1925. Crustacea Malacostraca. VI (Amphipoda II). Danish Ingolf-Exped. 3 (9): 101–178, figs. 23–53, charts.

Vinogradova, N. G. 1959. The zoogeographical distribution of the deep-water bottom fauna in the abyssal zone of the ocean. Deep-Sea Research 5 (3): 205–208, 3 figs. 1 table.

Walker, A. O. 1907. Crustacea. III.—Amphipoda. Nat. Antarctic Exped., Brit. Mus. (N.H.) 3: 1–39, 13 pls.

Wolff, T. 1956. Isopoda from depths exceeding 6000 meters. Galathea Rept. 2: 85–157, 56 figs., 16 tables.

1956a. Crustacea Tanaidacea from depths exceeding 6000 meters. Galathea Rept. 2: 187–241, 54 figs., 6 tables.

Zenkevich, L. A., and J. A. Birstein. 1956. Studies of the deep water fauna and related problems. Deep-Sea Research 4: 54–64, 4 figs., 8 tables.

Zenkevich, L. A., J. A. Birstein, and G. M. Belyaev. 1954. Izuchenie fauny Kurilo-Kamchatkoj vpadiny. Priroda, Feb.: 61–73, 15 figs., 1 table.

Zobell, C. E. 1956. The occurrence of bacteria in the deep sea and their significance for animal life. IUBS Deep Sea Colloquium, XIV Intern. Zool. Congr., Copenhagen, 1953.

The Isopods of Abyssal Depths in the Atlantic Ocean

by ROBERT J. MENZIES

Department of Biology, University of Southern California

SUMMARY

In this monograph 176 species are described. Prior to this work only 66 species were known from the Arctic-Atlantic below 2000 meters and only 143 were known from the abyss of the world oceans, excluding probably pelagic species. This means that the results of this work based upon 84 abyssal trawl samples taken by the R.V. *Vema* and M.V. *Theta* increase by roughly one-fifth the number of abyssal species known for the entire world in the order Isopoda. The number of species from the Atlantic, where the fauna was best known previously, is increased by over two times. One hundred and seven new species are described from the Atlantic abyss and near abyss for the first time. Species new to the abyss but previously known elsewhere, are *Antennuloniscus dimeroceras* (Barnard), *Stylomesus inermis* (Vanhöffen), *Nannoniscus oblongus* G. O. Sars, *Eurycope antarctica* Vanhöffen, and *Eurycope vicarius* Vanhöffen. Additionally five species previously recorded from the Atlantic abyss are excluded from this monograph due to the fact that they are too poorly known. These are *Eurycope abyssicola* Beddard, *Acanthocope acutispina* Beddard, *Eurycope* sp., *Ischnomesus bacillus* Beddard, and *Storthyngura fragilis* (Beddard). The list of the new species is contained in the table of contents.

A total of nine new genera is described. These are *Antennuloniscus* (formerly part *Haploniscus*), *Dendromunna*, *Spinianirella*, *Notoxenoides*, *Xostylus*, *Abyssijaera*, *Mesosignum*, *Glabroserolis*, and *Vemathambema*. This brings the known abyssal Atlantic genera to 41 when one adds the five genera that were previously known from Atlantic shallow water and are reported herein from the abyss, *Leptanthura*, *Antarcturus*, *Acanthomunna*, *Nannoniscoides*, and *Stylomesus*.

Where possible analytical keys are given to the species (world) of each genus; partial keys are given to the species of *Gnathia* and *Eurycope*, and no key is given to the poorly defined genus *Ilyarachna*.

It is intended that the zoogeographic, ecologic, and phylogenetic relationships of these collections will be subject to analytic study in the second part of this monograph.

INTRODUCTION

In this paper the marine isopods of the abyss of the North and South Atlantic, including the Arctic Ocean and Caribbean Sea, are described. Every old and new species known up to 1960 is illustrated at least once. This study is based mainly upon the collections made in recent years by the research vessel belonging to the Lamont Geological Observatory, the R.V. *Vema*. The principal objective of this work has been to define abyssal communities based upon modern systematic studies and to determine where possible the probable sites of origin of these highly important abyssal organisms from their morphologic affinities and geographic distribution. Additionally, however, a study has been made on the food of the abyssal isopods through dissection and study of their gut content. Records were maintained also regarding the weight, size, state of sexual maturity, and brood size.

The collections on which this study was based come from *Vema* cruises 7 to 15 inclusive. These cruises were supported by grants from the Office of Naval Research, the Bureau of Ships of the U.S. Navy, and the National Science Foundation, as part of the International Geophysical Year. The laboratory work has been supported by a grant from the Rockefeller Foundation and the National Science Foundation.

The aid of the following chief scientists is particularly appreciated: Dr. J. Lamar Worzel, *Vema* 7 and 15; Dr. Bruce C. Heezen, *Vema* 10; Mr. Walter Beckman and Captain Valvin Sinclair, *Vema* 12; Captain H. Kohler, *Vema* 14; Dr. Jack Nafe, Dr. Charles Drake, and Professor Maurice Ewing, *Vema* 14 and 15. The aid of the following shipboard biologists on various cruises is especially appreciated: Mr. Peter Trurnit, Mr. Thomas Dow, and Mr. Arthur Clarke, Jr.

Discussions at various times with Professor Maurice Ewing, Dr. William Donn, Dr. Bruce Heezen, and Mr. David B. Ericson, all of the Lamont staff, have been particularly helpful in this work.

The illustrations were made in pencil from projected images of the animals. Parts requiring higher magnificaton were drawn with the aid of a camera lucida. Penciled sketches were "inked in" by Mr. Donald Robinson and by myself. Previously described species were painstakingly copied from the publications involved by Mr. Donald Robinson. Sorting of the preserved samples was done by Mr. Thomas Dow, Mr. Michael Tinker, and myself.

MATERIALS AND METHODS

The material examined came from deep sea trawl samples. Various trawl designs were tried: first, the epibenthic trawl developed by Mr. Robert Bieri (in Hedgpeth, 1957, p. 77, Fig. 10) and, second, a large biology trawl (LBT), which was discarded in favor of a small biology trawl (SBT) designed at the suggestion of Mr. Walter Beckman of the Lamont Geological Observatory. The LBT had an opening one meter square, but otherwise was identical with the SBT. The latter has an orifice one meter wide by ten centimeters high and a steel frame. Attached to the frame is a tapered nylon net three meters long with a mesh diameter of 0.5 millimeters. A bridle of chain is attached to the front, at the yolk of which a eighty-pound lead weight is attached (Fig. 1). The bridle is attached with swivels at each joint, allowing the trawl and weight to wind or unwind freely as tension is released or increased. The cod end of the net is tied to the frame to prevent it from tangling around the trawl wire. The trawl wire was 5/32-inch hydrographic wire, and trawling operations were carried out with tensions nearing the breaking point. For this reason a heavier or larger trawl could not be used from wire of such small diameter. The SBT under normal conditions could be lowered and retrieved at maximum winch speed. This is a highly important disideratum of shipboard operations.

The trawl samples when retrieved on the deck of the ship were put into suitable containers and preserved with 10 percent neutral formalin sea water buffered with Hexamine.[1] The entire sample, usually consisting of a quart of sediment and animals, was then sorted in the laboratory with the binocular steroscopic microscope. Identified specimens are transferred into 70 percent alcohol.

The dissection of isopod specimens generally was done with the aid of a microscope while the specimens were immersed in glycerine on a microscope slide. Measurements were made with a calibrated ocular micrometer. The weight of specimens was determined from wet specimens which had been damp-dried with a paper towel after removal from the alcohol preservative. Food content analyses were usually made on material removed from the hind gut or gastric

---

[1] Trade name for hexamethylenamine (USP), available from the Amend Drug and Chemical Co. in New York.

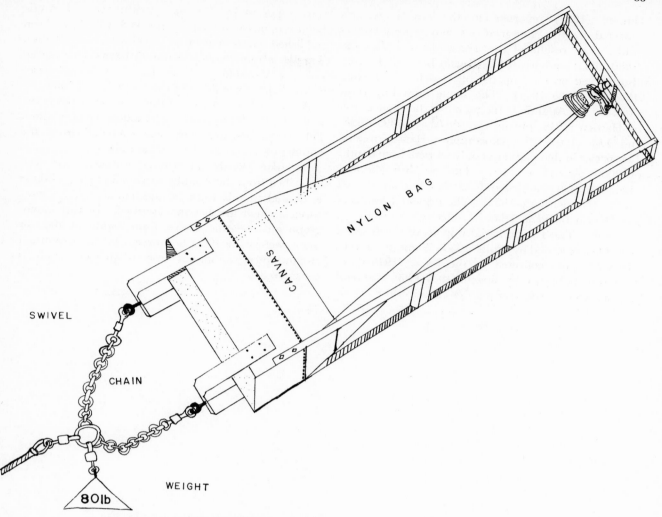

Figure 1. Small biology trawl (SBT) used in the majority of the Lamont collections from aboard *Vema*, frame length 3 meters, width 1 meter, diameter of orifice 10 centimeters.

mill, and in this way an uncontaminated sample was obtained.

Identified specimens were placed in cotton-stoppered vials in quart alcohol-filled jars. Entry in the catalogue provided each lot of a species from each trawl station from each cruise with a separate L.G.O. (Lamont Geological Observatory) catalogue number (cat. no.). Individual cruise biology trawl stations have been numbered consecutively (L.G.O. Biotrawl No.).

DEFINITION OF THE AREA SAMPLED

In this study the abyssal isopods of the Arctic Ocean, the North and South Atlantic, and the Caribbean are described and studied. The zoogeographical implications will be discussed separately as a significant second part of this monograph by Dr. Bruce C. Heezen and myself. Therefore, in this, the systematic part, details of zoogeography are purposely avoided.

The abyssal stations on which this study has been based are compiled in a separate section, "List of Stations"; accordingly, it has been possible to give with each species a minimum of station detail, and only the L.G.O. Biotrawl number and number of specimens are listed.

HISTORY OF PREVIOUS WORK

For a general review of oceanographic expeditions up to 1926, the reader is referred to Schott's *Geographie des Atlantischen Ozeans* (1926).

The first capture of abyssal isopods resulted from the cruises of the *Lightning* (1868), *Porcupine* (1869–1870), and *Valorous* (c. 1870). These were reported on by Norman and Stebbing (1886), three species, and by Stebbing (1913), one species. Next came Beddard's great work (1884–1886, 1886) on the *Challenger* (1872–1876) collections. Beddard reported on around 58 species, but only about 24 of these were from below 2000 meters depth. Richardson (1909, etc.) and

Hansen (1897) reported on the abyssal isopods collected by the American *Albatross* cruises (1898–1913). The results of the *Travailleur* and *Talisman* (1880–1883) were treated by Richardson (1911), who also worked on the isopods collected by the *Princess Alice* 1–2 (1885–1914). The single most important work for the Atlantic is the monumental monograph by Hansen (1916) on the Danish *Ingolf* (1895–1896) and *Thor* (1904–1910) expeditions. Hansen treated 164 species in that work, but only 38 were from depths of 2000 meters or more. The Swedish *Albatross* (1947–1948) has added only one additional abyssal species (Nordenstam, 1955). The principal results of the Danish *Galathea* Atlantic collections are not yet available. The Pacific hadal isopods of the *Galathea* have been recorded by Wolff (1956). Some of the ultra abyssal isopods collected by the *Vitjaz* (1949–date) have been published by Birstein (1957,1960). Several abyssal Atlantic species from the *Vema* 7 cruise (1955) were reported by Menzies (1956). Abyssal Arctic polar isopods gathered by the U.S.S.R. have been published most recently by Gurjanova (1946a). The *abyssal* isopods of the Antarctic have been reported only by Vanhöffen (1914), based on the German South Polar Expedition of the *Gauss* (1901–1903).

A reasonably complete listing of all known benthic abyssal isopods is given in the following tabulation. Pelagic species are purposely excluded from the enumeration and are listed separately.

To date 69 abyssal benthic isopods have been described from the Atlantic Ocean, and each of these is treated in this work in addition to the 107 new species which are herein described. In this monograph only benthic species from depths of 2000 or more meters are described except when in unusual circumstances a species from shallower depth is considered.

LIST OF ISOPODS FROM DEPTHS GREATER THAN 2000 METERS—BY REGION

Species	Depth Range (meters)
ARCTIC OCEAN: POLAR BASIN	
1. *Ilyarachna derjugini* Gurjanova	2500
2. *Eurycope hanseni* Ohlin, Gurjanova	460–2500
3. *Eurycope incisa* Gurjanova	2380
4. *Mesidothea megalura polaris* Gurjanova	1300–2500
NORTH ATLANTIC OCEAN	
5. *Abyssianira dentifrons* Menzies, 1956a	5104–5122
6. *Acanthaspidia decorata* Hansen, Nierstrasz, 1941	4000
7. *Ananthura abyssorum* (Norman and Stebbing), 1886	3199
8. *Anthelura truncata* (Hansen), 1916	2258–2702
9. *Calathura brachiata* (Stimpson), Hansen, 1916	18–2488
10. *Desmosoma coarctatum* Hansen, 1916	24–2702
11. *Desmosoma gracilipes* Hansen, 1916	2258–2702
12. *Desmosoma insigne* Hansen, 1916	2702
13. *Desmosoma intermedium* Hult, 1941	30–2258
14. *Desmosoma longispinum* Hansen, 1916	3521
15. *Desmosoma simile* Hansen, 1916	2258
16. *Echinothambema ophiuroides* Menzies, 1956a	5104–5122
17. *Eurycope abyssicola* Beddard, 1886b (insufficient data available on the species)	3977
18. *Eurycope complanata* Bonnier, 1896	950–2702
19. *Eurycope furcata* G. O. Sars, Hansen, 1916	150–2258
20. *Eurycope hanseni* Ohlin, Hansen, 1916	460–2669
21. *Eurycope murrayi* Walker, Hansen, 1916	1300–2775
22. *Eurycope nodifrons* Hansen, 1916	2702
23. *Eurycope parva* Bonnier, Hansen, 1916	872–2702
24. *Eurycope producta* G. O. Sars, Hansen, 1916	72–2087
25. *Gnathia caeca* Richardson	2638
26. *Gnathia stygia* (G. O. Sars)	552–2465
27. *Haplomesus angustus* Hansen, 1916	1373–2137
28. *Haplomesus insignis* Hansen, 1916	698–2702
29. *Haplomesus quadrispinosus* G. O. Sars, Hansen, 1916	510–2702
30. *Haplomesus modestus* Hansen, 1916	2258
31. *Haplomesus tenuispinis* Hansen, 1916	2258–3474
32. *Haploniscus bicuspis* (G. O. Sars) Hansen, 1916	360–2465
33. *Haploniscus excisus* Richardson, 1908a	3235
34. *Haploniscus spinifer* Hansen, 1916	2970–4061
35. *Haploniscus unicornis* Menzies, 1956a	5104–5122
36. *Heteromesus granulatus* Richardson, 1908a	713–3235
37. *Heteromesus longiremis* Hansen, 1916	698–2707
38. *Heteromesus similis* Richardson, 1911	2995
39. *Heteromesus spinescens* Richardson, 1908a	2155–3337
40. *Hydronisus abyssi* Hansen, 1916	3521
41. *Hyssura producta* Norman and Stebbing, 1886	2651
42. *Ianirella laevis* Hansen, 1916	2258–2702
43. *Ianirella lobata* Richardson, 1908a	2480–3235
44. *Ianirella vemae* Menzies, 1956a	5104–5122
45. *Ilyarachna abyssorum* Richardson, 1911	4060–4165
46. *Ilyarachna bicornis* Hansen, 1916	2702
47. *Ilyarachna longicornis* G. O. Sars, Hansen, 1916	18–2788
48. *Ilyarachna spinosissima* Hansen, 1916	2702–3521
49. *Ischnomesus armatus* Hansen, 1916	2702
50. *Ischnomesus profundus* Hansen, 1916	3521
51. *Macrostylis abyssicola* Hansen, 1916	3229–3521
52. *Mesidothea megalura megalura* G. O. Sars, Hansen, 1916	1996–2465
53. *Munna acanthifera* Hansen, 1916	552–2258
54. *Nannoniscus analis* Hansen, 1916	2258
55. *Nannoniscus armatus* Hansen, 1916	3521
56. *Nannoniscus inermis* Hansen, 1916	2258
57. *Nannoniscus spinicornis* Hansen, 1916	2465
58. *Rhacura pulchra* Richardson, 1908a	3235
59. *Storthyngura magnispinis* (Richardson), 1908b	2258–2702
60. *Storthyngura truncata* (Richardson), 1908b	2788–3235
61. *Syneurycope hanseni* Menzies, 1956a	5104–5122
62. *Syneurycope parallela* Hansen, 1916	3474
63. *Thambema amicorum* Stebbing, 1913	2486
SOUTH ATLANTIC OCEAN	
64. *Eurycope murrayi* Walker, Hansen, 1916	2–<2700
65. *Pseudanthura lateralis* Richardson, 1911	930–3200
66. *Serolis neaera* Beddard, 1886a	1097–3731
MEDITERRANEAN	
No abyssal species recorded	
NORTH PACIFIC	
67. *Acanthocope intermedia* Beddard, 1886a	5670
68. *Arcturus parvus* Richardson, 1910	2272
69. *Eurycope scabra* Hansen, 1897	2486
70. *Eurycope spinifrons* Gurjanova, Nierstrasz, 1941	308–3000
71. *Gnathia elongata* Hansen, 1916, Nierstrasz	120–3000
72. *Haplomesus quadrispinosus* G. O. Sars, Birstein, 1960	4000–4150
73. *Haplomunna coeca* Richardson, 1905	3993
74. *Heteromesus thomsoni* (Beddard), 1886	3750
75. *Ischnomesus andriashevi* Birstein, 1960	4000–6560
76. *Macrostylis latifrons* Beddard, 1886	3749
77. *Microthambema tenuis* Birstein, 1961	5680–5690
78. *Storthyngura pulchra* (Hansen), 1897	2490–2690
79. *Storthyngura chelata* Birstein, 1957	5345–6860
80. *Storthyngura bicornis* Birstein, 1957	6156–6207
81. *Storthyngura vitjazi* Birstein, 1957	7305–8430
82. *Storthyngura herculea* Birstein, 1957	6475–8100
83. *Storthyngura brachycephala* Birstein, 1957	5670–5680
84. *Storthyngura tenuispinis kurilica* Birstein, 1957	7210–7230
85. *Storthyngura tenuispinis tenuispinis* Birstein, 1957	7246
86. *Acanthomunna proteus* Beddard, 1886	1281–2011
87. *Antarcturus abyssicola* (Beddard), 1886	2560–4321
88. *Acanthocope acutispina* Beddard, 1886a	2650
89. *Naesicopea abyssorum* (Beddard), 1886a	1958

90. *Eurycope galatheae* Wolff, 1956	6960–7000
91. *Eurycope madseni* Wolff, 1956	6960–7000
92. *Eurycope nodifrons* Hansen, Wolff, 1956	6960–7000
93. *Haploniscus robinsoni* Menzies and Tinker, 1960	2860–2858
94. *Ianira abyssicola* Beddard, 1886	2468
95. *Ischnomesus bacilloides* (Beddard), 1886a	2652
96. *Stylomesus wolffi* Birstein, 1960	4000–5530
97. *Stylomesus pacificus* Birstein, 1960	5450
98. *Stylomesus gracilis* Birstein, 1960	5680–5690
99. *Stylomesus menziesi* Birstein, 1960	5680–5690
100. *Heteromesus gigas* (Birstein), 1960	6560–8430
101. *Heteromesus scabriusculus* (Birstein), 1960	5450
102. *Heteromesus robustus* (Birstein), 1960	5450–5817
103. *Haplomesus brevispinis* Birstein, 1960	5510–5690
104. *Haplomesus cornutus* Birstein, 1960	6471–6571
105. *Haplomesus orientalis* Birstein, 1960	4000–4150

SOUTH PACIFIC

106. *Ischnomesus bruuni* Wolff, 1956	6960–7000
107. *Ischnomesus spärcki* Wolff, 1956	6660–7000
108. *Leptanthura hendili* Wolff, 1956	6580
109. *Macrostylis galatheae* Wolff, 1956	9820–10,000
110. *Macrostylis hadalis* Wolff, 1956	7270
111. *Storthyngura benti* Wolff, 1956	5230–7000
112. *Storthyngura furcata* Wolff, 1956	5850–6770
113. *Storthyngura novaezelandiae* (Beddard), 1886a	2012
114. *Storthyngura pulchra* Hansen, Wolff, 1956	6620
115. *Acanthocope spinicauda* Beddard, 1886a	3290
116. *Antarcturus abyssicola* (Beddard), 1886a	2560–4359
117. *Antarcturus brunneus* (Beddard), 1886a	2928
118. *Antarcturus spinosus* (Beddard), 1886a	2516
119. *Eurycope* sp. Beddard, 1886a	2925
120. *Eurycope sarsii* Beddard, 1886a	2514–2926
121. *Eurycope spinosa* Beddard, 1886a	3565
122. *Ischnomesus bacillus* (Beddard), 1886a	3292
123. *Serolis antarctica* Beddard, 1884	2517–2925
124. *Serolis bromleyana* Suhm, Beddard, 1884	1280–2011

INDIAN OCEAN

125. *Antarcturus furcatus* (Studer), 1914	3062
126. *Antarcturus gaussianus* Vanhöffen, 1914	2450
127. *Antarcturus glacialis* (Beddard), 1886a	3062
128. *Desmosoma longimana* Vanhöffen, 1914	2735
129. *Eurycope ovalis* Vanhöffen, 1914	3423
130. *Eurycope vicarius* Vanhöffen, 1914	3423
131. *Haploniscus antarcticus* Vanhöffen, 1914	385–3397
132. *Haploniscus curvirostris* Vanhöffen, 1914	3423
133. *Iolanthe acanthonotus* Beddard, 1886a	3062
134. *Ilyarachna antarctica* Vanhöffen, 1914	252–3423
135. *Janthopsis nodosus* Vanhöffen, 1914 (and 65° 42′ S., 79° 49′ E.)	3423

ANTARCTIC

136. *Microprotus antarcticus* Vanhöffen, 1914	3398
137. *Serolis bromleyana* Suhm, Beddard, 1884	3612
138. *Serolis johnstoni* Hale	2267
139. *Serolis meridionalis* Hodgson, Vanhöffen, 1914	2725
140. *Stenetrium acutum* Vanhöffen, 1914	385–3397
141. *Storthyngura elegans* Vanhöffen, 1914	3423
142. *Storthyngura fragilis* (Beddard), 1886	? 2303
143. *Stylomesus inermis* (Vanhöffen), 1914	2450

EXCLUDED PROBABLE PELAGICS: NORTH ATLANTIC

1. *Asconiscus simplex* G. O. Sars, Vanhöffen, 1914	0–3000
2. *Bathyopsurus nybelini* Nordenstam, 1956	5500–7900
3. *Cumoechus insignis* Hansen, 1916	806–2465
4. *Eurydyce grimaldi* Dollfuss, Stephensen, 1915	0–2600
5. *Eurydyce stygia* G. O. Sars, Hansen, 1916	2465
6. *Holophryxus acanthophyrae* Stephensen, 1913	<2000
7. *Holophryxus richardi* Koehler, Hansen, 1916	0–2500
8. *Munneurycope tjalfiensis* Stephensen, 1913	1200–2500
9. *Munnopsoides eximius* Hansen, 1916	866–2702
10. *Munnopsurus longipes* Tattersall, Hansen, 1916	710–2702
11. *Paramunnopsus oceanica* Tattersall, Hansen, 1916	0–2702
12. *Pseudomunnopsis beddardi* (Tattersall), 1905 (1906)	354–2702
13. *Paramunnopsis spinifer* (Vanhöffen), 1914	400–3000
14. *Notophryxus longicaudatus* Vanhöffen, 1914	0–3000

EXCLUDED PROBABLE PELAGICS: SOUTH ATLANTIC

15. *Asconiscus simplex* G. O. Sars, Vanhöffen, 1914	0–3000
16. *Cryptoniscus* sp. Vanhöffen, 1914	30–3000
17. *Microniscus ornatus* Vanhöffen, 1914	3000
18. *Microniscus* sp. Vanhöffen, 1914	400–2500
19. *Paramunnopsis oceanica*, Vanhöffen, 1914	0–3000

EXCLUDED PROBABLE PELAGICS: SOUTH PACIFIC AND INDIAN OCEAN

20. *Anilocra meridionalis* Searle	2000–2500
21. *Microniscus* sp. Vanhöffen, 1914	400–2500
22. *Munnopsoides australis* Beddard, 1886a	2500–3000

SYSTEMATICS

The systematic arrangement of this monograph follows the scheme set forth by Menzies (in press). In outline this is:

Order: Isopoda
 Suborder: Gnathiidea
 Suborder: Quatuordecapoda (Isopoda, *sensu stricto*)
  Tribe 1: Asellota
  Tribe 2: Valvifera

Tribe 3: Flabellifera
Tribe 4: Epicaridea
Tribe 5: Oniscoidea
Tribe 6: Phreatoicidea

The Phreatoicidea and Oniscoidea, with terrestrial and fresh water species, lack abyssal representatives and are, therefore, outside of the scope of this work.

Suborder: GNATHIIDEA MONOD, 1926a

This major category of the Isopoda deserves mention in a treatise on abyssal organisms mainly because it is so poorly represented in the abyss. Only two species are known from below 2000 meters; these are *Gnathia stygia* (G. O. Sars) and *Gnathia caeca* Richardson. The majority of the species live in shelf depths (viz., down to 200 meters). The animals, by virtue of their parasitic mode of life, are intimately tied to a fish host. This is probably the major reason why they have not been successful in penetration of the deep sea.

The main zoogeographic conclusions that can be drawn from the great work by Monod (1926a) are that the gnathiid isopods are cosmopolitan in their distribution; that there are more species in the north and south temperate zones than elsewhere; and that the Antarctic has three times the number of species found in the Arctic. Bipolarity is not known in this group.

Diagnosis: Isopoda with five pairs of peraeopods. Mandibles of male project beyond cephalon as a pair of pincers. Last pair of appendages lost and seventh somite much reduced. Appendages of first peraeonal somite united into the cephalon as a second pair of maxillipeds (the pylopods). Adult male is the gnathia stage, adult female the praniza, and larval form the anceus.

Affinities: The gnathiidea have obviously been derived from a cirolanid-type ancestor, and as early as the Jurassic the probable precursor *Urda* was developed. The nearest relative to *Urda* living today, however, is probably *Gnatholana*, a shallow water genus from Africa.

I tend to favor the consideration that the gnathiids represent a group which has evolved since the Mesozoic from an *Urda*-like ancestor. Since then they have become highly specialized fish parasites. *Gnatholana*, on the other hand, probably represents a relict descendant from the *Urda* type.

Two new species of *Gnathia* were found in the *Vema* collections from bathyal depths off the South African coast. These are described here together with the only two known abyssal species, *G. stygia* and *G. caeca*.

A KEY TO THE FOURTEEN DESCRIBED SPECIES OF GNATHIIDEA KNOWN FROM DEPTHS OF 500 METERS AND GREATER
(Modified from Monod, 1926a, pp. 282–339)

1. Pylopods with five articles 2
1. Pylopods with three articles 5
2. Frons produced as a triangulate process as far as the apex of the mandibles . *Bathygnathia* . . . 3
2. Frons not produced . . . . *Akidognathia* . . . 4
3. Apex of rostrum with a patch of setae . . . . *bathybia* (Beddard) (1638 meters, *Challenger*, 38° 11′ N., 27° 9′ W.)
3. Apex of rostrum nude . . . . *curvirostris* Richardson (709–1232 meters, *Albatross*, N. Atlantic, south of Martha's Vineyard and east of Georges Bank)
4. Pylopods operculate . . . . . . *cristatipes* (Stebbing) (980 meters, *Porcupine*, 48° 6′ N., 9° 18′ W.)
4. Pylopods pediform . . . . . . *poteriophora* Monod (914 meters, *Ingolf*, St. Croix, Antilles)
5. Frons produced 7
5. Frons not produced 6
6. Frontal process bifid . . . . . *abyssorum* (G. O. Sars) (N. Atlantic, Norwegian fjords, 128–887 meters)
6. Frontal process trifid . . . . . *oxyuraea* (Lilljeborg) (Norway, England, Mediterranean, 0–533 meters)
7. With eyes 8
7. Without eyes 11
8. Eyes produced on immovable swellings . . . . *elongata* (Krøyer) (0–890 meters, circumpolar, Norway, etc.)
8. Eyes not produced, sessile 9
9. Supraocular lobe produced . . . *hirsuta* (G. O. Sars) (208–1755 meters, Norway, Davis Strait)
9. Supraocular lobe not produced 10

10. Head subcircular, mandibles small and not
    extending to margin of frons . . . *serrata* Richardson
    (709 meters, *Albatross*, N. Atlantic, south of Martha's
    Vineyard)

10. Head quadrate, mandibles
    normal . . . . *tuberculata* Richardson
    (1132 meters, *Albatross*, 37° 22′ .30″ N., 137° 47′ E.,
    off Japan)

11. Peraeopods strongly spinous, head small
    (much narrower than peraeon) . . *stygia* (G. O. Sars)
    (535–2391 meters, N. Atlantic)

11. Peraeopods weakly spinous, head large (nearly as
    wide as peraeon) 12

12. Somite 4 of peraeon with a sulcus on
    dorsal suface at midline . . . . . *caeca* Richardson
    (2638 meters, N. Atlantic)

12. Somite 4 of peraeon without a sulcus on dorsal
    surface at midline 13

13. Lateral border of head strongly convex.
    Lateral margin of peraeon convex . . *bicolor* Hansen
    (1537 meters, N. Atlantic)

13. Lateral border of head scarcely convex, borders
    of peraeon subparallel . . . . . . *albescens* Hansen
    (842–1018 meters, N. Atlantic)

Genus: GNATHIA Leach

Gnathia vemae, new species
Figure 2

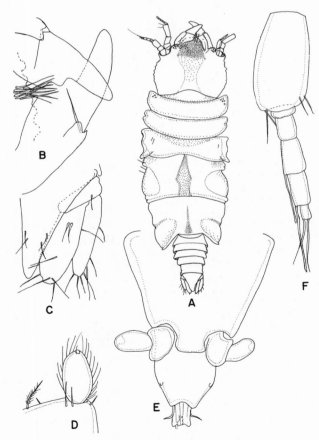

Figure 2. *Gnathia vemae*, n. sp. A: male holotype; B: mandible and frons; C: pleotelson
and uropod; D: pylopod; E: frons of praniza;
F: first antenna, male.

Synonyms: None.

Diagnosis: *Gnathia* with a produced and entire
frons, eyes lacking. Mandible with a pronounced
redan and three teeth. Pylopod with three articles,
last article minute. Flagellum of first antenna with
five articles, second also with five articles. Last two
large peraeonal somites with a dorsal medial sulcus.
Peraeopods not markedly spinous. Pleopoda lacking
setae.

Measurements: Holotype male length 2.8 mm.,
width pleotelson 0.2 mm.

Type locality: South Atlantic, L.G.O. Biotrawl No.
55, type plus two male paratypes and one praniza,
cat. no. I-41.

Distribution: Known only from the type locality.

Affinities: This species is closely allied to *Gnathia
caeca* Richardson, from which it differs in having teeth
on the mandible; otherwise the two are very similar.

Gnathia caeca Richardson
Figure 3 A–B

Synonyms: *Gnathia caeca* Richardson, 1911, pp.
519–520; Stephensen, 1915, p. 7; Monod, 1926a,
pp. 406–408.

Diagnosis: Pylopods with three articles. Head as
wide as thorax. Eyes lacking. Frons produced but
not as far as mandible apex. Supraocular lobes
strongly tuberculate. Peraeopods without many stout
spines. Fourth peraeonal somite with a pronounced
dorso-medial sulcus. Margins of uropods and telson
entire, without teeth.

Measurements: Length 5 mm. (Monod, op. cit.,
p. 407).

Type locality: North Atlantic, *Talisman* Station 76,
latitude 25° 1′ N., longitude 19° 15′ W., 2638 meters
(Monod, op. cit., p. 408).

Distribution: Known only from type locality.

Affinities: The species appears to be most nearly
related to *G. bicolor* Hansen in key characteristics at
least (*vide* Monod, op. cit., p. 332).

Gnathia stygia (G. O. Sars)
Figure 3 C–E

Synonyms: *Anceus stygius* G. O. Sars, 1877, p.
348; — 1885, pp. 85–92; — 1886, pp. 27, 85. *Gnathia
stygius* (G. O. Sars), Stebbing, 1893, p. 338; — Ohlin,
1901, p. 22, Fig. 3. *Caecognathia stygia* (G. O. Sars),
Dollfus, 1901, p. 244. *Caecognathia sarsi* A. Dollfus,
1901, pp. 244–245, Fig. 3. *Bathygnathia stygia* (err.
typ.), Stephensen, 1915, p. 6. *Caecognathia stygia*
(G. O. Sars), Stephensen, 1915, p. 7. *Gnathia Stygia*
(G. O. Sars), Hansen. 1916, pp. 230–232; Monod,
1926a, pp. 398–405.

Diagnosis: Pylopods with three articles. Head
narrower than thorax. Eyes lacking. Frons produced

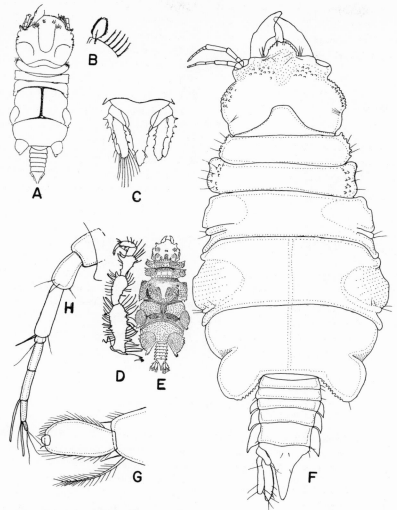

Figure 3. A–B: *Gnathia caeca* Richardson. A: male; B: pylopod (after Monod, 1926a, p. 406, Fig. 162). C–E: *Gnathia stygia* (G. O. Sars). C: pleotelson; D: fifth peraeopod; E: male (after Monod, 1926a, pp. 400–401, Figs. 159–160). F–H: *Gnathia albescenoides*, n. sp. F: male holotype; G: pylopod; H: first antenna.

but not as far as the mandible apex. Supraocular lobes ramose. Peraeopods with many stout spines. Fourth peraeonal somite with a pronounced dorsomedial sulcus. Margin of uropods and telson dentate. Pleopoda elongate and smooth. Entire body provided with sharp tubercles. Flagellum of first antenna with five articles. That of second antenna with seven articles.

Measurements: Length to 11 mm. (Monod, op. cit., p. 402).

Type locality; North Atlantic, latitude 65° 53′ N., longitude 7° 18′ W., 2127 meters.

Distribution: Arctic Ocean (Gurjanova) to Norwegian Basin of North Atlantic, 552–2465 meters (Hansen, op. cit). Taken by the *Ingolf* from the following stations:

North of the Faeroes: Station 141, latitude 63° 22′ N., longitude 6° 58′ W., 1279 meters, temperature —0.6°, six specimens (five male); Station 139.

East of Iceland: Station 105, latitude 65° 34′ N., longitude 7° 31′ W., 1435 meters, temperature —0.8°, one specimen (male). Station 103, latitude 66° 23′ N., longitude 8° 52′ W., 1090 meters, temperature —0.6°, one specimen (male); Station 102, latitude 66° 23′ N., longitude 10° 26′ W., 1412 meters, temperature —0.9°, five specimens (one male).

North of Iceland: Station 126, latitude 67° 19′ N., longitude 15° 52′ W., 552 meters, temperature —0.5°, one specimen (larva); Station 124, latitude 67° 40′ N., longitude 15° 40′ W., 932 meters, temperature —0.6°, one and one-half specimens (male).

North east of Iceland: Station 120, latitude 67° 29′ N., longitude 11° 32′ W., 1666 meters, temperature —1.0°, two specimens (male); Station 119, latitude 67° 53′ N., longitude 10° 19′ W., 1902 meters, temperature —1.0°, one specimen (larva).

South of Jan Mayen: Station 117, latitude 69° 13′ N., longitude 8° 23′ W., 1889 meters, temperature —1.0.

two specimens (both larvae, one of them on *Liparis frigidus*); Station 113, latitude 69° 31′ N., longitude 7° 06′ W., 2465 meters, temperature −1.0°, one specimen (larva, taken on *Liparis frigidus*).

Gnathia albescenoides, new species
Figure 3 F–H

Synonyms: None.

Diagnosis: *Gnathia* with produced frons, eyes lacking. Mandible with slight redan but lacking teeth on cutting edge. Pylopod triarticulate, last article minute. Last two large peraeonal somites without a dorsal medial sulcus. Flagellum of first antenna with five articles, second with six articles.

Measurements: Holotype male length 5.4 mm., width pleon 0.4 mm., allotype length 5.5 mm., width pleon 0.5 mm.

Type locality: South Atlantic, L.G.O. Biotrawl No. 54, types plus five male paratypes, cat. no. I-42.

Distribution: Known only from type locality.

Affinities: This species is closely allied to *Gnathia albescens* H. J. Hansen. It differs from that species in having a narrower frons and in having six instead of eight articles to the flagellum of the second antenna. Otherwise the two are very similar.

Suborder: QUATUORDECAPODA (Isopoda, *sensu stricto*)

The quatuordecapods contain the majority of the abyssal isopods, but even here the abundance of abyssal species is strongly skewed toward the Asellota. The generally detritus-feeding habits of asellotes and the low incidence of parasitism (none known), commensalism (*Caecijera horvathi*, *Iais* spp., *Antias unirameus*), and carnivorous feeding (none known) are probably the most important factors related to the ability of the asellotes to penetrate the abyss. Parasitic isopods in general are rare in the abyss. The anthurids perhaps constitute an exception.

Tribe: ASELLOTA

It is possible to divide the Asellota into three groups of equivalent rank, as shown in the following key. The characteristics used are shown in Figure 4.

A KEY TO THE SUBTRIBES OF THE TRIBE ASELLOTA
(After Menzies, in press)

1. Male first pair of pleopods fused along midline; consisting of an elongate sympod, lacking rami. Second male pleopods coupled loosely with first pairs. First pair of female pleopods lacking; second fused along midline to form a large operculum covering the remaining pleopods. Pleon with one or two somites . . . . *Paraselloidea*
1. Male first pair of pleopods consist of a short sympod and a short ramus, neither coupled with second pair. First pair of pleopods of female not covering the remaining pleopods. Pleon with three somites . . . . *Stenetrioidea*
1. Basal article of male first pleopods free, not joined medially into a single piece. Neither the first pair of pleopods of female nor the basal article of male first pleopods fused together . . . . *Aselloidea*

It is perhaps well to add also that the Paraselloidea (Fig. 4) never have more than two somites comprising the pleon, whereas the Aselloidea and Stenetrioidea always have more than two complete pleonal somites. The structure of the pleon and pleopods shows definitely that the Paraselloidea represent a specialized advanced group, whereas the Stenetrioidea and Aselloidea conserve the greatest number of primitive characteristics. The Aselloidea contain only fresh water species, whereas the Stenetrioidea are exclusively marine, most extensively developed in the shallow water of the subtropics, and have only one abyssal representative. To the Paraselloidea belongs the majority of the abyssal species. It is possible to divide the Paraselloidea into two additional previously unrecognized groups. The first category embraces species in which the anal opening is separated from the branchial cavity, and the second includes species in which the anus is enclosed within the branchial cavity. As obvious as this characteristic is in some genera (viz., separated from the branchial chamber in *Haploniscus*, and contained within the branchial chamber in *Pleurogonium*), it is nevertheless impossible to utilize it at this date, due to the fact that it is not well enough described for the majority of asellote genera. At first I thought there might be a correlation between the separation of the anus from the branchial chamber and abyssal habitat, but this turns out not to be the case because in *Abyssijaera*, a genus in which the anus is enclosed within the branchial chamber, an abyssal habitat is typical, whereas in *Munna*, an intertidal genus, the anus is terminal and separated from the branchial chamber.

A separation of families in the number of pleonites comprising the pleon is a more hopeful one, but here again only in those cases where it is perfectly certain and obvious—e.g., *Haploniscus* with one and *Ilyarachna* with two pleonal somites.

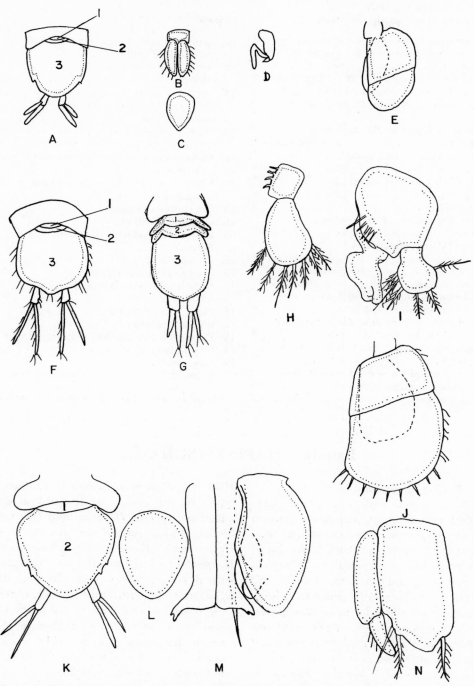

Figure 4. Characteristics of asellota. A–E: Stenetrioidea. A: pleon; B: male first pleopod; C: female first (second) pleopod; D: male second pleopod; E: third pleopod, either sex. F–J: Aselloidea. F: pleon *Asellus*; G: pleon *Stenasellus*; H: male first pleopod; I: male second pleopod; J: third pleopod, either sex. K–M: Paraselloidea. K: pleon *Janira*; L: female first (second) pleopod; M: first and second male pleopod; N: third pleopod, either sex. (Figures A–E after Hansen, 1916, from Richardson, 1905; F–J after Birstein, 1951; K–N after Menzies, 1952.)

A KEY TO THE FAMILIES OF THE TRIBE ASELLOTA, SUBTRIBE PARASELLOIDEA[a]

(Modified after Menzies, in press)

1. None of the peraeopods modified for swimming . 5
1. Some of the peraeopods modified for swimming . 2
2. All peraeopods except first pair modified for swimming, similar in structure . . . *Desmosomidae**
2. Only peraeopods 5–6 or 7 inclusive paddle-like. Others simple walking legs or fossorial appendages 3
3. Only peraeopods 5–6 paddle-like, seventh a simple walking leg . . . . *Ilyarachnidae**
3. Peraeopods 5–7 inclusive paddle-like 4
4. Peraeopods 5–7 inclusive lack dactyls . *Munnopsidae*
4. Peraeopods 5–7 inclusive with dactyls . . *Eurycopidae**
5. Uropoda lack peduncle 6
5. Uropoda with peduncle 7
6. Molar process of mandible normal, strong, truncated at denticulate grinding apex . . *Munnidae**
6. Molar process of mandibles weak, pointed . . . . *Pleurogonidae**
7. Fourth and fifth peraeonal somites sometimes elongated twice as long as wide . . . . *Ischnomesidae**
7. All peraeonal somites similar in width, none twice as long as wide, most wider than long 8
8. Palp of maxilliped with narrow similar articles all less than one-half the width of endite 9
8. Palp of maxillipeds with last two articles narrow, others twice as wide 12
9. Molar process of mandible normal, strong, truncated at denticulate grinding apex 10
9. Molar process spiniform . . . . *Jaeropsidae*

10. Dactyl of seventh peraeopod with one elongated terminal claw 11
10. Dactyl of seventh peraeopod with two short claws . . . . *Antiasidae*
11. Coxal plates developed . . . . *Dendrotiondae*
11. Coxal plates lacking . . . . *Haploniscidae**
12. Articles of maxillipedal palp one-half the width of endite . . . . *Acanthaspididae**
12. Articles of maxillipedal palp about as wide as endite 13
13. Dactyls of peraeopods 2–7 inclusive with two principal claws and a smaller accessory claw . . . . *Ianiridae**
13. Dactyls of peraeopods 2–7 inclusive with one or two terminal claws but never three 14
14. Molar process of mandible reduced to short setiferous tubercle . . . . *Nannoniscidae*
14. Molar process normal, expanded apically and truncated, grinding 15
15. Coxal plates present 17
15. Coxal plates absent 16
16. First peraeopod with two stout dactyls . . . . *Echinothambemidae**
16. First peraeopod with one dactyl only *Macrostylidae**
17. Body not markedly elongated 18
17. Body length exceeds four times its width . . . . *Thambematidae**
18. Pleon with one somite, uropoda uniramous . . . . *Ianirellidae**
18. Pleon with two somites, uropoda biramous . . . 19
19. Coxal plates spiniform . . . . *Schistosomidae*
19. Coxal plates rounded . . . . . *Abyssianiridae** and some *Munnidae*

[a] Families with abyssal representatives marked with asterisk.

Family: HAPLONISCIDAE

Type genus: *Haploniscus* Richardson.

Diagnosis: Paraselloidea with free head. Eyes lacking. Mandibles normal with palp and expanded molar, lacinia, and setal row. Antennae shorter than body. All peraeopods simple walking legs; dactyl with at last one terminal claw, never three. Uropoda ventral, with peduncle and one ramus only. All peraeonal somites of similar width, wider than long. First three articles of maxillipedal palp narrow, less than one-half the width of endite. Pleon with one somite only. Anus widely separated from branchial chamber. (Modified after Menzies, 1956a, p. 9.)

Composition: This family contains *Haploniscus* Richardson, *Hydroniscus* Hansen, and a proposed new genus, *Antennuloniscus*. All are now known from the North and South Atlantic. The majority of the species are abyssal, although shallow water species are known.

Genus: HAPLONISCUS Richardson.

Type species: *Nannoniscus bicuspis* G. O. Sars, 1885, Richardson, 1908a, p. 75.

Richardson (op. cit.) established this species in 1908 with *Nannoniscus bicuspis* G. O. Sars, 1885, as the type. At the same time Richardson described two additional species, *H. excisus* and *H. retrospinis*. Vanhöffen, 1914, described two species, *H. antarcticus* and *H. curvirostris*. Hansen, 1916, added two more species, *H. spinifer* and *H. armadilloides*. Barnard, 1920, described *H. dimeroceras*, and Menzies, 1956a, added *H. unicornis*, and with Tinker (1960), *H. robinsoni*.

Menzies (op. cit.) constructed a key to the species based upon the presence or absence of a complete seventh peraeonal somite. The collections now available show that this characteristic is not the best one to use, as the segmentation may be obscure, even though present, in certain species and is not described accurately for the known species. A more obvious characteristic divides the species of this genus into two groups which are tentatively considered as separate genera.

Generic diagnosis: Haploniscidae with uniramous uropoda. Peraeon with 6–7 articulated somites. Epimera (coxal plates) not visible in dorsal view. Third article of the peduncle of the second antenna about as long as wide. (After Menzies, 1956a.)

Composition: To this genus belong all the species mentioned above except *dimeroceras* Barnard, which is transferred to *Antennuloniscus*. The 20 following new species described herein also belong to *Haploniscus*.

Depth distribution:	Meters	
bicuspis (G. O. Sars)	360–2465	Hansen, 1916, p. 30
spinifer Hansen	2970–3474	Hansen, 1916, p. 31
armadilloides Hansen	1301–1301	Hansen, 1916, p. 32
antarcticus Vanhöffen	385–3397	Vanhöffen, 1914, p. 557
curvirostris Vanhöffen	3423–3423	Vanhöffen, 1914, p. 558
excisus Richardson	3235–3235	Richardson, 1908a, p. 76
retrospinis Richardson	713–713	Richardson, 1908a, p. 77
unicornis Menzies	5104–5122	Menzies, 1956a, p. 1
robinsoni Menzies and Tinker	2860–2858	Menzies and Tinker, 1960, pp. 2–4.

The genus is obviously eurybathyal, extending from bathyal depths to the abyss. To date it is unknown from hadal depths (viz., below 6000 meters).

Diagnostic characteristics: The diagnostic characteristics are shown in Figure 5. The cephalon frontal margin (frons) may be quadrate, excavate, or convex

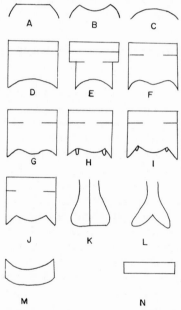

Figure 5. Key characteristics of *Haploniscus*. A–C: frons of cephalon; D–F: shape of pleon; G–J: posterior margin of pleon and uropods; K–L: male first pleopods; M–N: fourth peraeonal somite.

and with or without medial projections (Fig. 5 A–C). The lateral margin of the seventh peraeonal somite may project beyond the margin of the pleon or may be continuous with it (Fig. 5 D–E). The postero-lateral angles of the pleon may or may not project beyond the postero-medial margin of the pleon (Fig. 5 F–G). The uropods may or may not extend to the margin of the pleon or may be concealed from dorsal view (Fig. 5 H–J). The sympod of the first pleopod of the male may or may not be separated at the apex

(Fig. 5 K–L). The antero-lateral margin of the fourth peraeonal somite may be produced forward in various degrees or may not be produced (Fig. 5 M–N). Additionally, the flagellum of the first antenna may have a differing number of articles and the frontal border of the cephalon may or may not conceal the first article of the first antenna. The spine on the peduncle of the second antenna may be present or absent. These characteristics not only serve to distinguish one species from another but also serve to indicate the genetic similarities between various species. It is on the characteristics that the following natural key to the species is based.

A KEY TO THE SPECIES OF HAPLONISCUS

1. First article of first antenna concealed by cephalon dorsally 2
1. First article of first antenna not concealed by cephalon dorsally 8
2. Postero-lateral angles of pleon project beyond medial margin . . . . *curvirostris* Vanhöffen
2. Postero-lateral angles of pleon not projecting beyond medial margin 3
3. Uropoda extending to posterior margin of pleon . 4
3. Uropoda not extending to posterior margin of pleon 6
4. Frontal margin with medial projection . . . . *armadilloides* Hansen
4. Frontal margin entire, without medial projection. 5
5. Lateral border of pleon and peraeon continuous, body tuberculate . . . . *tuberculatus*, n. sp.
5. Pleon set in from peraeon at lateral margin . . . . *parallelus*, n. sp.
6. Uropoda concealed in dorsal view 7
6. Uropoda exposed in dorsal view . . . . *ovalis*, n. sp.
7. Pleon quadrate . . . . *trituberculatus*, n. sp.
7. Pleon pointed . . . . *telus*, n. sp.
8. Frontal margin of cephalon excised 9
8. Frontal margin of cephalon straight or convex . 14
9. Frontal margin with medial projection 10
9. Frontal margin entire, without medial projection 22
10. Postero-lateral angles of pleon produced beyond medial margin 24
10. Postero-lateral angles of pleon not produced beyond medial margin 11
11. Medial projection of front with a projected base . 12
11. Medial projection of front entire 13
12. Pleon set in from peraeon . . . . *tricornoides*, n. sp.
12. Pleonal and peraeonal margins continuous . . . . *tricornis*, n. sp.
13. Frontal projection with a broad base, tapering to a point . . . . . . *bicuspis* (G. O. Sars)
13. Frontal projection widest at least one-half its length . . . . *spatulifrons*, n. sp.
14. Frontal margin with a medial projection 15
14. Frontal margin without a medial projection . . . 20
15. Pleon set in from peraeon 16
15. Pleonal and peraeonal lateral margins continuous 18
16. Medial projection bifid . . . . *rugosus*, n. sp.
16. Medial projection a single knob 17
17. Flagellum of first antenna with four articles . . . . *polaris*, n. sp.
17. Flagellum of first antenna with five articles . . . . *antarcticus* Vanhöffen

18. Medial projection a simple knob 19
18. Medial projection longer than
wide . . . . *unicornis* Menzies
19. Postero-lateral angles of pleon exceed twice
the length of uropoda . . . . *retrospinis* Richardson
19. Postero-lateral angles of pleon equal the
length of uropoda . . . . *percavix*, n. sp.
20. Lateral border of fourth peraeonal somite
produced forward . . . . *quadrifrons*, n. sp.
20. Lateral border of fourth peraeonal somite not
produced forward 21
21. Uropoda extending almost to the margin of the
postero-lateral angles of the pleon . . . *acutus*, n. sp.
21. Uropoda very short, less than one-half the
length of the pleon postero-lateral
angles . . . . *spinifer* Hansen
22. Lateral borders of fourth peraeonal somite
produced forward and pointed at antero-lateral
angle . . . . *elevatus*, n. sp.
22. Lateral borders of fourth peraeonal somite not
produced forward or with blunt lateral angles 23
23. Pleon set in from peraeon 27
23. Lateral border of pleon and peraeon
continuous . . . . *minutus*, n. sp.
24. Frontal projection trifid 25
24. Frontal projection entire 26
25. Lateral border peraeon and pleon
continuous . . . . *tridens*, n. sp.
25. Lateral border pleon set in from
peraeon . . . . *capensis*, n. sp.
26. Uropods extending to postero-lateral
margin of pleon . . . . *nondescriptus*, n. sp.
26. Uropods not extending to postero-lateral
margin of pleon . . . . *princeps*, n. sp.
27. Uropods extending beyond postero-lateral
margin of pleon . . . . *excisus* Richardson
27. Uropods not extending to postero-lateral
margin of pleon . . . . *tropicalis*, n. sp.

Haploniscus bicuspis (G. O. Sars)
Figure 6 A–D

Synonyms: Nannoniscus bicuspis G. O. Sars, 1877,
p. 352. *Haploniscus bicuspis* (G. O. Sars); —
Richardson, 1908a, p. 75; — Hansen, 1916, pp.
29–30, Pl. II (incomplete).

Diagnosis: Frontal border of cephalon with a
median projection, base broad tapering to a point.
Flagellum of first antenna with six articles. Lateral
margins of peraeon and pleon continuous. Antero-
lateral margin of fourth peraeonal somite not produced forward, lateral angles blunt. First article of
first antenna not concealed by cephalon dorsally.
Uropods extending to posterior margin of pleon and
to the end of the postero-lateral angles.

Measurements: Length 2.90 mm. (G. O. Sars,
1885, p. 122).

Type locality: North Atlantic, west of Norway,
latitude 63° 5′ N., 988 meters (Hansen, 1916, p. 30)
or possibly latitude 69° 46′ N., 1220 meters.

Distribution: Hansen (op. cit.) records the species
from 15 *Ingolf* stations, and one—Station 113, latitude
69° 31′ N., longitude 7° 06′ W., 2465 meters—is

from abyssal depth. Presumably it is eurybathial,
extending from 360 meters to 2465 meters.

Here it is recorded from the South Atlantic,
L.G.O. Biotrawl No. 12, one male and two females,
cat. no. I-5; and L.G.O. Biotrawl No. 53, one male
and four females, cat. no. I-4.

It is highly probable that Hansen (op. cit.) confused at least two species in what he called *bicuspis*;
his illustrations, Pl. II, show specimens in which the
uropoda do and do not reach the posterior margin of
the pleon. For this reason not all of his distributional
data is cited here. I have not seen his specimens.
The male that he figures is doubtless a distinct
bathyal species and probably is identical with Richardson's *retrospinis*. It differs from the true *bicuspis* in
having the apex of the male pleopod swollen and the
uropods not reaching the posterior margin of the
pleon; that is, the postero-lateral angles of the pleon
are much produced.

Affinities: This species is related to *tricornis* and
tricornoides, from both of which it differs in lacking a
projected base on the medial spine of the frontal
margin of the cephalon.

Haploniscus unicornis Menzies
Figure 6 E–G

Synonym: Haploniscus unicornis Menzies, 1956a, p. 9.

Diagnosis: Frontal border of cephalon convex,
with elongated (longer than breadth of base) spine-
like horn. Lateral borders of pleon and peraeon
continuous. Flagellum of first antenna with five
articles. Postero-lateral angles of pleon produced
beyond medial margin. First article of first antenna
not concealed by cephalon dorsally. Antero-lateral
border of fourth peraeonal somite not produced
forward; lateral margin quadrate. Uropoda extending beyond apex of pleon but not to tips of postero-
lateral angles of pleon.

Measurements: Female length 1.45 mm., width at
second peraeonal somite 0.60 mm. (Menzies, 1956a,
p. 9).

Type locality: North Atlantic, L.G.O. Biotrawl
No. 1, 5104–5122 meters, cat. no. 11759, A.M.N.H.

Distribution: Known only from type locality.

Affinities: The elongate spine which is much larger
than its base on the front of the cephalon distinguishes
this species from the others.

Haploniscus excisus Richardson
Figure 6 H

Synonyms: Haploniscus excisus Richardson, 1908a,
pp. 75–77, Figs. 4–5.

Diagnosis: Frontal border of cephalon excavated,
entire. Flagellum of first antenna with five articles.
Pleon set in from peraeon. Lateral borders of fourth

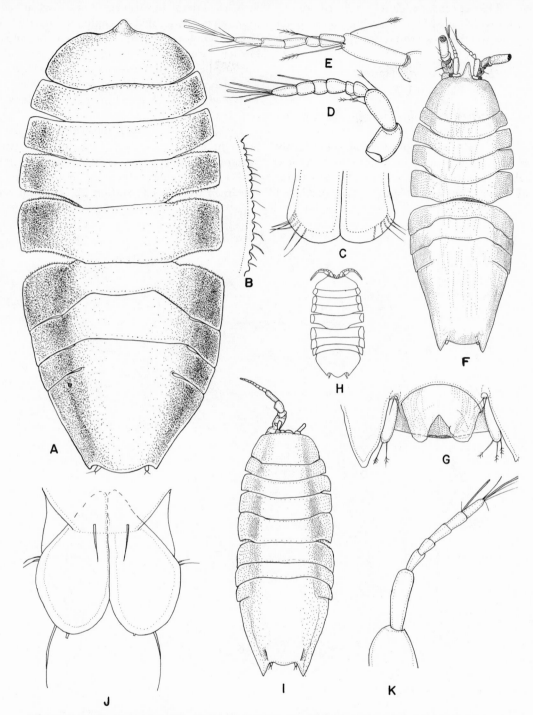

Figure 6. A–D: *Haploniscus bicuspis* (G. O. Sars). A: male dorsal view, 5.1 mm. long, 2.1 mm. wide, L.G.O. Sta. 12; B: anterior border fifth peraeonal somite; C: male first pleopod; D: first antenna. E–G: *Haploniscus unicornis* Menzies. E: first antenna; F: dorsal view type; G: ventral view pleotelson (after Menzies, 1956a). H: *Haploniscus excisus* Richardson, dorsal view type (after Richardson, 1908a). I–K: *Haploniscus spinifer* Hansen. I: dorsal view male; J: male first pleopod; K: first antenna (after Hansen, 1916, Pl. II).

peraeonal somite not produced forward, lateral edges blunt. First article of first antenna not concealed by cephalon dorsally. Uropods extending beyond postero-lateral margin of pleon.

Measurements: None available.

Type locality: North Atlantic, east of Georges Bank, *Albatross* Station 2572, 3235 meters.

Distribution: Known only from type locality.

Affinities: This species is closely related to *H. tropicalis,* from which it differs in having the uropoda extending beyond the postero-lateral margin of the pleon.

Haploniscus spinifer Hansen
Figure 6 I–K

Synonyms: *Haploniscus spinifer* Hansen, 1916, p. 31, Pl. II.

Diagnosis: Frontal border of cephalon very slightly convex, entire. Flagellum of first antenna with five articles. Pleon set in from peraeon. Antero-lateral margin of fourth peraeonal somite not produced forward, lateral borders straight. First article of first antenna not concealed by cephalon dorsally. Postero-lateral angles of pleon produced beyond medial border, uropods extending beyond medial border but not beyond postero-lateral angles. Apex of male first pleopod separated, swollen with two apical setae.

Measurements: Largest male 2.8 mm. length (Hansen, 1916, p. 31).

Type locality: This is uncertain because Hansen lists three *Ingolf* stations and further cites some variability which seems too wide for a single species. The male pleopod which he figures came from a specimen from *Ingolf* Station 22, and this seems the

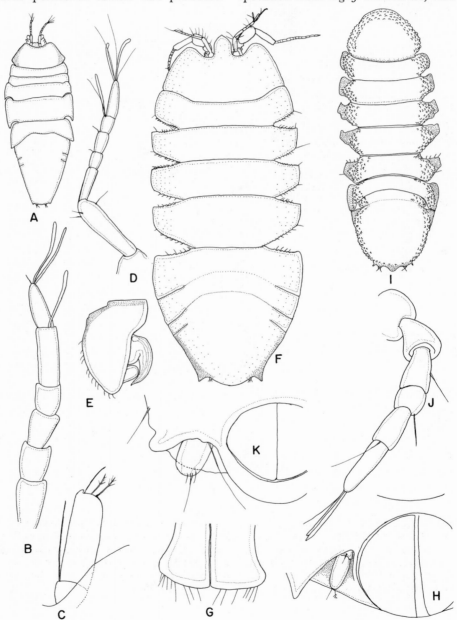

Figure 7. A–C: *Haploniscus minutus,* n. sp. A: female dorsal view; B: first antennal flagellum; C: uropod. D–H: *Haploniscus spatulifrons,* n. sp. D: first antenna; E: second pleopod; F: male dorsal view; G: first pleopod; H: anus and uropod. I–K: *Haploniscus tuberculatus,* n. sp. I: female dorsal view; J: first antenna; K: anus and uropods.

logical choice of type locality; latitude, 58° 10′ N., longitude 48° 25′ W., 3474 meters, temperature 1.4° C., four specimens.

Distribution: Uncertain. It was collected from North Atlantic, *Ingolf* Station 22; South Atlantic, L.G.O. Biotrawl No. 18, one female, one male, cat. no. I-22, and L.G.O. Biotrawl No. 16, three females, cat. no. I-23.

Affinities: This species appears to be most closely related to *acutus*, n. sp.

Haploniscus minutus, new species
Figure 7 A–C

Synonyms: None.
Diagnosis: Frontal border excised, entire. Pleon and peraeonal lateral borders continuous. Flagellum of first antenna with six articles. Postero-lateral angles of pleon not projected beyond medial margin. Dorsum of pleon smooth. First article of first antenna not concealed by cephalon. Uropoda extending beyond posterior medial margin of pleon. Antero-lateral borders of fourth pleonal somite not projected forward. Dorsum of head not tuberculate.
Measurements: Holotype female length 2.5 mm., width pleon 0.8 mm.
Type locality: South Atlantic, L.G.O. Biotrawl No. 12, one female, cat. no. I-15.
Distribution: Known only from type locality.
Affinities: The species is close to *H. excisus*, differing markedly from it in having the lateral borders of the pleon and peraeon continuous.

Haploniscus spatulifrons, new species
Figure 7 D–H

Synonyms: None.
Diagnosis: Frontal border deeply excavate and with a pronounced pointed spatulate projection. Pleon and peraeon lateral borders continuous. Flagellum of first antenna with five articles. Postero-lateral angles of pleon not produced beyond medial margin. Dorsum of pleon smooth. First article of first antenna not concealed by cephalon. Uropods not extending to posterior border of pleon. Rami of sympod of male first pleopod round at apex. Antero-lateral borders of fourth peraeonal somite not produced forward.
Measurements: Holotype male length 5.3 mm., width pleon 2.0 mm. Allotype female length 2.6 mm., width pleon 0.9 mm.
Type locality: South Atlantic, types and only specimens from L.G.O. Biotrawl No. 51, cat. no. I-10.
Distribution: Known only from type locality.
Affinities: The species is perhaps most nearly allied to *H. bicuspis* (G. O. Sars), but its spatulate rostrum distinguishes it.

Haploniscus tuberculatus, new species
Figure 7 I–K

Synonyms: None.
Diagnosis: Frontal border of cephalon convex, entire. Lateral borders of pleon and peraeon continuous. Flagellum of first antenna with four articles. Postero-lateral angles of pleon not projecting beyond medial margin. Dorsum of pleon tuberculate. First article of first antenna concealed by cephalon. Uropods extending beyond posterior margin of pleon. Antero-lateral borders of fourth peraeonal somite not produced forward.
Measurements: Holotype female length 1.7 mm., width pleon 0.4 mm.
Type locality: South Atlantic, type and only specimen collected from L.G.O. Biotrawl No. 51, cat. no. I-20.
Distribution: Known only from type locality.
Affinities: This species is most nearly related to *H. parallelus*, n. sp., from which it differs in having the lateral borders of the pleon and peraeon continuous.

Haploniscus tridens, new species
Figure 8

Synonyms: None.
Diagnosis: Frontal border deeply excavate and with a sharp trifid median projection. Pleon and peraeon lateral borders continuous. Flagellum of first antenna with five articles. Postero-lateral margins of pleon produced beyond medial margin. Dorsum of pleon smooth. First article of first antenna not concealed by cephalon. Uropods extending to posterior border of pleon. Rami of sympod of male first pleopod separated slightly at apex. Antero-lateral borders of fourth peraeonal somite not produced forward.
Measurements: Male holotype length 3.2 mm., width pleotelson 1.6 mm., allotype 4.2 mm. length, width pleotelson 2.0 mm.
Type locality: South Atlantic, types and one fragment from L.G.O. Biotrawl No. 12, cat. no. I-1.
Distribution: Known from type locality and from South Atlantic, L.G.O. Biotrawl No. 212, one intersex, cat. no. I-59, one intersex, cat. no. I-61.
Affinities: The species is most closely allied to *H capensis*, n. sp., differing from it most obviously in having the lateral borders of the pleon and peraeon continuous.

Haploniscus elevatus, new species
Figure 9 A–D

Synonyms: None.
Diagnosis: Frontal border excavate with a very slight, wide medial lobe. Pleon strongly set in from

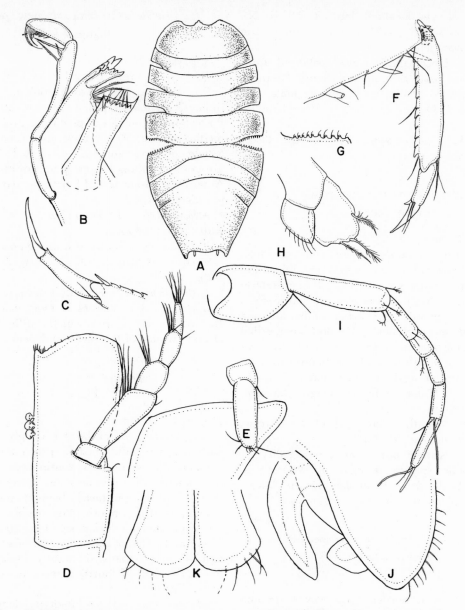

Figure 8. *Haploniscus tridens*, n. sp.   A: dorsal view male holotype; B: left mandible; C: sixth peraeopod; D: maxilliped; E: uropod; F: second peraeopod; G: proximal border fifth peraeonal somite; H: third pleopod; I: first antenna; J: second pleopod; K: first pleopod.

lateral border of peraeon. Flagellum of first antenna with five articles. Postero-lateral angles of pleon not produced beyond medial margin. Dorsum of pleon with large swelling medially near apex. First article of first antenna not concealed by cephalon. Uropods not extending to posterior border of pleon. Rami of sympod of male first pleopod united at apex. Antero-lateral border of fourth peraeonal somite produced forward.

Measurements: Male holotype length 1.9 mm., width pleon 0.8 mm.

Type locality: South Atlantic, type only from L.G.O. Biotrawl No. 52, cat. no. I-11.

Distribution: Known only from type locality.

Affinities: In general aspect *H. elevatus* resembles *H. princeps*, but the antero-lateral borders of peraeonal somites 3–4 are not as greatly produced forward.

Haploniscus quadrifrons, new species
Figure 9 E–G

Synonyms: None.

Diagnosis: Frontal border of cephalon entire and straight. Pleon set in from peraeon at lateral margins. Flagellum of first antenna with five articles. Postero-lateral angles of pleon produced much beyond medial margin. Dorsum of pleon smooth. First article of first antenna not concealed by cephalon. Uropods not extending to postero-lateral margin of pleon. Rami of sympod of male first pleopoda separated. Antero-lateral border of fourth peraeonal somite strongly produced forward.

Measurements: Holotype male length 2.1 mm., width pleon 0.6 mm.

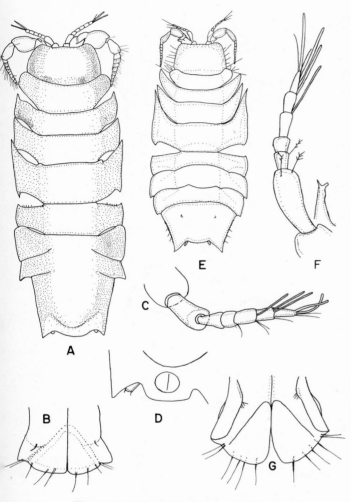

Figure 9. A–D: *Haploniscus elevatus*, n. sp. A: dorsal view male; B: first pleopod; C: first antenna; D: anus and uropod. E–G: *Haploniscus quadrifrons*, n. sp. E: dorsal view male type; F: first antenna; G: first pleopod.

Type locality: South Atlantic, holotype and two fragments from L.G.O. Biotrawl No. 22, cat. no. I-16.

Distribution: Also found at L.G.O. Biotrawl No. 23, one male, cat. no. I-17.

Affinities: This species is closely allied to *H. princeps* and *H. elevatus*, from which it is distinguished by the two dorsal tubercles on the pleon.

Haploniscus princeps, new species
Figure 10 A–C

Synonyms: None.

Diagnosis: Frontal border of cephalon excised, with a median slight but wide projection. Pleon

set in from peraeon. Flagellum of first antenna with four articles. Postero-lateral angles of pleon projecting beyond medial margin. Dorsum of pleon smooth. First article of peduncle of first antenna not concealed by cephalon. Uropods not extending to postero-lateral border of pleon. Rami of sympod of male first pleopod joined at apex. Antero-lateral margins of fourth peraeonal somite produced forward.

Measurements: Holotype female length 2.1 mm., width pleotelson 0.65 mm. Male allotype length 2.2 mm., (fragment).

Type locality: South Atlantic, types plus three female paratypes, L.G.O. Biotrawl No. 53, cat. no. I-14.

Distribution: Also found at L.G.O. Biotrawl No. 14, eleven females and one male, cat. no. I-203.

Affinities: *H. princeps* is closely allied to *H. elevatus*, *H. nondescriptus*, and *H. quadrifrons*. The absence of dorsal tubercles on the pleon and the short uropoda distinguish it.

Haploniscus percavix, new species
Figure 10 D–E

Synonyms: None.

Diagnosis: Frontal border of cephalon straight but with minute medial knob. Lateral margins of pleon and peraeon continuous. Flagellum of first antenna with five articles. Postero-lateral angles of pleon projecting beyond medial margin. Dorsum of pleon smooth. First article of first antenna not concealed by cephalon. Uropods extending to posterior margin of pleon. Antero-lateral angles of fourth peraeonal somite not produced forward.

Measurements: Male holotype intersex length 2.4 mm., width pleotelson 0.7 mm., female allotype length 3.4 mm., width pleotelson 1.5 mm.

Type locality: South Atlantic, types plus one male intersex paratype, L.G.O. Biotrawl No. 53, cat. no. I-6.

Distribution: Also found at L.G.O. Biotrawl No. 16, one male, one female, cat. no. I-7, and North Atlantic, *Atlantis* Station 15, one female, cat. no. I-207.

Affinities: This species is related to *H. retrospinis* Richardson, from which it differs in having the postero-lateral angles of the pleon two times the length of the uropoda.

Haploniscus tricornis, new species
Figure 10 F–I

Synonyms: None.

Diagnosis: Frontal border cephalon excavate but with a medial apically trifid projection. Lateral margins of pleon and peraeon continuous. Flagellum of first antenna with six articles. Postero-lateral angles of pleon not projecting beyond medial pleonal

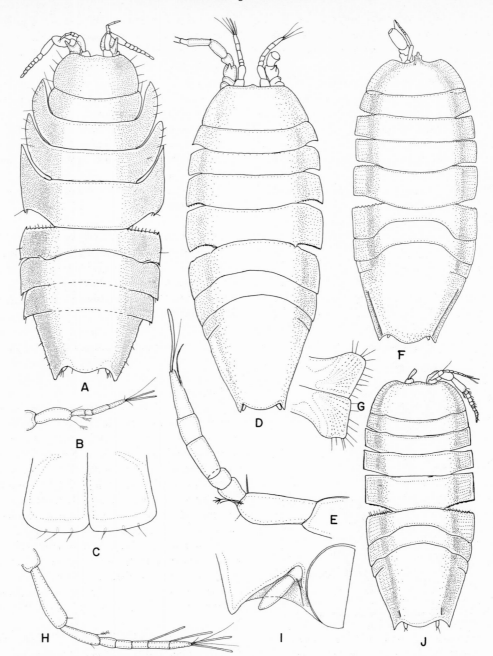

Figure 10. A–C: *Haploniscus princeps*, n. sp. A: female allotype dorsal view; B: first antenna; C: first pleopod male. D–E: *Haploniscus percavix*, n. sp. D: intersex holotype dorsal view; E: first antenna. F–I: *Haploniscus tricornis*, n. sp. F: dorsal view male type; G: first pleopod; H: first antenna; I: uropod and anus. J: *Haploniscus nondescriptus*, n. sp., female type dorsal view.

margin. Dorsum of pleon with a ridge on each side of pleon. First article of first antenna not concealed by cephalon. Uropods not extending to posterior margin of pleon. Rami of sympod of male first pleopod joined at apex. Antero-lateral angles of fourth peraeonal somite not produced forward.

Measurements: Holotype male length 4.2 mm., width pleotelson 1.3 mm.

Type locality: South Atlantic, holotype only, L.G.O. Biotrawl No. 51, cat. no. I-18.

Distribution: Also found at L.G.O. Biotrawl No. 47, one male, one female, cat. no. I-19.

Affinities: The species *H. tricornis* and *H. tricornoides* seem closely related; in the latter the pleon is set in from the peraeonal lateral margin, but not in the former.

Haploniscus nondescriptus, new species

Figure 10 J

Synonyms: None.

Diagnosis: Frontal border of cephalon excised with a broad low median projection. Pleon and peraeon lateral margins continuous. Flagellum of first antenna with five articles. Postero-lateral angles of pleon slightly exceeding median margin. Dorsum of pleon with a pair of slight short ridges above uropodal insertion. First article of peduncle of first antenna concealed from dorsal view by cephalon. Uropods not extending to postero-lateral margin of pleon. Antero-lateral margins of fourth peraeonal somite not produced forward.

Measurements: Holotype female length 3.6 mm., width pleon 1.3 mm.

Type locality: South Atlantic, holotype female, plus two female paratypes, L.G.O. Biotrawl No. 53, cat. no. I-21.

Distribution: Known only from type locality.

Affinities: This species is allied to *H. princeps*, but the uropoda extend to the posterior margin of the pleon at the postero-lateral angles.

Haploniscus acutus, new species
Figure 11 A–C

Synonyms: None.

Diagnosis: Frontal border of cephalon excavate, entire. Pleon inset from peraeonal lateral margin. Flagellum of first antenna with five articles. Postero-lateral angles of pleon projecting beyond medial pleonal margin. Dorsum of pleon smooth. First article of first antenna not concealed by cephalon. Uropods not extending to postero-lateral margin of pleon. Antero-lateral angles of fourth peraeonal somite not produced forward.

Measurements: Holotype female length 3.3 mm., width pleotelson 1.2 mm.

Type locality: South Atlantic, holotype female, L.G.O. Biotrawl No. 51, cat. no. I-13.

Distribution: Known only from type locality.

Affinities: Closely related to *H. spinifer* Hansen, but with the uropoda much longer—that is, extending almost to the tip of the postero-lateral angles of the pleon.

Haploniscus parallelus, new species
Figure 11 D–H

Synonyms: None.

Diagnosis: Frontal margin of cephalon convex, entire. Pleon set in from lateral margins of peraeon. Flagellum of first antenna with four articles. Postero-lateral angles of pleon not projecting beyond medial pleonal margin. Dorsum of pleon smooth. First article of first antenna concealed by cephalon. Rami of sympod of first male pleopod joined at apex. Uropods extending beyond posterior margin of pleon. Antero-lateral angles of fourth pleonal somite produced forward.

Measurements: Holotype male length 1.8 mm., width pleon 0.55 mm., allotype length 2.1 mm., width pleon 0.6 mm.

Type locality: South Atlantic, types plus one female and two fragmentary paratypes, L.G.O. Biotrawl No. 12, cat. no. I-2.

Distribution: Also taken from L.G.O. Biotrawl No. 52, two females, cat. no. I-3.

Affinities: This species is related to *H. tuberculatus*, but has the pleonal margin set in from the peraeonal margin.

Haploniscus capensis, new species
Figure 11 I–K

Synonyms: None.

Diagnosis: Frontal border of cephalon excavated and with very short trifid projection medially. Pleon set in from peraeon. Flagellum of first antenna with five articles. Postero-lateral angles of pleon projecting beyond medial pleonal margin and are medially recurved. Dorsum of pleon with short carinae above uropods. First article of first antenna not concealed by cephalon. Rami of male first pleopods not separated at apex. Uropods not extending to posterior margin of pleon. Antero-lateral angles of fourth pleonal somite not produced forward.

Measurements: Holotype male length 2.9 mm., width pleotelson 0.5 mm., allotype gravid length 2.7 mm., width pleotelson 1.1 mm., and nine male, ten female, one juvenile paratypes.

Type locality: South Atlantic, types only, L.G.O. Biotrawl No. 55, cat. no. I-25.

Distribution: Known only from type locality.

Affinities: This species resembles *H. tridens* in many respects, differing from it in having the lateral borders of the peraeon and pleon discontinuous.

Haploniscus trituberculatus, new species
Figure 11 L–Q

Synonyms: None.

Diagnosis: Frontal border of cephalon excavate, entire. Pleon set in from peraeon. Flagellum of first antenna with four articles. Postero-lateral angles of pleon not projecting beyond medial pleonal margin. Dorsum of pleon with two tubercles located on anterior third of pleon and a large dorsally indented swelling medially near posterior margin. First article of first antenna concealed by cephalon. Rami of male first pleopods not separated at apex. Uropods concealed, extending to posterior margin of pleon.

Measurements: Holotype male length 2.25 mm., width pleotelson 0.55 mm., allotype length 2.6 mm., width pleotelson 0.7 mm., plus two male, three female, and two fragmentary paratypes.

Type locality: South Atlantic, types, L.G.O. Biotrawl No. 51, cat. no. I-24.

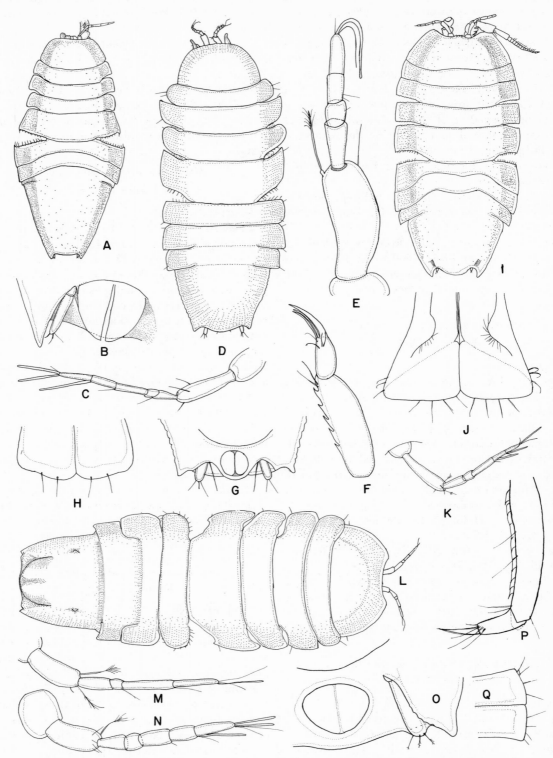

Figure 11. A–C: *Haploniscus acutus*, n. sp. A: holotype dorsal view; B: anus and uropod; C: first antenna. D–H: *Haploniscus parallelus*, n. sp. D: holotype dorsal view; E: first antenna; F: first peraeopod; G: anus and uropods; H: first pleopod. I–K: *Haploniscus capensis*, n. sp. I: holotype dorsal view; J: first pleopod; K; first antenna. L–Q: *Haploniscus trituberculatus*, n. sp. L: holotype dorsal view; M: first antenna allotype; N: first antenna holotype; O: anus and uropod; P: first peraeopod; Q: first pleopod.

Distribution: Also found at L.G.O. Biotrawl No. 14, one female fragment, cat. no. I-202.

Affinities: This species closely resembles *H. telus*, but has the pleon more quadrate than tapering or pointed.

Haploniscus polaris, new species
Figure 12 A–B

Synonyms: None.

Diagnosis: Frontal border convex, with minute medial projection. Pleon set in from peraeon. Flagellum of first antenna with four articles. Postero-lateral angles of pleon projecting beyond medial margin. Dorsum of pleon with a slight ridge forward of each uropod. Uropods not extending to postero-lateral border of pleon. Antero-lateral border of

fourth peraeonal somite not produced forward.

Measurements: Holotype female length 2.1 mm., width pleon 0.8 mm.

Type locality: South Atlantic, type only, L.G.O. Biotrawl No. 52, cat. no. I-32.

Distribution: Known only from type locality.

Affinities: This species is closely related to *H. antarcticus* Vanhöffen, from which it differs in having a relatively longer pleon and in having only four articles, not five, to the flagellum of the first antenna.

Haploniscus telus, new species
Figure 12 C–E

Synonyms: None.

Diagnosis: Frontal border excised, entire. Pleon

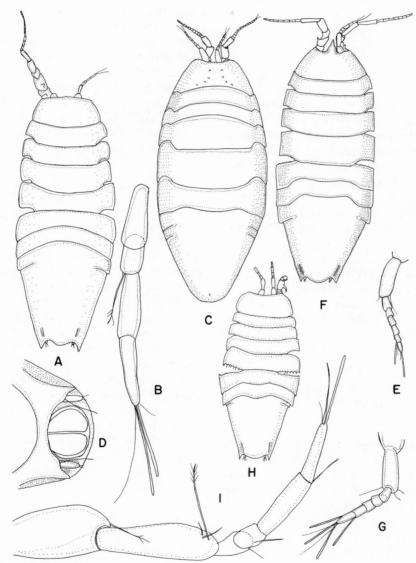

Figure 12. A–B: *Haploniscus polaris*, n. sp. A: female holotype dorsal view; B: first antennal flagellum. C–E: *Haploniscus telus*, n. sp. C: female holotype dorsal view; D: anus and uropods; E: first antenna. F–G: *Haploniscus tricornoides*, n. sp. F: female holotype dorsal view; G: first antenna. H–I: *Haploniscus tropicalis*, n. sp. H: immature female holotype dorsal view; I: first antenna.

and peraeonal lateral borders continuous. Flagellum of first antenna with six articles. Postero-lateral angles of pleon not projecting beyond medial margin. Dorsum of pleon smooth. First article of first antenna concealed by cephalon. Uropods not extending beyond posterior margin of pleon. Antero-lateral borders of fourth peraeonal somite not projected forward. Dorsum of cephalon tuberculate.

Measurements: Holotype female, length 2.5 mm., width pleon 0.8 mm.

Type locality: South Atlantic, type only L.G.O. Biotrawl No. 52, cat. no. I-20.

Distribution: Known only from type locality.

Affinities: This species may be distinguished from *H. trituberculatus*, its nearest relative, because of its tapering pleon.

Haploniscus tricornoides, new species
Figure 12 F–G

Synonyms: None.

Diagnosis: Frontal border excised, with pronounced medial projections. Pleon set in from peraeon. Flagellum of first antenna with five articles. Postero-lateral angles of pleon equal median projection in extent. Dorsum of pleon with slight carina above each uropod. First article of first antenna not concealed by cephalon. Uropods not extending to posterior margin of pleon. Antero-lateral borders of fourth peraeonal somite not projected forward.

Measurements: Holotype female, length 2.5 mm., width pleon 0.75 mm.

Type locality: South Atlantic, type only, L.G.O. Biotrawl No. 52, cat. no. I-31.

Distribution: Known from type locality.

Affinities: This species appears closely related to *H. tricornis*, from which it differs in having a longer cephalic projection and in having the pleon set in from the peraeon.

Haploniscus tropicalis, new species
Figure 12 H–I

Synonyms: None.

Diagnosis: Frontal border of cephalon excavated, entire. Flagellum of first antenna with four articles. Pleon set in from peraeon. Lateral border of fourth peraeonal somite not produced forward, lateral edges blunt. First article of first antenna not concealed by cephalon dorsally. Uropod not extending to posterolateral margin of pleon.

Measurements: Holotype immature female length 1.5 mm., width pleon 0.5 mm.

Type locality: North Atlantic, Caribbean, holotype only, L.G.O. Biotrawl No. 100, cat. no. I-65.

Distribution: Also taken from L.G.O. Biotrawl No. 101, one female with oostegites, cat. no. I-66.

Affinities: Closely related to *H. excisus* Richardson, from which it differs in having shorter uropods and a narrower pleon.

Haploniscus rugosus, new species
Figure 13 A–C

Synonyms: None.

Diagnosis: Frontal border of cephalon almost transverse, with a bifid medial projection. Flagellum of first antenna with six articles. Pleon set in from peraeon. Lateral border of fourth peraeonal somite not produced forward, lateral edges blunt. First article of first antenna not concealed by cephalon dorsally. Uropod extending to posterior lateral margin of pleon. Dorso-lateral areas of peraeon tuberculate. Carina and tubercles located above uropodal insertion.

Measurements: Length female holotype 3.1 mm., width pleotelson 1.1 mm., plus five juvenile paratypes.

Type locality: South Atlantic, types from L.G.O. Biotrawl No. 53, cat. no. I-8.

Distribution: One male and one female also collected from L.G.O. Biotrawl No. 14, cat. no. I-9.

Affinities: This species is unique in having a bifid frons and a tuberculate peraeon.

Haploniscus ovalis, new species
Figure 13 D–G

Synonyms: None.

Diagnosis: Frontal margin of cephalon straight, entire. Flagellum of first antenna with four articles. Pleon set in from peraeon. Antero-lateral areas of peraeonal somite 4 not produced forward, lateral borders convex. First article of first antenna concealed dorsally by cephalon. Uropods not extending to posterior margin of pleon.

Measurements: Holotype male length 2.0 mm., width pleotelson 0.5 mm., allotype length 2.1 mm., width pleotelson 0.6 mm., plus six female, one fragmentary male paratype.

Type locality: South Atlantic, types, L.G.O. Biotrawl No. 12, cat. no. I-12.

Distribution: Known only from type locality.

Affinities: Closely related to *H. armadilloides* Hansen, from which it differs in lacking the median projection on the cephalon.

Haploniscid Fragments

Fragmentary specimens of species of indeterminable *Haploniscus* were obtained from the following L.G.O. stations: 12, five fragments; 18, one fragment; 22, one fragment; 49, one fragment; 51, five fragments; 52, one female crushed; 208, one fragment; 218, one female crushed; 229, one related closely to *H.*

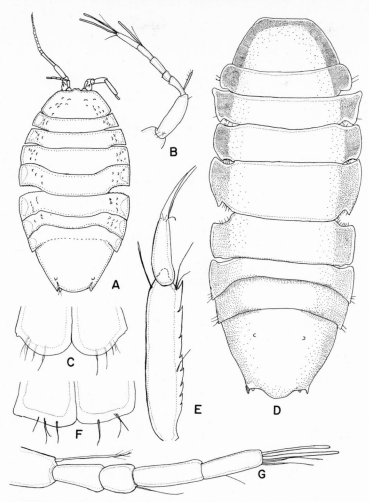

Figure 13. A–C: *Haploniscus rugosus*, n. sp. A: female holotype dorsal view; B: first antenna; C: male first pleopod. D–G: *Haploniscus ovalis*, n. sp. D: male holotype dorsal view; E: third peraeopod; F: first pleopod; G: first antenna.

parallelus; 231, one female crushed possibly related to *H. minutus*; 232, one female fragment related to species in L.G.O. Biotrawl No. 229.

ANTENNULONISCUS, new genus

Type species: *Haploniscus dimeroceras* Barnard, 1920, pp. 406–408, Pl. XVII, Figs. 4–7.

Generic diagnosis: Haploniscidae with the third article of the peduncle of the second antenna much longer than wide. First five peraeonal somites always distinct.

Composition: In addition to the new species described herein and the type, none other is yet known in this genus.

Depth distribution: The species of this genus vary in depth from 1280 meters (bathyal) to 5843 meters (abyssal).

A KEY TO THE SPECIES OF ANTENNULONISCUS

1. Postero-lateral angles of pleon not projecting
beyond medial margin . . . . *ornatus*, n. sp.
1. Postero-lateral angles of pleon projecting beyond
medial margin 2
2. Frontal border excised but with slight medial
convexity . . . . *dimeroceras* (Barnard)
2. Frontal border convex, with pronounced medial
projection 3
3. Lateral borders of peraeonal somites 5–7
inclusive continuous . . . . *armatus*, n. sp.
3. Lateral border of peraeonal somites 5–6
inclusive produced outward . . . . . *rostratus*, n. sp.

Antennuloniscus dimeroceras (Barnard)
Figure 14 A–B

Synonyms: *Haploniscus dimeroceras* Barnard, 1920, pp. 406–408, Pl. XVII, Fig. 4–7.

Diagnosis: Frontal border excised, with even slight median convexity. Pleon set in from lateral border of peraeon. Flagellum of first antenna with six articles. Postero-lateral angles of pleon projecting beyond medial margin. Dorsum of pleon with a pair of tubercles halfway from distal margin. Sympod of male first pleopods separate at apex. First article of

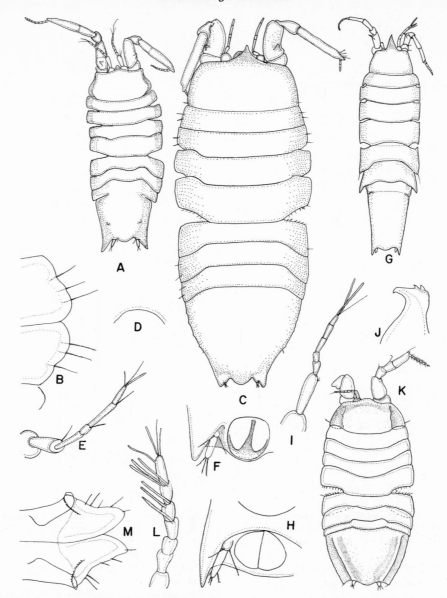

Figure 14. A–B: *Antennuloniscus dimeroceras* (Barnard), male length 2.2 mm., width pleon 0.6 mm. A: dorsal view male; B: first pleopod. C–F: *Antennuloniscus armatus*, n. sp. C: dorsal view; D: apex of pleon; E: first antenna; F: anus and uropod. G–J: *Antennuloniscus rostratus*, n. sp.   G: dorsal view type female; H: anus and uropod; I: first antenna; J: cephalic horn. K–M: *Antennuloniscus ornatus*, n. sp.   K: dorsal view male type; L: first antenna flagellum; M: first pleopod.

first antenna not concealed by cephalon. Uropods not extending to postero-lateral margin of pleon. Antero-lateral borders of fourth peraeonal somite not produced forward.

Measurements: Length 2.5 mm., width 1.0 mm., (Barnard, op. cit., 408).

Type locality: 34° 25′ S., 17° 55′ E., 700 fathoms. Bottom green mud. Several males and females, S.S. *Pieter Faure*, 20 August 1903 (S.A.M. No. A 4069).

Distribution: South Atlantic, L.G.O. Biotrawl No. 14, three females, cat. no. I-40; L.G.O. Biotrawl No. 22, three males, eight females, cat. no. I-39; L.G.O. Biotrawl No. 23, one female, cat. no. I-38; L.G.O.

Biotrawl No. 54, eight males, nineteen females, cat. no. I-37; L.G.O. Biotrawl No. 212, one female, cat. no. I-60, North Atlantic, L.G.O. Biotrawl No. 231, one female, cat. no. I-52.

Affinities: The excised frontal border of the cephalon sets this species apart from the others.

Antennuloniscus armatus, new species
Figure 14 C–F

Synonyms: None.

Diagnosis: Frontal borders convex, with sharp, elongate, median spine. Lateral margins of pleon and peraeon continuous. Flagellum of first antenna with four articles. Postero-lateral angles of pleon extending beyond medial margin. Dorsum of pleon smooth. First article of first antenna not concealed by cephalon. Uropods not extending to posterior border of pleon.

Measurements: Length 2.6 mm, width pleon 0.8 mm.

Type locality: South Atlantic, L.G.O. Biotrawl No. 51, one female, cat. no. I-34.

Distribution: Known also from L.G.O. Biotrawl No. 52, one male, two female, cat. no. I-35.

Affinities: This species appears most closely related to *A. rostratus*, from which it differs mainly in having the lateral margins of the peraeon and pleon continuous.

Antennuloniscus rostratus, new species
Figure 14 G–J

Synonyms: None.
Diagnosis: Frontal border convex with a sharp upcurved spine medially. Lateral margin of pleon peraeon continuous. Flagellum of first antenna with five articles. Postero-lateral angles of pleon extending beyond medial margin. Dorsum of pleon smooth. First article of first antenna not concealed by cephalon. Uropods not extending to postero-lateral border of pleon.

Measurements: Holotype female length 3.3 mm., width pleon 0.55 mm.

Type locality: South Atlantic, L.G.O. Biotrawl No. 52, three females, cat. no. I-36.

Distribution: Known only from type locality.

Affinities: The long and broad rostrum of this species is distinctive; also the lateral border of the sixth peraeonal somite is produced outward from that of the seventh.

Antennuloniscus ornatus, new species
Figure 14 K–M

Synonyms: None.
Diagnosis: Frontal margin of cephalon convex. Pleonal and peraeonal lateral margins continuous. Flagellum of first antenna with six articles. Postero-lateral angles of pleon not projecting beyond medial pleonal margin. Dorsum of pleon with ridge near each lateral margin. First article of first antenna not concealed by cephalon. Rami of male first pleopod separated at apex. Uropods extending to posterior margin of pleon. Antero-lateral borders of fourth peraeonal somite not produced forward.

Measurements: Holotype male length 1.9 mm., width pleon 0.8 mm.

Type locality: South Atlantic, L.G.O. Biotrawl No. 47, two males, cat. no. I-33.

Distribution: Also known from L.G.O. Biotrawl No. 201, one male, cat. no. I-223.

Affinities: The dorsal elevation of the cephalon and the carinae on the pleon separate this species from all the others. Its nearest known relative is possibly *A. dimeroceras* (Barnard), a species also known from the South Atlantic.

Genus: HYDRONISCUS Hansen

Type species: *Hydroniscus abyssi* Hansen, 1916
Diagnosis: Haploniscidae with the pleon and last three peraeonal somites fused into a solid piece. Uropoda extremely reduced or entirely absent. Third article of peduncle of first antenna longer than wide but lacking the angulate projection characterizing *Haploniscus*.

Composition: The genus contains three species, two from the North Atlantic and one from the South Atlantic. They are markedly different from one another. According to Wolff (1960), Birstein has found a species of Hydroniscus in the North Pacific.

A KEY TO THE SPECIES OF HYDRONISCUS

1. Uropoda present . . . . *ornatus*, n. sp.
1. Uropoda absent 2
2. Rostrum pointed . . . . *abyssi* Hansen
2. Rostrum blunt . . . . *quadrifrons*, n. sp.

Hydroniscus ornatus, new species
Figure 15 A–H

Synonyms: None.
Diagnosis: *Hydroniscus* with distinct pointed postero-lateral angles projecting laterally from pleon. Single-jointed uropoda present, not extending beyond posterior margin of pleon. Flagellum of first antenna with four articles, that of second with 12 articles.

Measurements: Holotype male length 3.5 mm., width pleon 1.7 mm., allotype female length 4.0 mm., width pleon 1.75 mm.

Type locality: South Atlantic, types plus three female paratypes from L.G.O. Biotrawl No. 51, cat. no. I-43.

Distribution: Known also from L.G.O. Biotrawl No. 217, one female, cat. no. I-211, in the South Atlantic.

Affinities: *Ornatus* is possibly closely related to *quadrifrons*, from which it differs in having a rounded rostrum and in having very pronounced postero-lateral angles on the pleon.

Hydroniscus quadrifrons, new species
Figure 15 I–M

Synonyms: None.
Diagnosis: *Hydroniscus* with minute postero-lateral angles on pleon. Quadrate single-jointed uropods

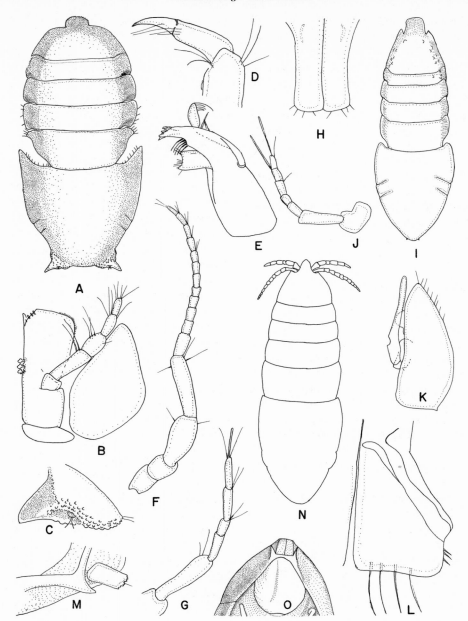

Figure 15. A–H: *Hydroniscus ornatus*, n. sp.   A: dorsal view female allotype; B: maxilliped; C: dorsal view uropod; D: first peraeopod; E. mandible; F: second antenna; G: first antenna; H: first pleopod. I–M: *Hydroniscus quadrifrons*, n. sp.   I: dorsal view male holotype; J: first antenna; K: second pleopod; L: first pleopod; M: uropod. N–O: *Hydroniscus abyssi* Hansen (after Hansen, 1916). N: dorsal view female; O: pleon and anus.

present. Flagellum of first antenna with five articles. Dorsum of cephalon tuberculate, rostrum blunt at apex.

Measurements: Male holotype length 2.7 mm., width pleon 1.0 mm., allotype length 3.2 mm., width pleon 1.1 mm., and four male and six female paratypes.

Type locality: North Atlantic, L.G.O. Biotrawl No. 231, types, cat. no. I-51.

Distribution: Also known from L.G.O. Biotrawl No. 214, one female, cat. no. I-53; L.G.O. Biotrawl No. 229, one male and one fragment, cat. no. I-58; L.G.O. Biotrawl No. 232, one fragment, cat. no. I-55; L.G.O. Biotrawl No. 233, one male, one frag-

ment, cat. no. I-56; L.G.O. Biotrawl No. 234, three males, cat. no. I-57.

Affinities: This species is related to *H. abyssi* Hansen, from which it differs in having a blunt rostrum and in having uropods, and to *ornatus*, from which it differs in having a blunt rostrum.

Hydroniscus abyssi Hansen
Figure 15 N–O

Synonyms: *Hydroniscus abyssi* Hansen, 1916, p. 33, Pl. II.

Diagnosis: *Hydroniscus* with a spearpoint-shaped pleon lacking lateral projections. Uropoda absent. Flagellum of first antenna with five articles, that of second antenna with nine articles.

Measurements: Female holotype length 2.8 mm.

Type locality: North Atlantic, *Ingolf* Station 38, latitude 59° 12′ N., longitude 51° 05′ W., 3521 meters. One female specimen.

Distribution: An abyssal species known only from type locality.

Family: ISCHNOMESIDAE

Type genus: *Ischnomesus* Richardson, 1908a.

Diagnosis: Paraselloidea with head and first peraeonal somite joined. Eyes lacking. Mandibles generally lacking palp, molar expanded, lacinia and setae row present. Antennae shorter than body. All peraeopods simple walking legs; dactyl with at least one terminal claw, never three. Uropoda terminal uniramous. Fifth peraeonal somite generally much longer than wide. Last two articles of maxillipedal palp narrow, others as wide as endite. Pleon with one–two distinct separated somites. Anus widely separated from branchial chambers.

Composition: This family contains *Ischnomesus*, *Haplomesus*, *Heteromesus*, and *Stylomesus*. The genus *Ischnosoma* was replaced by *Ischnomesus*, and the genus *Rhabdomesus* was subsequently found to be a synonym of *Ischnomesus* (see Wolff, 1956). Like Haploniscidae, the family is characteristically abyssal but contains shallow water representatives as well. The absence of a mandibular palp is not a constant characteristic of the family: a triarticulate palp is present in *I. simplissimus*, but only a rudimentary seta remains in *I. paucispinis* and nothing at all in the remaining species.

A KEY TO THE GENERA OF
THE ISCHNOMESIDAE
(Modified after Wolff, 1956)

1. Uropoda with a single article 2
1. Uropoda with two articles 3
2. Pleon and three posterior peraeonal somites fused into a single piece. Third article of first antenna markedly elongate . . . . *Haplomesus*
2. Pleon and two posterior peraeonal somites fused into a single piece. Third article of first antenna minute . . . . *Heteromesus*
3. First pleonal somite separate from pleotelson . . . . *Ischnomesus*
3. First pleonal somite fused with pleotelson . . . . *Stylomesus*

Genus: ISCHNOMESUS Richardson, 1908a

Synonyms: *Ischnosoma* G. O. Sars, 1868. *Rhabdomesus*, Richardson, 1908a, p. 81. *Ischnomesus* Richardson 1908a, p. 81.

Type species: *Ischnosoma bispinosum* G. O. Sars, 1868.

Diagnosis: Ischnomesidae with a distinctly two-jointed pleonal somite. Uropoda with two articles.

Remarks: The genus may be indistinctly split into two groups on the basis of the fundamental structure of the male first and second pleopods. Unfortunately,

these characteristics are not known for all species and therefore have not been used in the key. To the most primitive group belong those species in which the stylus of the male second pleopod is shorter than the exopod and the lateral projections of each ramus at the apex of the first pleopod are quite evident. To this group belong the species *I. bispinosum*, *I. paucispinis*, *I. multispinis*, *I. spärcki*, *I. decemspinosus*, *I. bidens*, etc.

A secondarily derived group has a long semi-coiled stylus which inserts into depressions on the interior surface of the sympod of the male first pleopod. The lateral expansions of the sympod are generally coalesced with the sympod, giving the apex a blunt appearance under low magnification. To this group belong the remaining species, *I. caribbicus*, *I. bruuni*, *I. bacilloides*, *I. wolffi*, etc.

Depth distribution:	*Meters*
1. *bispinosum* (G. O. Sars)	94–1100
2. *bacillopsis* Barnard	1280–1280
3. *armatus* Hansen	2702–2702
4. *bacilloides* (Beddard)	2652–2652
5. *profundus* Hansen	3521–3521
6. *spärcki* Wolff	6660–7000
7. *bruuni* Wolff	6960–7000
8. *bacillus* (Beddard)	3292–3292
9. *andriashevi* Birstein	4000–6560

Nine new species may be added to the list of known species. All are considered in the following key.

A KEY TO THE SPECIES OF
ISCHNOMESUS

1. Dorsum of pleon with stout spines 2
1. Dorsum of pleon smooth, lacking spines 4
2. Postero-medial margin of pleon with spines . . . . *magnificus*, n. sp.
2. Postero-medial margin of pleon entire, lacking spines 3
3. Lateral borders of pleon each with only three spines . . . . *multispinis*, n. sp.
3. Lateral borders of pleon each with more than ten spines . . . . *spärcki* Wolff
4. Sixth peraeonal somite with a long lateral spine on either side 5
4. Sixth peraeonal somite without a lateral spine on either side 8
5. Lateral spine of fifth peraeonal somite directed posteriorly at about 20° angle to peraeonal axis 16
5. Lateral spine of fifth peraeonal somite directed more laterally, about perpendicular from peraeonal axis 6

6. Posterior margin of seventh peraeonal somite
   with a medial projection . . . . *bacilloides* (Beddard)
6. Posterior margin of seventh peraeonal somite
   entire medially 7
7. Lateral spine of sixth peraeonal somite directed
   at a 45° angle from peraeonal
   axis . . . . *wolffi*, n. sp.
7. Lateral spine of sixth peraeonal somite
   directed at a 75° angle from peraeonal
   axis . . . . *bruuni* Wolff
8. Pleon with postero-lateral angles projecting
   beyond medial margin . . . . *bidens*, n. sp.
8. Pleon lacking projecting postero-lateral angles . . 9
9. Fifth peraeonal somite with long lateral spine . . 10
9. Fifth peraeonal somite without lateral spines . . 12
10. Dorsum of fourth peraeonal somite with
    spines at anterior part . . . . . *decemspinosus*, n. sp.
10. Dorsum of fourth peraeonal somite smooth, without
    spines 11
11. Pleonal lateral borders strongly
    convex . . . . *elegans*, n. sp.
11. Pleonal lateral borders
    subparallel . . . . *bacillus* (Beddard)
12. Lateral border of pleon each with a stout
    seta and three small setae . . . . *paucispinis*, n.sp.
12. Lateral borders of pleon lack stout setae 13
13. First peraeonal somite with a stout antero-lateral
    spine 14
13. First peraeonal somite without a stout antero-
    lateral spine . . . . *simplissimus*, n. sp.
14. Postero-lateral margin of pleon without angles,
    entire and smooth 17
14. Postero-lateral margin of pleon with distinct
    postero-lateral angles 15
15. Pleon with a pair of minute projections anterior
    to uropodal insertion
    (postero-lateral angles) . . . . *caribbicus*, n. sp.
15. Pleon without a pair of projections anterior to
    postero-lateral angles . . . . . . *profundus* Hansen
16. Pleon constricted in front of
    uropods . . . . *armatus* Hansen
16. Pleon not constricted in front of
    uropods . . . . *bacillopsis* (Barnard)
17. Hand of first peraeopod about as wide
    as long . . . . *bispinosum* (G. O. Sars)
17. Hand of first peraeopod three times longer
    than wide . . . . *andriashevi* Birstein

Ischnomesus profundus Hansen
Figure 16 A–D

Synonyms: *Ischnomesus profundus* Hansen, 1916, pp.
56–57, Pl. 4; — Wolff, 1956, pp. 88–89, Fig. 1.

Diagnosis: *Ischnomesus* with lateral spines on first
peraeonal somite only, other somites lacking lateral
spines. Pleon with sharp postero-lateral angles at
uropods; posterior margin convex and lacking spines
or setae. Male first pleopods with pronounced lateral
extensions at apex (uropods lost). (From Hansen, op.
cit., illustration and description.)

Measurements: Male length 4.0 mm. (Hansen, op.
cit.)

Type locality: North Atlantic, south of Davis
Strait, *Ingolf* Station 38, latitude 59° 12′ N., longitude
51° 05′ W., 3521 meters, temperature 1.3° C. type
only (Hansen, op. cit.).

Distribution: Known only from type locality.

Affinities: This species appears to be related to the
Caribbean species *I. caribbicus*, n. sp., from which it
differs in lacking pleonal projections anterior to the
uropodal insertion.

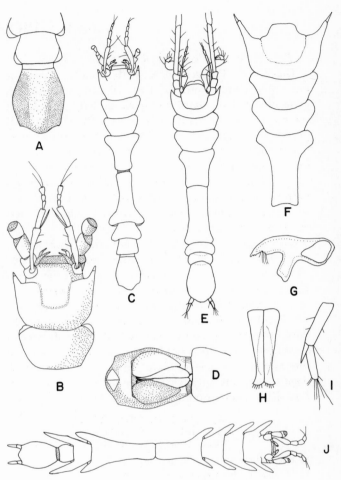

Figure 16. A–D: *Ischnomesus profundus* Hansen
(after Hansen, 1916). A: dorsal view posterior; B: dorsal view head; C: dorsal view
male; D: ventral view pleon. E–I: *Ischnomesus
bispinosum*, (G. O. Sars) (after G. O. Sars,
1896). E: dorsal view female; F: dorsal
view head and anterior thoracic segments,
male; G: mandible; H: first pleopod;
I: uropod. J: *Ischnomesus armatus* Hansen
(after Hansen, 1916), dorsal view male.

Ischnomesus bispinosum (G. O. Sars)
Figure 16 E–I

Synonyms: *Ischnosoma bispinosum* G. O. Sars, 1865,
p. 34; — 1897, pp. 123–124, Pl. 52; Hult, 1941, pp.
62–66, Figs. 16–18, and references (incomplete).

Diagnosis: *Ischnomesus* with a spine on lateral
border of first peraeonal somite only; dorsal spine
lacking. Pleon pyriform, without postero-lateral
angles. Lateral projections on apex of male first

pleopods scarcely evident, endite of male second pleopod short, not coiled. Uropoda biramous (derived from Sars' illustrations, 1897; this may be an error in illustration).

Measurements: Adult female length 3 mm., male length 2.5 mm. (G. O. Sars, 1897, p. 124).

Type locality: Christiania Fjord, Norway.

Distribution: Lofoten, Norway, Ireland, to Gulf of Naples in the Mediterranean (Hult, 1941, p. 65), depth range 90 to 1100 meters.

Affinities: The smooth spineless pleon of this species sets it apart from the others as a fundamentally more primitive species.

Ischnomesus armatus Hansen
Figure 16 J

Synonyms: Ischnomesus armatus Hansen, 1916, pp. 59–60, Pl. 4;—Wolff, 1956, pp. 89–90, Fig. 2.

Diagnosis: Ischnomesus with lateral spines on peraeonal somites 1–6 inclusive. Lateral spines of first four somites directed acutely forward, those of somites 5 and 6 directed acutely hindward. Pleon constricted above uropods, lateral and posterior margins smooth and lacking setae or spines. Lateral projection at apex of male first pleopods joined with sympod. (From Hansen, op. cit.)

Measurements: Length male 4.8 mm. (Hansen, op. cit.)

Type locality: North Atlantic, Davis Strait, *Ingolf* Station 36, latitude 61° 50′ N., longitude 56° 21′ W., 2702 meters, temperature 1.5° C., two males (Hansen, op. cit.).

Distribution: Known also from the North Atlantic from L.G.O. Biotrawl No. 234, one male, cat. no. I-68.

Affinities: This species appears related to the South Atlantic *I. bacillopsis* (Barnard), from which it differs in having the pleon constricted in front of the uropods.

Ischnomesus caribbicus, new species
Figure 17 A–B

Synonyms: None.

Diagnosis: Ischnomesus with lateral spines on first peraeonal somite only. Dorsal spines lacking. Pleon with distinct sharp but small angles above uropodal insertion. Medial posterior margin of pleon truncated, smooth, lacking spines or setae. Lateral projection at apex of male first pleopod largely joined to sympod, distal margin with nine setae.

Measurements: Length holotype male 7.8 mm., width pleon 0.9 mm.

Type locality: North Atlantic, Caribbean, L.G.O. Biotrawl No. 100, type only, cat. No. I-72.

Distribution: Known only from type locality.

Affinities: This species appears to be most nearly related to *I. profundus* Hansen, from which it differs in having a minute angle projecting anterior in front of each uropodal insertion.

Ischnomesus simplissimus, new species
Figure 17 C–F

Synonyms: None.

Diagnosis: Ischnomesus lacking lateral or dorsal spines on peraeonal or pleonal somites. Mandible with triarticulate palp, last article minute and with a single apical seta. Pleon margins smooth, lacking angles, setae, or spines, apex pointed.

Measurements: Female holotype length 9.1 mm., width pleon 1.1 mm.

Type locality: South Atlantic, L.G.O. Biotrawl No. 52, one holotype female and one paratype female, cat. no I-98.

Distribution: Taken also at L.G.O. Biotrawl No. 53, eight fragmentary females, cat. no. I-99.

Affinities: The presence of a triarticulate mandibular palp sets this species apart; otherwise it is distinct in lacking a stout antero-lateral spine from the first peraeonal somite.

Ischnomesus multispinis, new species
Figure 17 G–H

Synonyms: None.

Diagnosis: Ischnomesus with dorsal spines on all body somites. First, third, fourth, and fifth somites with lateral spines. Pleon with three spines on either side, dorsum with a pair of spines. Sympodal apex with lateral projections directed caudad; rami separated at apex. Posterior margin of pleon without spines or setae.

Measurements: Injured male holotype length 7.4 mm., width pleon 0.7 mm.

Type locality: North Atlantic, Caribbean, L.G.O. Biotrawl No. 107, holotype only, cat. no. I-77.

Distribution: Known only from type locality.

Affinities: By virtue of the three spines on each lateral margin of the pleon this species is most closely related perhaps to *I. spärcki* Wolff, from which it differs in having fewer lateral pleonal spines. The apex of the male pleopods also indicates the affinity between the two.

Ischnomesus wolffi, new species
Figure 18 A–C

Synonyms: None.

Diagnosis: Ischnomesus with lateral spines on peraeonal somites 1–6 inclusive. Those of somites 5 and 6 projecting posteriorally. Pleon with posterolateral angles at uropod insertion, otherwise smooth,

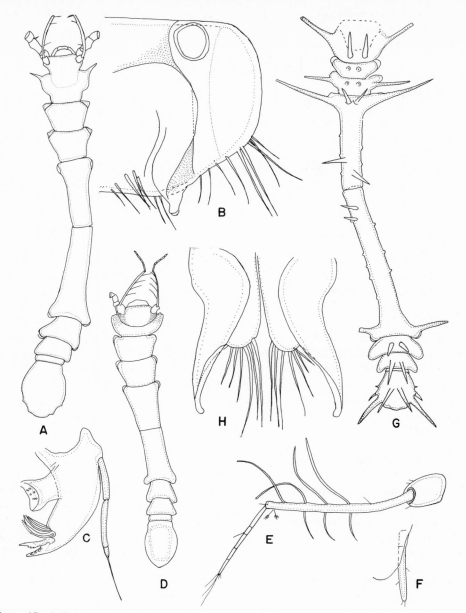

Figure 17. A–B: *Ischnomesus caribbicus*, n. sp.   A: dorsal view male holotype; B: first pleopod. C–F: *Ischnomesus simplissimus*, n. sp. C: mandible holotype; D: dorsal view female holotype; E: first antenna; F: paratype uropod. G–H: *Ischnomesus multispinis*, n. sp. G: dorsal view male holotype; H: first pleopod.

entire; posterior margin broadly convex, smooth. Lateral projection of first male pleopod largely coalesced with sympod, apex of each with six setae.

Measurements: Holotype fragment male length 5.8 mm., width pleon 1.1 mm.

Type locality: South Atlantic, L.G.O. Biotrawl No. 52, type only, cat. no. I-96.

Distribution: Known also from L.G.O. Biotrawl No. 18, six fragmentary males, cat. no. I-45.

Affinities: This species appears most closely related to the Pacific species *I. bruuni* Wolff, from which it differs in having the lateral spines of the

sixth peraeonal somite less laterally projecting—that is, at a 45° angle instead of a 75° angle from the peraeonal axis.

Ischnomesus magnificus, new species
Figure 18 D

Synonyms: None.

Diagnosis: *Ischnomesus* with lateral and dorsal spines on fifth peraeonal somite (other anterior somites missing). Sixth and seventh peraeonal somites lacking lateral spines but having small dorsal spines. Pleon with seven spines on each side, 16

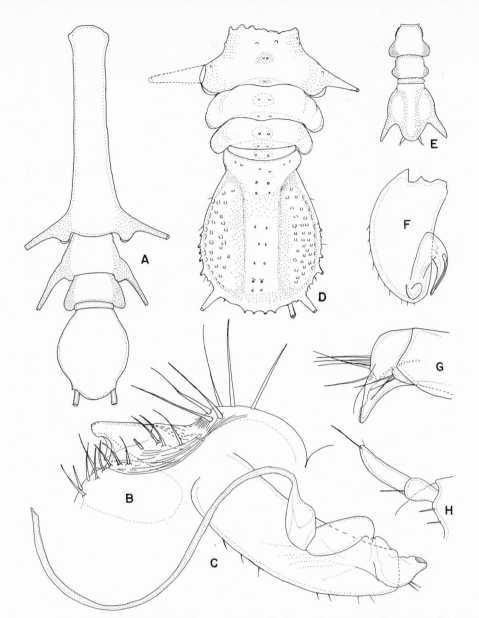

Figure 18. A–C: *Ischnomesus wolffi*, n. sp.   A: dorsal view male holotype fragment; B: apex male pleopod; C: second male pleopod. D: *Ischnomesus magnificus*, n. sp., dorsal view female holotype fragment. E–H: *Ischnomesus bidens*, n. sp.   E: dorsal view male holotype fragment; F: second male pleopod; G: male first pleopod; H: uropod.

dorsal spines, and four terminal spines. Pleopods missing.

Measurements: Female holotype fragment, length pleonal somites: first, 0.5 mm.; second, 4.5 mm.; peraeonal somites: sixth, 1.2 mm.; seventh, 1.05 mm.; width pleon 3.8 mm.

Type locality: South Atlantic, L.G.O. Biotrawl No. 12, type only, cat. no. I-91.

Distribution: Known only from type locality.

Affinities: This highly spinous species most nearly resembles *I. spärcki* Wolff, but differs from it in having spines on the distal border of the pleon. The species is obviously among the largest of the known asellotes.

Ischnomesus bidens, new species
Figure 18 E–H

Synonyms: None.

Diagnosis: *Ischnomesus* with angular postero-lateral projections on pleon, extending to postero-medial margin of pleon. Sympod of male first pleopod with acute lateral projection at apex. Endite of male second pleopod short, not projecting beyond apex of exopod. Sixth and seventh peraeonal somites without dorsal or lateral spines. Dorsum of pleon smooth, without spines.

Measurements: Holotype male fragment, length 1.8 mm., width of pleotelson 1.0 mm.

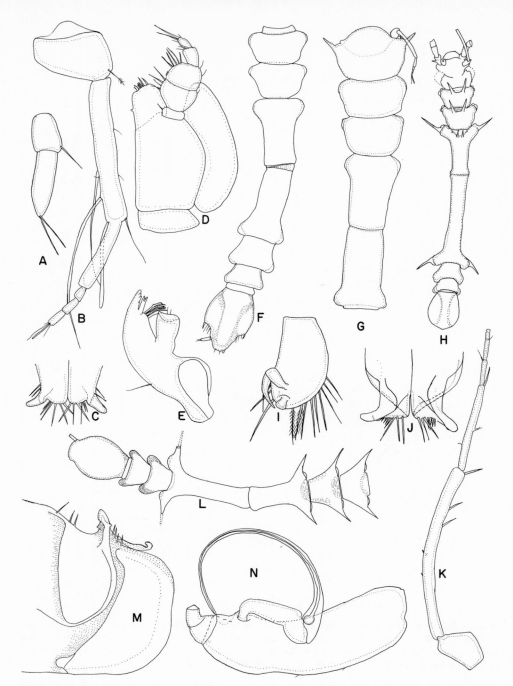

Figure 19. A–G: *Ischnomesus paucispinis*, n. sp.   A: uropod; B: first antenna; C: first male pleopod; D: maxilliped; E: mandible; F: dorsal view male holotype minus cephalon; G: dorsal view male paratype fragment. H–K: *Ischnomesus decemspinosus*, n. sp.   H: dorsal view male holotype; I: second male pleopod; J: first male pleopod; K: first antenna. L–N: *Ischnomesus elegans*, n. sp.   L: dorsal view male holotype; M: first male pleopod; N: second male pleopod.

Type locality: South Atlantic, L.G.O. Biotrawl No. 12, type plus one male paratype fragment, cat. no. I-95.

Distribution: Known only from type locality.

Affinities: This species is unique in having the postero-lateral angles of the pleon projecting beyond the medial distal border. Otherwise it belongs with the group of species lacking a lateral spine from the sixth peraeonal somite.

Ischnomesus paucispinis, new species
Figure 19 A–G

Synonyms: None.

Diagnosis: Ischnomesus with lateral spines only on first peraeonal somite. Dorsal spines lacking. Pleon with stout setae on either side of pronounced postero-lateral angle, three smaller setae follow, apex with two minute setae. Lateral projections at apex of male first pleopod well developed, apex each with six stout setae.

Measurements: Holotype male fragment length 4.3 mm. (minus cephalon), width pleon 0.65 mm.

Type locality: South Atlantic, L.G.O. Biotrawl No. 12, holotype and one male fragment, cat. no. I-93.

Distribution: Known only from type locality.

Affinities: The stout setae on the lateral margin of the pleon distinguish this species from the others, as does the fact that the fifth peraeonal somite lacks lateral spines.

Ischnomesus decemspinosus, new species
Figure 19 H–K

Synonyms: None.

Diagnosis: Ischnomesus with lateral spines on peraeonal somites 4–5 inclusive; somites 2–4 each with a pair of dorsal spines. Pleon ovoid, smooth, devoid of spines, setae, or sharp postero-lateral angles. Lateral projections at apex of first male pleopod well developed, apex of each with seven stout setae.

Measurements: Male holotype length 8.4 mm., width pleon 0.9 mm.

Type locality: South Atlantic, L.G.O. Biotrawl No. 14, type and one fragment, cat. no. I-44.

Distribution: Known only from type locality.

Affinities: The fact that the dorsal surface of the fourth peraeonal somite has spines sets this species apart from the majority, plus the fact that the fifth peraeonal somite has long lateral spines.

Ischnomesus elegans, new species
Figure 19 L–N

Synonyms: None.

Diagnosis: Ischnomesus with lateral spines on peraeonal somites 2–5 inclusive. Dorsal spines lacking. Pleon with sharp postero-lateral angles at uropods, margins entire and smooth, posterior margin truncated and smooth. Lateral projection at apex of male first pleopod largely joined to sympod, distal margin without setae.

Measurements: Holotype male length 10.01 mm. (minus cephalon), width pleon 1.5 mm.

Type locality: South Atlantic, L.G.O. Biotrawl No. 214, type only, cat. no. I-76.

Distribution: Known only from type locality.

Affinities: This species is closely related to *I. bacillus* (Beddard), but has the pleonal border swollen and not subparallel.

Ischnomesus species indeterminate

Unidentifiable fragments of *Ischnomesus* were collected at L.G.O. Biotrawl no. 12, eleven fragments; 18, five fragments; 52, two fragments; 53, three fragments; 98, one fragment; 217, one fragment; 220, one fragment; 233, one fragment.

Genus: HAPLOMESUS Richardson

Synonyms: Haplomesus Richardson, 1908a, p. 81; — Hansen, 1916, p. 59; — Wolff, 1956, p. 87.

Type species: Ischnosoma quadrispinosa G. O. Sars, 1879, p. 435.

Diagnosis: Ischnomesidae with third article of first antennae elongate, two and a half times or more longer than the fourth. Pleon with a single somite only. Uropoda with a single article. Fifth to seventh peraeonal somites fused with pleon.

Remarks: Eight species, all from the Atlantic and Pacific, are presently known from this genus:

Species	Depth Range (Meters)	
	Least	Greatest
1. *quadrispinosus* (G. O. Sars)	510	4150
2. *angustus* Hansen	698	2137
3. *insignis* Hansen	698	2707
4. *tenuispinis* Hansen	698	3474
5. *modestus* Hansen	—	2258
6. *brevispinis* Birstein	5510	5690
7. *cornutus* Birstein	6471	6571
8. *orientalis* Birstein	4000	4150

Additionally, three new species are described in this paper from abyssal depths of the North and South Atlantic.

A KEY TO THE SPECIES OF HAPLOMESUS

1. Third peraeonal somite with lateral spines . . . 2
1. Third peraeonal somite without lateral spines . . 5
2. Fourth peraeonal somite with lateral spines . . . . *modestus* Hansen
2. Fourth peraeonal somite without lateral spines . . 3
3. Apex of pleon medially incised . . . . *bifurcatus,* n. sp.
3. Apex of pleon truncated or curved not medially incised 4
4. Dorsum of pleon medially with paired carinae . . . . *ornatus,* n. sp.
4. Dorsum of pleon medially with a single sweling . . . . *quadrispinosus* (G. O. Sars)
5. Fourth peraeonal somite with lateral spines . . . 6
5. Fourth peraeonal somite without lateral spines . . 8
6. Dorsum of pleon with at least one pair of stout spines near midline . . . . . *tenuispinis* Hansen
6. Dorsum of pleon without paired stout spines . . . 7
7. Lateral spines of first and fourth peraeonal somites massive, longer than wide . . . . . . *insignis* Hansen
7. Lateral spines of first and fourth peraeonal somites short, no longer than wide . . *tropicalis,* n. sp.
8. Posterior border of pleon trilobed . . . *angustus* Hansen
8. Posterior border of pleon with one median lobe only . . . . *gorbunovi* Gurjanova[a]

[a] More probably this species belongs in the genus *Stylomesus.*

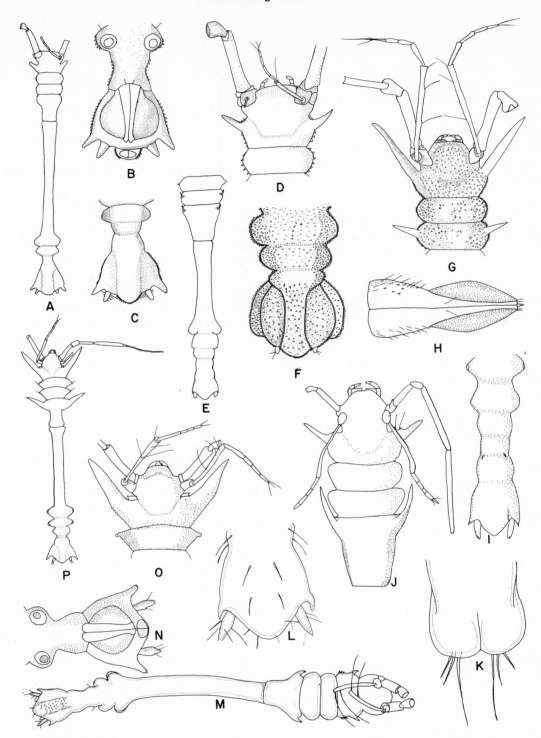

Figure 20. A–D: *Haplomesus angustus* Hansen. A: dorsal view immature male; B: ventral view male pleon; C: dorsal view male pleon; D: dorsal view head of male. E: *Haplomesus modestus* Hansen, dorsal view mutilated female. F–H: *Haplomesus quadrispinosus* (G. O. Sars). F: ventral view male pleon from *Ingolf* Sta. 36; G: dorsal view male cephalon from *Ingolf* Sta. 36; H: ventral view median lamella of male abdominal operculum from *Ingolf* Sta. 36. I–J: *Haplomesus tenuispinis* Hansen. I: dorsal view fragment of mutilated female from *Ingolf* Sta. 22; J: dorsal view of cephalon of female from *Ingolf* Sta. 24. K–M: *Haplomesus tropicalis*, n. sp. K: apex of male pleopod; L: dorsal view of male pleon and uropods; M: dorsal view male holotype. N–P: *Haplomesus insignis* Hansen. N: ventral view male pleon; O: dorsal view male cephalon; P: dorsal view male.

Haplomesus angustus Hansen
Figure 20 A–D

Synonyms: *Haplomesus angustus.* Hansen, 1916, pp. 61–62. Pl, V.

Diagnosis: *Haplomesus* with lateral spines on the first peræonal somite only. Uropoda longer than wide. Pleon with pronounced postero-lateral angles dorsum without carinae.

Measurements: Juvenile male 4.8 mm. long. Full-grown males 9–12 mm. Length presumed (Hansen, op. cit.).

Type locality: North Atlantic, south of Denmark Strait, *Ingolf* Station 18, latitude 61° 44′ N., longitude 30° 29′ W., 1135 fathoms (2137 meters), temperature 3.0° C. (Hansen, op. cit.).

Distribution: Also found by *Ingolf* Station 125, latitude 68° 08′ N., longitude 16° 02′ W., 729 fathoms (1373 meters), temperature −0.8° C. This species was not represented in *Vema* collections, which appear to lie too far south of the distributional area of the species. Gorbunov (1946, p. 123) reports this species in the Arctic from 698 meters.

Affinities: This species superficially resembles *S. gorbunovi* Gurjanova from the Arctic; however, the postero-medial margin of the pleon is trilobed rather than a single lobe as in the latter.

Haplomesus modestus Hansen
Figure 20 E

Synonyms: *Haplomesus modestus.* Hansen, 1916, pp. 65–66, Pl. V.

Diagnosis: *Haplomesus* with lateral spines on somites 2, 3, and 4 and probably also on 1. Pleon without projecting postero-lateral angles, dorsum smooth and lacking spines or carinae. Uropoda not much longer than wide and not extending beyond posterior margin.

Measurements: 1.8 mm., fragment (Hansen, op. cit.).

Type locality: North Atlantic, Davis Strait, *Ingolf* Station 24, latitude 63° 06′ N., longitude 56° 00′ W., 1199 fathoms (2258 meters), temperature 2.4° C., one mutilated female specimen (Hansen, op. cit.).

Distribution: Known only from type locality.

Affinities: The presence of lateral spines on peraeonal somites 2–4 inclusive distinguishes this species from the others that are known.

Haplomesus quadrispinosus (G. O. Sars)
Figure 20 F–H

Synonyms: *Ischnosoma quadrispinosum* G. O. Sars, 1879, p. 435; — 1885, p. 126, Pl. II. *Haplomesus quadrispinosus* (G. O. Sars), Richardson, 1908a, p. 81; — Hansen, 1916, pp. 59–61, Pl. II.

Diagnosis: *Haplomesus* with lateral spines on the first and third peraeonal somites only. Uropoda short, no longer than wide. Peraeon and pleon markedly tuberculate. Pleon without postero-lateral angles, dorsum with a single medial swelling. Apex of male first pleopods without lateral projections and with three terminal setae.

Measurements: Three males, largest 5 mm. (after Hansen, op. cit.).

Type locality: West of Norway, latitude 67° 56′ N., longitude 4° 11′ E., 1423 meters, temperature −1.4°C (Hansen, op. cit.).

Distribution: North Atlantic. The *Ingolf* collected it at nine stations:

Davis Strait: Station 24, latitude 63° 06′ N., longitude 56° 00′ W., 2258 meters, temperature 2.4° C., two specimens; Station 36, latitude 61° 50′ N., longitude 56° 21′ W., 2702 meters, temperature 1.5° C., two specimens.

South of Davis Strait: Station 38, latitude 59° 12′ N., longitude 51° 05′ W., 3521 meters, temperature 1.3° C., one specimen.

North of the Faeroes: Station 139, latitude 63° 36′ N., longitude 7° 30′ W., 1322 meters, temperature −0.6° C., two specimens.

East of Iceland: Station 102, latitude 66° 23′ N., longitude 10° 26′ W., 1412 meters, temperature −0.9° C., five specimens.

Northeast of Iceland: Station 120, latitude 67° 29′ N., longitude 11° 32′ W., 1666 meters, temperature −1.0° C., one specimen; Station 119, latitude 67° 53′ N., longitude 10° 19′ W., 1902 meters, temperature −1.0° C., one specimen.

South of Jan Mayen: Station 113, latitude 69° 31′ N., longitude 7° 06′ W., 2465 meters, temperature −1.0° C., five specimens; Station 116, latitude 70° 05′ N., longitude 8° 26′ W., 699 meters, temperature −0.4° C., one specimen.

The species was not represented in the Lamont collections. Gorbunov (1946, p. 123) records it from 510 and 698 meters in the Arctic, and Birstein (1960, p. 15) cites it from the North Pacific at 4000–4150 meters.

Affinities: This species resembles the new species *ornatus* considerably, but lacks paired carinae on the dorsum of the pleon.

Haplomesus tenuispinis Hansen
Figure 20 I–J

Synonyms: *Haplomesus tenuispinis* Hansen, 1916, pp. 64–65, Pl. V.

Diagnosis: *Haplomesus* with lateral spines on peraeonal somites 1 and 4 only. Pleon with pronounced postero-lateral angles, dorsum with paired stout spines. Uropoda longer than wide and extending beyond the posterior border of the pleon.

Measurements: 3.1 mm. long (estimated, Hansen, op. cit.).

Type locality: North Atlantic, Davis Strait, *Ingolf* Station 24, latitude 63° 06′ N., longitude 56° 00′ 1199 fathoms (2258 meters), temperature 2.4° C. (Hansen, op. cit.).

Distribution: Also taken from North Atlantic, south of Davis Strait, *Ingolf* Station 22, latitude 58° 10′ N., longitude 48° 25′ W., 1845 fathoms (3474 meters), temperature 1.4° C. (perhaps a distinct species) (Hansen, op. cit.). Also reported by Gorbunov (1946, p. 123) from 698 meters in the Arctic.

Remarks: A specimen, female fragment, with an additional pair of stout spines on the dorsum of the seventh peraeonal somite was captured by *Vema* at L.G.O. Biotrawl No. 231, cat. no. 231. It may represent a distinct species. The spines (actually stout setae) on the pleon distinguish this species from the others.

Haplomesus tropicalis, new species
Figure 20 K–M

Synonyms: None.

Diagnosis: *Haplomesus* with lateral spines on first and fourth peraeonal somites in male, and on first only in female. Pleon with sharp incurved posterolateral angles, dorsum without stout spines or carinae; apex convex. Uropoda longer than wide styliform, extending beyond apical margin of pleon. Male

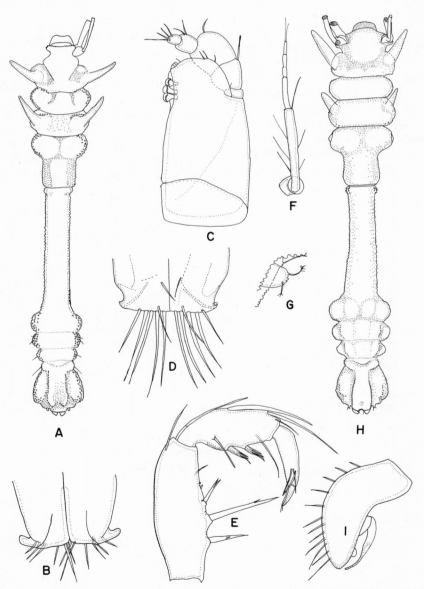

Figure 21. A–B: *Haplomesus ornatus*, n. sp. A: dorsal view male holotype; B: first pleopod. C–I: *Haplomesus bifurcatus*, n. sp. C: maxilliped; D: first male pleopod; E: first male paraeopod; F: first antenna; G: male uropod; H: dorsal view male holotype; I: second male pleopod.

pleopods each with simple rounded apex bearing three setae.

Measurements: Male holotype length 3.1 mm., width pleon 0.2 mm. Allotype length 4.1mm., width pleon 0.4 mm.

Type locality: North Atlantic, Mediterranean, L.G.O. Biotrawl No. 76, holotype and allotype, cat. no. I-105.

Distribution: Also taken at L.G.O. Biotrawl No. 95, one male fragment, cat. no. I-106, Caribbean.

Affinities: This species appears most closely related to *H. insignis* Hansen, from which it differs in having much smaller lateral body spines.

Haplomesus insignis Hansen
Figure 20 N–P

Synonym: *Haplomesus insignis* Hansen, 1916, p. 63, Pl. V.

Diagnosis: *Haplomesus* with massive lateral spines on peraeonal somites 1 and 4 only. Pleon with pronounced postero-lateral angles, dorsum without stout setae or carinae. Uropoda longer than wide and extending beyond posterior margin of pleon.

Measurements: Male 4.5 mm. long (Hansen, op. cit.).

Type locality: North Atlantic, Davis Strait, *Ingolf* Station 36, latitude 61° 50′ N., longitude 56° 21′ W., 1435 fathoms (2702 meters), temperature 1.5° C. (Hansen, op. cit.).

Distribution: Taken also by *Vema* at L.G.O. Biotrawl No. 234, one anterior fragment, cat. no. I-69. Reported by Gorbunov (1946, p. 123) from 698 meters in the Arctic.

Affinities: This species appears to be related to *H. tropicalis*, but has much more massive lateral body spines.

Haplomesus ornatus, new species
Figure 21 A–B

Synonyms: None.

Diagnosis: *Haplomesus* with lateral spines on peraeonal somites 1 and 3 only. Peraeon strongly tuberculate. Apex of pleon truncated, posterolateral angles lacking, dorsum with paired medial carinae. Apex of male pleopods each with blunt lateral process and six setae.

Measurements: Holotype male length 6.8 mm., width pleon 0.9 mm.

Type locality: South Atlantic, L.G.O. Biotrawl No. 18, one male and one male fragment, cat. no. I-49.

Distribution: Also from L.G.O. Biotrawl No. 52, one male, cat. no. I-47, and L.G.O. Biotrawl No. 214, two fragments, cat. no. I-78.

Affinities: This species is near to the North Atlantic *I. quadrispinosis* (G. O. Sars), but has carinae on the dorsum of the pleon which the latter lacks.

Haplomesus bifurcatus, new species
Figure 21 C–I

Synonyms: None.

Diagnosis: *Haplomesus* with lateral spines on peraeonal somites 1 and 3 only. Peraeon strongly tuberculate. Pleon without pronounced posterolateral angles; apex incised, dorsum with mid-central swelling with deep pit. Uropoda minute, as wide as long and not extending to apex of pleon. Male first pleopods each with minute lateral projections and six setae.

Measurements: Holotype male length 5.0 mm., width pleon 0.7 mm.

Type locality: South Atlantic, L.G.O. Biotrawl No. 12, holotype and one male fragment paratype, cat. no. I-48.

Distribution: Known only from type locality.

Affinities: This species resembles *H. ornatus*, but the indentation of the posterior border of the pleon distinguishes it.

Genus: HETEROMESUS Richardson

Synonyms: *Heteromesus* Richardson, 1908a, p. 81; — Hansen, 1916, p. 66; — Wolff, 1956, p. 141.

Type species: *Ischnosoma thomsoni* Beddard.

Diagnosis: Ischnomesidae with the third article of the first antenna minute. Pleon with a single somite only. Uropoda with a single article. Sixth and seventh peraeonal somites fused with pleon.

Composition: Thirteen species of this genus are known. Additionally, one new one is described in this paper. They are bathyal to abyssal in depth distribution and are known from only the Arctic, the North Atlantic (including the Caribbean), and the North Pacific (four species).

Species	Depth Range (Meters)	
	Least	Greatest
1. *thomsoni* (Beddard)	3750	3750
2. *spinosus* (Beddard)	1829	1829
3. *greeni* (Tattersall)	364	700
4. *spinescens* Richardson	2155	3337
5. *granulatus* Richardson	713	3235
6. *dentatus* Hansen	1505	1505
7. *longiremis* Hansen	698	2707
8. *schmidtii* Hansen	956	956
9. *frigidus* Hansen	698	1435
10. *similis* Richardson	—	2995
11. *gigas* (Birstein)	6560	8430
12. *scabriusculus* (Birstein)	5450	5450
13. *robustus* (Birstein)	5450	5817

A KEY TO THE SPECIES OF HETEROMESUS[a]

It is not easy to provide a key to the species of Heteromesus because entire specimens are not yet known for all the species. The following key therefore is incomplete but probably useful.

1. Pleon with spines or spine-like projections at the lateral margins 2
1. Pleon without spines or spine-like projections at lateral margins 5
2. Posterior border of pleon with a pair of spine-like projections . . . . . *thomsoni* (Beddard)
2. Posterior border of pleon without spine-like projections 3
3. Posterior border of pleon medially excised . . . . *bifurcatus*, n. sp.
3. Posterior border of pleon rounded 4
4. First peraeonal somite laterally with two spines . . . . *similis* Richardson
4. First peraeonal somite laterally with only one spine . . . . *dentatus* Hansen
5. Uropoda over five times longer than their greatest width . . . . *longiremis* Hansen
5. Uropoda considerably less than five times longer than wide 6
6. Lateral borders of first peraeonal somite with one spine each 7
6. Lateral borders of first peraeonal somite with 2–3 spines 8
7. Uropoda only two times as long as wide . . . . *granulatus* Richardson
7. Uropoda four times as long as wide . . . . *schmidtii* Hansen
8. Lateral border of first peraeonal somite with three spines each . . . . *spinosus* (Beddard)
8. Lateral border of first peraeonal somite with two spines each 9
9. Uropoda curving toward midline of pleon . . . . *frigidus* Hansen
9. Uropoda straight 10
10. Last peduncular article of second antenna without a spine in distal inner extremity . . . . *greeni* (Tattersall)
10. Last peduncular article of second antenna with a prominent spine at distal inner extremity . . . . . . *spinescens* Richardson

a Birstein's three species not included; these are deep Pacific species.

Heteromesus longiremis Hansen
Figure 22 A–B

Synonyms: *Heteromesus longiremis* Hansen, 1916, pp. 68–69, Pl. VI.

Diagnosis: *Heteromesus* having pleon smooth laterally, lacking spines. Uropoda over five times as long as wide.

Measurements: Length mutilated female specimen 3.5 mm. (Hansen, op. cit.).

Type locality: North Atlantic, Davis Strait, *Ingolf* Station 36, latitude 61° 50′ N., longitude 56° 21′ W., 2707 meters, temperature 1.5° C., type only.

Distribution: Known only from type locality.

Affinities: The very long uropods and the lack of lateral spines on the pleon distinguish this species from the others.

Heteromesus bifurcatus, new species
Figure 22 C

Synonyms: None.

Diagnosis: *Heteromesus* with a single spine (curved

toward apex) on each side of the pleon. Apex of pleon medially incised. Uropoda about three times as long as wide. Last free peraeonal somite without spines at postero-lateral border.

Measurements: One female fragment 3.5 mm. long, width pleon 0.5 mm.

Type locality: North Atlantic, Caribbean, L.G.O. Biotrawl No. 94, type only, cat. no. I-107.

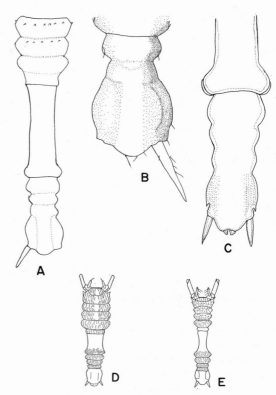

Figure 22. A–B: *Heteromesus longiremis* Hansen. A: dorsal view mutilated female; B: dorsal view mutilated male. C: *Heteromesus bifurcatus*, n. sp., dorsal view female fragment. D: *Heteromesus granulatus* Richardson, dorsal view female. E: *Heteromesus spinescens* Richardson, dorsal view male.

Distribution: Known only from type locality.

Affinities: This species is very close to *H. dentatus* Hansen, from which it differs in having the apex of the pleon incised.

Heteromesus granulatus Richardson
Figure 22 D

Synonyms: *Heteromesus granulatus* Richardson, 1908a, pp. 82–83, Figs. 14–17.

Diagnosis: *Heteromesus* with spines lacking from lateral border of pleon, apex of pleon rounded, entire, lacking spine-like projections. Uropoda only about twice as long as wide.

Measurements: None available.

Type locality: North Atlantic, *Albatross* Station 2547, south of Martha's Vineyard, 713 meters, 41 females, four males, cat. no. 38969 U.S.N.M., Washington (Richardson, op. cit.).

Distribution: Known also from *Albatross* Station 2572, southeast of Georges Bank, 3235 meters, two males, one female; *Albatross* Station 2571, southeast of Georges Bank, 2479 meters, one male; *Albatross* Station 2208, south of Block Island, 2155 meters, one male, six females; *Albatross* Station 2078, off Georges Bank, 912 meters, one female (Richardson, op. cit.).

Affinities: This species appears closely related to *H. schmidtii* Hansen, but has much shorter uropods.

Heteromesus spinescens Richardson
Figure 22 E

Synonyms: *Heteromesus spinescens* Richardson, 1908a, pp. 83–84, Fig. 18.

Diagnosis: *Heteromesus* with pleon lacking lateral spines, apex rounded, entire, lacking spine-like projections. Uropoda less than five times as long as wide, not bent toward midline. Lateral border of first peraeonal somite with two spines. Last peduncular article of first antenna with a prominent spine at distal extremity (Richardson, op. cit. illustration.).

Measurements: None available.

Type locality: North Atlantic, *Albatross* Station 2105, off Virginia, 2557 meters, one male, cat. no. 38970 U.S.N.M., Washington (Richardson, op. cit.).

Distribution: Also taken from *Albatross* Station 2714, south of Martha's Vineyard, 3337 meters, two females; *Albatross* Station 2208, south of Block Island, 2155 meters, two females *Albatross* Station 2084, off Georges Bank, 2361 meters, one female; *Albatross* Station 2571, southeast of Georges Bank, 2479 meters, five females.

Affinities: This species seems related to *H. greeni* (Tattersall) and differs from it in having the long spine in the inner angle of the last peduncular article of the second antenna.

Heteromesus similis Richardson
Figure: none available

Synonyms: *Heteromesus similis* Richardson, 1911, pp. 531–532.

Diagnosis: *Heteromesus* with spines at lateral border of pleon, posterior border entire, rounded, without spine-like projections or excisions. First peraeonal somite laterally with two spines.

Measurements: None available.

Type locality: *Talisman* Station 31, northeast of San Miguel in the Azores, 22 August 1883, 2995 meters, one fragment.

Distribution: Known only from type locality.

Affinities: This species is perhaps related to *H. dentatus* Hansen, from which it differs in having two spines instead of one at the lateral margin of the first peraeonal somite.

Genus: STYLOMESUS Wolff

Synonyms: *Stylomesus* Wolff, 1956, pp. 87–88, 97.

Type species: *Rhabdomesus inermis* Vanhöffen, Wolff, 1956, pp. 87–88, 97.

Diagnosis: Ischnomesidae having uropods with two articles. Seventh peraeonal somite fused with pleon. Third article of first antenna more than twice as long as fourth.

Composition: Wolff (1956) put only *inermis* in this genus. The species *S. inermis* was collected by the German South Polar Expedition (1901–1903) in the Antarctic Indian Ocean northwest of the *Gauss* station from a depth of 2450 meters. Four additional new species are described in this paper. Birstein (1960) described four abyssal species from the North Pacific, and Gurjanova (1946) described one from the Arctic.

A KEY TO THE SPECIES OF STYLOMESUS[a]

1. Pleon composed of three fused somites 2
1. Pleon composed of two fused somites 4
2. Apex of male first pleopod with lateral projections 6
2. Apex of male first pleopod without lateral projections 3
3. Inner margin of uropodal peduncle spinulate . . . . *spinulosus*, n. sp.
3. Inner margin of uropodal peduncle smooth . . . . *simplex*, n. sp.
4. Uropodal peduncle just extending to end of pleon . . . . *inermis* (Vanhöffen)
4. Uropodal peduncle extending beyond end of pleon by about one-half its length 5
5. Dorsum of pleon strongly granulate, without central depression . . . . *granulosus*, n. sp.
5. Dorsum of pleon smooth with central transverse depression . . . . *elegans*, n. sp.
6. Apex of pleon between uropods triangulate . . . . *regularis*, n. sp.
6. Apex of pleon between uropods evenly rounded 7
7. Lateral margin of male first pleopods with two distinct lobes at distal half . . . . *productus*, n. sp.
7. Lateral margin of male first pleopods with one distinct lobe at distal half . . . . . . *simulans*, n. sp.

[a] Following species not included:
1. *gorbunovi* (Gurjanova)
2. *wolffi* Birstein
3. *menziesi* Birstein
4. *gracilis* Birstein
5. *pacificus* Birstein

Stylomesus inermis (Vanhöffen)
Figure 23

Synonyms: *Rhabdomesus inermis* Vanhöffen, 1914, pp. 560–561, Fig. 88. *Stylomesus inermis* (Vanhöffen), Wolff, 1956, pp. 87, 97–99.

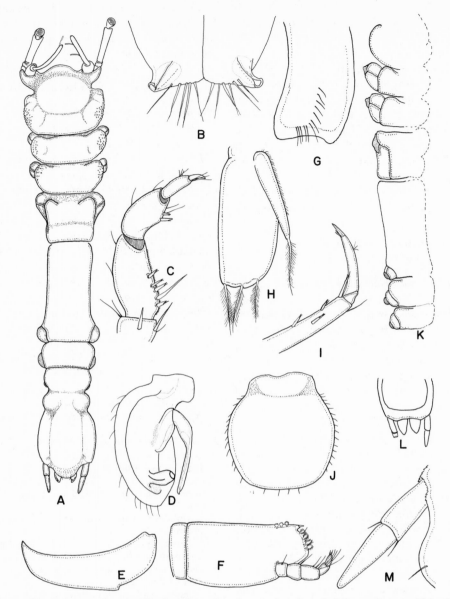

Figure 23. *Stylomesus inermis* (Vanhöffen). A: dorsal view female 5.8 mm. long, width pleon 0.8 mm.; B: first male pleopod; C: first paraeopod; D: second male pleopod; E: maxillipedal epipod; F: maxilliped; G: mandibular molar; H: second female pleopod; I: sixth paraeopod; J: female operculum; K: lateral view female; L: female anus and uropods; M: male uropod.

Diagnosis: *Stylomesus* without lateral spines on peraeonal or pleonal somites. Body granulate. Pleon with lateral swellings indicating only one coalesced somite. First article of uropod extending to apex of pleon. Apex of male pleopods with slight lateral process and each with six apical setae.

Measurements: 5.1 mm. total length; width somite one is 0.9 mm. (Wolff, op. cit.).

Type locality: Antarctic Indian Ocean, near *Gauss* Station, latitude 65° 31′ S., longitude 85° 17′ E., 2450 meters (Wolff, op. cit.).

Distribution: This species was collected by *Vema* from the South Atlantic Ocean at: L.G.O. Biotrawl

No 12, three female, two male, one fragment, cat. no. I-71; L.G.O. Biotrawl No. 210, one female, one fragment, cat. no. I-70; L.G.O. Biotrawl No. 214, three female, three fragments, cat. no. I-75.

Affinities: The pleon of this species has only two fused somites. Because the uropodal peduncles are short, the species is distinguished from *granulosus* and *elegans*, both of which have longer uropodal peduncles.

Stylomesus granulosus, new species
Figure 24 A–C

Synonyms: None.

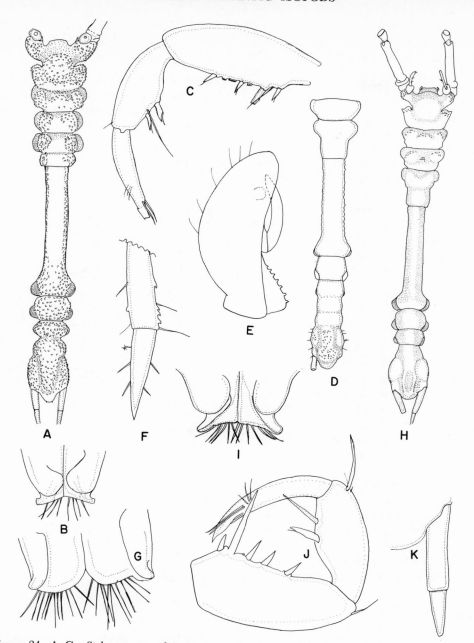

Figure 24. A–C: *Stylomesus granulosus*, n. sp. A: dorsal view male holotype; B: first male pleopod, C: first male paraeopod. D–G: *Stylomesus spinulosus*, n. sp. D: dorsal view fragment female holotype; E: second pleopod male paratype; F: uropod male; G: first pleopod male. H–K: *Stylomesus elegans*, n. sp. H: dorsal view male holotype; I: first pleopod male; J: first male paraeopod; K: male uropod.

Diagnosis: *Stylomesus* without lateral spines on peraeon or pleon. Body strongly granulate. Pleon with lateral swellings indicating only one coalesced somite. First article of uropoda extending beyond apex of pleon by one-half its length. Apex of male first pleopods with short truncated lateral processes and each with four apical setae.

Measurements: Male holotype length 8.9 mm., width pleon 1.1 mm., female allotype length 7.2 mm., width pleon 0.8 mm.

Type locality: South Atlantic, L.G.O. Biotrawl No.

51, types plus one male and four fragmentary paratypes, cat. no. I-101

Distribution: Known only from type locality.

Affinities: This species is allied with *S. elegans*, from which it differs in lacking a central transverse depression from the dorsum of the pleon

Stylomesus spinulosus, new species
Figure 24 D–G

Synonyms: None.

Diagnosis: Stylomesus without lateral spines on peraeon or pleon. Body strongly granulate. Pleon with lateral swellings indicating two coalesced somites. First article of uropoda marginally spinulous and extending to apex of pleon. Apex of male first pleopods with short blunt lateral processes, each apex with 10–11 setae.

Measurements: Female holotype fragment length 3.0 mm., width pleon 0.35 mm.

Type locality: South Atlantic, L.G.O. Biotrawl No. 12, holotype and three fragmentary paratypes, cat. no. I-102.

Distribution: Known only from type locality.

Affinities: This species appears most closely related to *S. simplex*, from which it differs in having the inner margin of the uropodal peduncle spinulate.

Stylomesus elegans, new species
Figure 24 H–K

Synonyms: None.

Diagnosis: Stylomesus with a short lateral spine on first peraeonal somite; other somites and pleon without lateral spines. Pleon with lateral swellings indicating only one coalesced somite. First article of uropod extending beyond apex of pleon by one-half its length. Second article shorter than first. Apex of male pleopods with blunt lateral processes; six setae at apex.

Measurements: Holotype male length 7.2 mm., width pleon 1.1 mm.

Type locality: South Atlantic, L.G.O. Biotrawl No. 51, type only, cat. no. I-100.

Distribution: Also taken from the North Atlantic, L.G.O. Biotrawl No. 208, one pleon fragment, cat. no. I-220.

Affinities: This species resembles *granulosus* most closely, but has a depressed area on the dorsum of the pleon.

Stylomesus regularis, new species
Figure 25 A–D

Synonyms: None.

Diagnosis: Stylomesus without lateral spines on peraeon, pleon with three fused somites. Margin of uropoda spinulate. Uropodal peduncle extending slightly beyond apex of pleon. Dorsum of pleon without central depressed area. Apex of male first pleopod with lateral expansions and with eight setae.

Measurements: Holotype male length 5.75 mm, with pleon 0.6 mm., allotype length 6.0 mm., width pleon 0.55 mm., plus cephalon fragment.

Type locality: South Atlantic, L.G.O. Biotrawl No. 218, types only, cat. no. I-219.

Distribution: Found only at type locality.

Affinities: This species is related to *S. simulans* and *S. productus*, from which it differs in having a triangulate pleonal apex between the uropods.

Stylomesus simplex, new species
Figure 25 E–J

Synonyms: None.

Diagnosis: Stylomesus without lateral spines on pleon. Body with few granules. Pleon with lateral swellings indicating two coalesced somites. First

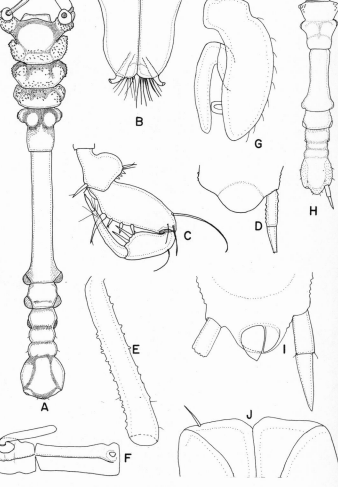

Figure 25. A–D: *Stylomesus regularis*, n. sp. A: dorsal view male holotype; B: first male pleopod; C: male gnathopod; D: ventral view uropod female allotype. E–J: *Stylomesus simplex*, n. sp. E: fourth male paraeopod; F: lateral view male holotype; G: second male pleopod; H: dorsal view male holotype (minus cephalon); I: ventral view female pleon; J: first male pleopod.

article of uropod extending to apex of pleon; margin smooth. Apex of male pleopods without lateral processes and each with a single apical seta.

Measurements: Male holotype (minus cephalon) length 3.0 mm., width pleon 0.4 mm.

Type locality: South Atlantic, L.G.O. Biotrawl No. 12, type and one female allotype fragment, cat. no. I-73.

Distribution: Known also from the South Atlantic, from L.G.O. Biotrawl No. 53, one female, cat. no. I-204, and from L.G.O. Biotrawl No. 212, one female, cat. no. I-74.

Affinities: This species is close to *S. spinulosus*, from which it differs in lacking spines from the uropodal peduncle.

Stylomesus productus, new species
Figure 26 A–C

Synonyms: None.

Diagnosis: *Stylomesus* with three fused pleonal somites. Uropodal peduncle extending far beyond apex of pleon. Dorsum of pleon with two pits, one at apex, one in front of apex. Apex of male first pleopod with seven setae and lateral expansions. Lateral margin male first pleopods with two large swellings just behind apex. Seventh peraeonal somite not separated from pleon.

Measurements: Length last six somites (inclusive of pleon) 3.0 mm., width pleon 0.6 mm.

Type locality: South Atlantic, L.G.O. Biotrawl No. 214, type male fragment only, cat. no. I-214.

Distribution: Known only from type locality.

Affinities: This species is near to *S. simulans*, but differs in having an additional lobe along the lateral border of the male first pleopods at its distal half.

Stylomesus simulans, new species
Figure 26 D–F

Synonyms: None.

Diagnosis: *Stylomesus* with three fused pleonal somites. Uropodal peduncle just extending beyond apex of pleon. Dorsum of pleon with two pits, one at apex, one in front of apex. Apex of each male first pleopod with seven setae and lateral expansions. Lateral margins male first pleopod with only one swelling just behind apex. Seventh peraeonal somite fused with pleon.

Measurements: Length male last five somites 1.9 mm., width pleon 0.7 mm.

Type locality: South Atlantic, L.G.O. Biotrawl No. 214, type only, cat. no. I-243.

Distribution: Known only from type locality.

Affinities: This species resembles *S. productus*

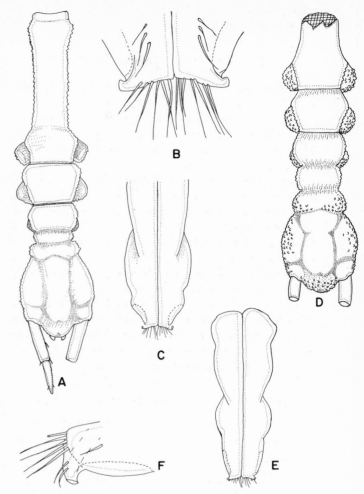

Figure 26. A–C: *Stylomesus productus*, n. sp. A: dorsal view male (minus cephalon); B: first male pleopod; C: male pleopod. D–F: *Stylomesus simulans*, n. sp. D: dorsal view male fragment; E: first male pleopod; F: first male pleopod.

rather closely, but has only one lobe instead of two along lateral margin of the male first pleopods at its distal half.

Stylomesus species indeterminable

Indeterminate species of *Stylomesus* were taken in L.G.O. Biotrawl No. 12, two fragments, and L.G.O. Biotrawl No. 47, two fragments.

Family: MACROSTYLIDAE

Type genus: *Macrostylis* G. O. Sars, 1863.

Diagnosis: Paraselloidea with free first peraeonal somite. Mandible with pointed molar bearing setae at apex; palp lacking. First three articles of maxillipedal palp as wide as endite, last two narrow, small. Uropoda styliform; uniramous. First pair of antennae shorter than peduncle of second pair of antennae. All peraeopods ambulatory. Pleon consisting of a single somite only. Anus separated from branchial chamber.

Composition: This family contains only one genus, *Macrostylis*. It is quite possible that *Pseudomesus* Hansen should be referred to this family, and in that event the Pseudomesidae should be canceled. I have not seen specimens of *Pseudomesus* and therefore hesitate to make that assignment.

Genus: MACROSTYLIS G. O. Sars, 1863

Type species: *Macrostylis spinifera* G. O. Sars, 1863, p. 15.

Diagnosis: Macrostylidae with the fourth peraeopods shorter than the others. Uropoda elongate. First three peraeonal somites almost fused into a single unit.

Composition: Although Wolff (1956) correctly indicates that ten species are known from the genus, he omitted *M. spinifera* from his key to the species. In depth the species range from the shallow water of Christiania Fjord to the floor of the Philippine trench at 10,000 meters. Here eight additional species are described from the abyssal Atlantic, where previously only one abyssal species was known.

The uropods are terminal and two-jointed in *Macrostylis*, and above them there is often a deep notch in the dorsum of the pleon. The uropoda are not dorsal in insertion as shown by Wolff, 1956, p. 100, Fig. 13, but terminal.

THE KNOWN SPECIES OF MACROSTYLIS

	Depth Range (Meters)	
Species	Least	Greatest
1. *spiniceps* Barnard	—	1280
2. *longipes* Hansen	—	1412
3. *subinermis* Hansen	1090	1902
4. *longiremis* (Meinert)	149	218
5. *elongata* Hansen	—	1591
6. *hadalis* Wolff	—	7270
7. *galatheae* Wolff	9820	10,000
8. *latifrons* Beddard	—	3749
9. *abyssicola* Hansen	3229	3521
10. *spinifera* G. O. Sars	4	1761

A KEY TO THE SPECIES OF MACROSTYLIS

1. Apical margin of pleon with conspicuous setae . 2
1. Apical margin of pleon without conspicuous setae 8
2. Postero-lateral margins of fourth peraeonal somite pointed and projecting 3
2. Postero-lateral margins of fourth peraeonal somite evenly rounded 4
3. Uropodal peduncle longer than pleon . . . . *hirsuticaudis*, n. sp.
3. Uropodal peduncle not as long as pleon 5
4. Postero-lateral angles of peraeonal somites 5–7 with a stout seta 6
4. Postero-lateral angles of peraeonal somites 5–7 without stout spine . . . . . . *longipes* Hansen
5. Peduncle of uropods longer than greatest width of pleon . . . . . . *spinifera* (G. O. Sars)
5. Peduncle of uropods shorter than greatest width of pleon . . . . *longiremis* (Meinert)
6. Fourth somite of peraeon narrower than third and fifth somites . . . . *setifer*, n. sp.

6. Fourth peraeonal somite as wide as third and fifth 7
7. Postero-lateral angles of cephalon sharply pointed . . . . *caribbicus*, n. sp.
7. Postero-lateral angles of cephalon evenly rounded . . . . *subinermis* Hansen
8. Medial apex of pleon emarginate . . . . *bifurcatus*, n. sp.
8. Medial apex of pleon convex or truncated, never bifurcated 9
9. Apex of pleon truncated . . . . . *truncatex*, n. sp.
9. Apex of pleon pointed or rounded 10
10. Cephalon wider than peraeon with postero-lateral angles projecting . . . . *spiniceps* Barnard
10. Cephalon not wider than peraeon, postero-lateral angles not projecting beyond peraeonal margin . 11
11. Pleon with bulbous swellings at uropod insertion making the pleon appear constricted cephalad of uropods . . . . *vemae*, n. sp.
11. Pleon not swollen laterally in front of uropod insertion 12
12. First and second peraeonal somites subequal in length 13
12. First peraeonal somite much shorter or longer than second 14
13. Cephalon quadrate in shape, as wide in front as behind . . . . *abyssicola* Hansen
13. Cephalon narrower in front than behind 15
14. First peraeonal somite much shorter than second . . . . *minutus*, n. sp.
14. First peraeonal somite much longer than second . . . . *hadalis* Wolff
15. Cephalon narrower than peraeon 17
15. Cephalon as wide as peraeon 16
16. Postero-lateral angles of cephalon rounded, lacking setae . . . . *galatheae* Wolff
16. Postero-lateral angles of cephalon pointed with stout seta at apex . . . . . . *bipunctatus*, n. sp.
17. Pleon with statocysts . . . . *elongata* Hansen
17. Pleon without statocysts . . . . . *latifrons* Beddard

Macrostylis truncatex, new species
Figure 27 A–C

Synonyms: None.

Diagnosis: Cephalon narrower in front than rear, front rounded. Fourth peraeonal somite as wide as third and fifth, lateral borders rounded. First peraeonal somite slightly longer than second. Uropodal peduncle not longer than pleon width; dorsum of pleon with a pair of carinae in front of uropods, pits and sensory organs lacking, apical border truncated lacking plumose setae. Apex of male first pleopods simple, rounded, without stout spines or lateral projections but with nine setae. First antenna with five-articles (male).

Measurements: Holotype male length 3.5 mm., width pleon 0.6 mm.

Type locality: North Atlantic, L.G.O. Biotrawl No. 246, one male, cat. no. I-117.

Distribution: Known only from type locality.

Affinities: The truncated nature of the pleonal apex distinguishes this species.

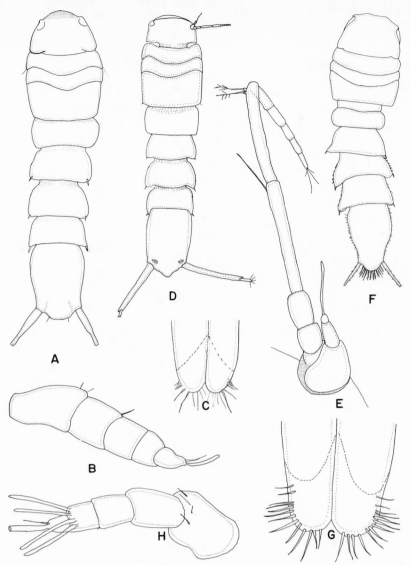

Figure 27. A–C: *Macrostylis truncatex*, n. sp. A: dorsal view holotype; B: first antenna;
C: first male pleopod. D–E: *Macrostylis abyssicola* Hansen. D: dorsal view female (3.9 mm.);
E: first and second antenna. F–H: *Macrostylis setifer*, n. sp. F: dorsal view male holotype;
G: first male pleopod; H: first antenna.

Macrostylis abyssicola Hansen
Figure 27 D–E

Synonyms: *Macrostylis abyssicola* Hansen, 1916, pp. 77–79, Pl. VII.

Diagnosis: Cephalon quadrate. Peraeonal somite 4 slightly narrower than 3 but not narrower than 5; lateral borders rounded slightly. First and second peraeonal somites subequal in length. Uropoda as long as pleon; peduncle produced at apex and five times as long as second article. Dorsum of pleon with pits above uropods; plumose setae absent, apex produced, convex. Apex male first pleopods simple. First antenna with only three articles (female).

Measurements: Female without marsupium 3.1mm., male 2.4 mm. (Hansen, op. cit.).

Type locality: North Atlantic, Davis Strait, *Ingolf* Station 37, latitude 60° 17′ N., longitude 54° 05′ W., 3229 meters, temperature 1.4° C., three specimens.

Distribution: Also collected south of Davis Strait, *Ingolf* Station 38, latitude 59° 12′ N., longitude 51° 05′ W., 3521 meters, temperature 1.3° C., about ten specimens, and south of Davis Strait at *Ingolf* Station 22, latitude 58° 10′ N., longitude 48° 25′ W., 3474 meters, temperature 1.4° C., six specimens, and from the South Atlantic from L.G.O. Biotrawl No. 23, two females, cat. no. I-120.

Affinities: The quadrate shape of the cephalon distinguishes this species.

Macrostylis setifer, new species
Figure 27 F–H

Synonyms: None.

Diagnosis: Cephalon narrower in front than rear, front slightly emarginate. Fourth peraeonal somite narrower than third and fifth, lateral borders rounded. First peraeonal somite slightly longer than second. Uropodal peduncle shorter than width of pleon. Dorsum of pleon lacking pits or sensory organs, lateral borders not constricted, apex produced, convex, with at least 12 plumose setae. Apex of male pleopods simple, rounded, lacking stout spines or lateral projections, apex with 13 setae. First antenna with five articles (male).

Measurements: Holotype male length 6.1 mm., width pleon 1.1 mm.

Type locality: North Atlantic, L.G.O. Biotrawl No. 234, type only, cat. no. I-113.

Distribution: Known only from type locality.

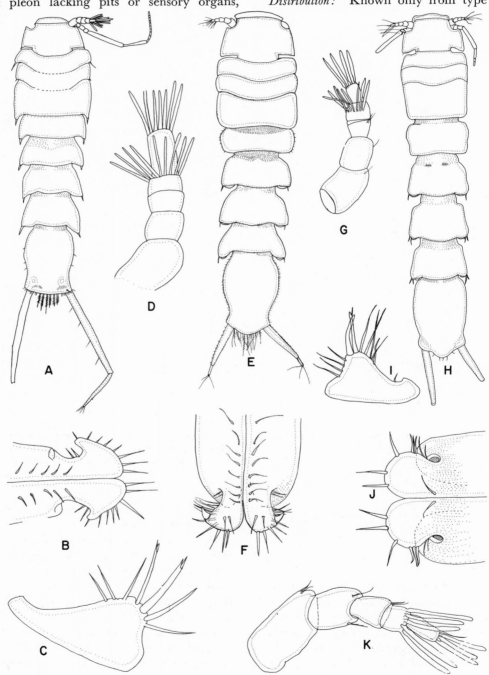

Figure 28. A–D: *Macrostylis hirsuticaudis*, n. sp. A: dorsal view male holotype; B: first male pleopod; C: third paraeopod; D: first antenna. E–G: *Macrostylis caribbicus*, n. sp. E: dorsal view male holotype; F: first pleopod; G: first antenna. H–K: *Macrostylis vemae*, n. sp. H: dorsal view male holotype; I: third paraeopod; J: first pleopod; K: first antenna.

Affinities: The fact that the fourth peraeonal somite is narrower than the third and fifth sets this species apart from *M. caribbicus* and *M. subinermis*.

Macrostylis hirsuticaudis, new species
Figure 28 A–D

Synonyms: None.

Diagnosis: Cephalon narrower in front than behind, front straight. Peraeonal somite 4 slightly narrower than 3 but as wide as 5, postero-lateral angles sharp, each with a stout seta. First and second peraeonal somites subequal in length. Uropodal peduncle much longer than length of pleon and twice as wide as pleon. Dorsum of pleon with pits in front of uropods, sensory organs present, apex almost straight bearing at least six plumose setae. Apex of male first pleopods laterally without stout spines, lateral part recurved, apex with eight setae. First antenna with five articles (male).

Measurements: Holotype male length 2.7 mm., width pleon 0.5 mm., allotype length 3.2 mm., width pleon 0.6 mm.

Type locality: South Atlantic, L.G.O. Biotrawl No. 22, types plus two male and two female paratypes, cat. no I-197.

Distribution: Known only from type locality.

Affinities: This species is allied to *M. longiremis,* Meinert but has uropoda longer than the pleon not shorter.

Macrostylis caribbicus, new species
Figure 28 E–G

Synonyms: None.

Diagnosis: Cephalon narrower in front than behind, front slightly convex. Peraeonal somite 4 as wide as 3 and 5, lateral borders rounded. First and second peraeonal somites subequal in length. Uropodal peduncle not as long as width of pleon. Dorsum of pleon without pits or sensory organs, lateral borders constricted in front of uropods; apical margin with 16 plumose setae. Apex of male first pleopods with stout spine laterally and five apical setae. First antenna with six articles (male).

Measurements: Male holotype length 4.8 mm., width pleon 0.9 mm.

Type locality: North Atlantic, Caribbean, L.G.O. Biotrawl No. 98, type, cat. no. I-118.

Distribution: Known only from type locality.

Affinities: This species is close to *M. subinermis* Hansen except that the postero-lateral angles of the cephalon are sharp and pointed, not rounded.

Macrostylis vemae, new species
Figure 28 H–K

Synonyms: None.

Diagnosis: Cephalon narrower in front than behind, front straight. Peraeonal somite 4 as wide as 3 and 5 and with rounded sides. First and second peraeonal somites subequal in length. Uropodal peduncle longer than width of pleon. Dorsum of pleon without dorsal pits or sensory organs; lateral border constricted in front of uropods; apical border convex and produced and lacking plumose setae. Apex of male first pleopods lacking lateral projections or stout spines, each rounded and with eight apical setae. First antenna with five articles.

Measurements: Male holotype length 3.9 mm., width pleon 0.6 mm., allotype length 3.8 mm., width pleon 0.7 mm.

Type locality: North Atlantic, L.G.O. Biotrawl No. 231, types and two male and two female paratypes, cat. no. I-110.

Distribution: Known also from L.G.O. Biotrawl No. 229, one female, cat. no. I-116.

Affinities: The bulbous swelling of the pleon in front of the uropods distinguishes this from a group of species lacking the swollen lateral border.

Macrostylis bifurcatus, new species
Figure 29 A–E

Synonyms: None.

Diagnosis: Cephalon quadrate, front slightly emarginate. Peraeonal somite 4 slightly narrower than 3 but as wide as 5. First and second peraeonal somites subequal in length. Peduncle of uropoda longer than width of pleon. Dorsum of pleon with slight pits above uropods. Apex of male first pleopods without stout lateral spine but with spoon-shaped lateral projections and each with five apical setae. Pleonal lateral margin not constricted in front of uropods. First antenna with five articles (male). Apex of pleon with deep medial incision; plumose setae lacking.

Measurements: Holotype male length 2.7 mm., width pleon 0.4 mm.

Type locality: South Atlantic, L.G.O. Biotrawl No. 51, type, cat. no. I-188.

Distribution: Known also from L.G.O. Biotrawl No. 52, one male, cat. no. I-187.

Affinities: The bifurcated nature of the apex of the pleon sets this species apart from the others.

Macrostylis minutus, new species
Figure 29 F–G

Synonyms: None.

Diagnosis: Cephalon narrower in front than behind, front with three lobes. Peraeonal somite 4 narrower than 5 but not narrower than 3, lateral margins rounded. First peraeonal somite shorter than second. Uropodal peduncle as long as pleon. Dorsum of pleon with slight pits above uropods and

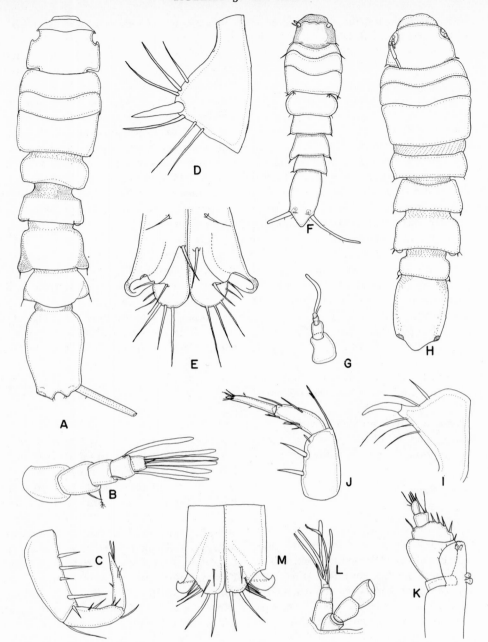

Figure 29. A–E: *Macrostylis bifurcatus*, n. sp. A: dorsal view male holotype; B: first antenna; C: first paraeopod; D: fourth paraeopod; E: apex of male first pleopod. F–G: *Macrostylis minutus*, n. sp. F: dorsal view female holotype; G: female first antenna. H–M: *Macrostylis bipunctatus*, n. sp. H: dorsal view male holotype; I: third paraeopod; J: first paraeopod; K: maxilliped; L: first and second antenna; M: apex first pleopod.

with sensory organ. Pleonal lateral margin not constricted in front of uropods; hind margin produced pointed, devoid of plumose setae. First antenna with four articles (female).

Measurements: Holotype female length 2.5 mm., width pleon 0.4 mm.

Type locality: North Atlantic, L.G.O. Biotrawl No. 234, two female paratypes, cat. no. I-114.

Distribution: Known also from L.G.O. Biotrawl No. 231, ten females, cat. no. I-115, and L.G.O. Biotrawl No. 232, one female, cat. no. I-111.

Affinities: This species resembles the Pacific *M. hadalis* Wolff except that the first peraeonal somite is shorter than the second, rather than longer.

Macrostylis bipunctatus, new species
Figure 29 H-M

Synonyms: None.

Diagnosis: Cephalon narrower in front than rear, front rounded. Peraeonal somite 4 as wide as somites 3 and 5. First and second peraeonal somites subequal in length; postero-lateral angles acute. Uropoda missing. Dorsum of pleon with pits above uropodal insertion. Apex of male first pleopods each with a stout recurved spine at lateral margin and six apical setae. Apex of pleon devoid of plumose setae. Pleonal lateral margin entire, not constricted in front of uropods; apical margin convex devoid of plumose setae. First antenna with only three articles (male).

Measurements: Holotype male length 2.5 mm., width pleon 0.4 mm., allotype female length 2.1 mm., width pleon 0.4 mm.

Type locality: South Atlantic, L.G.O. Biotrawl No. 12, types plus three fragments, cat. no. I-119.

Distribution: Taken also from the South Atlantic

at L.G.O. Biotrawl No. 51, one female, two fragments, cat. no. I-51; L.G.O. Biotrawl No. 52, sixteen specimens, cat. no. I-198; L.G.O. Biotrawl No. 53, one male, cat. no. I-189; and L.G.O. Biotrawl No. 217, one female (with statocysts, and perhaps a distinct species).

Affinities: This species is closely allied to *M. galatheae* Wolff, but has the postero-lateral angles of the cephalon pointed, not rounded.

Macrostylis species indeterminable

Indeterminate species of *Macrostylis* were taken from L.G.O. Biotrawl no. 53, three fragments.

Family : NANNONISCIDAE

Type genus: Nannoniscus G. O. Sars.

Diagnosis: Peraeopods not modified (flattened) for swimming but with plumose setae. Uropoda with peduncle, usually biramous. Peraeonal somites all of similar length; first free from cephalon. Maxillipedal palp with last two articles narrow; others equal width of endite. Dactyl of peraeopods with two terminal claws. Molar process of mandible reduced to a short setiferous lobe.

Composition: This family contains *Nannoniscus* Richardson, *Austroniscus* Vanhöffen, and *Nannoniscoides* Hansen. These are distinguished from one another in the following key:

A KEY TO THE GENERA OF NANNONISCIDAE

1. First antenna with a bulbous organ
   attached to distal article . . . . *Nannoniscus*
1. First antenna normal, without bulbous organ . . 2
2. Last two peraeonal somites incompletely
   fused . . . . *Nannoniscoides*
2. Last two peraeonal somites entirely
   separated . . . . *Austroniscus*

The first two genera are represented by abyssal species. It is highly probable that *Nannoniscella* Hansen, 1916, is a synonym of *Austroniscus* Vanhöffen, 1914.

Genus: NANNONISCOIDES Hansen, 1916

Type species: Nannoniscoides angulatus Hansen, 1916, pp. 86–87, Pl. VIII.

Diagnosis: Nannoniscidae with last two peraeonal somites incompletely fused. Pleon with single somite. Uropoda biramous. First antenna normal, without a bulbous organ attached to last article.

This genus contains only the type, from 702 fathoms in the North Atlantic, and the new abyssal species described herein from the South Atlantic.

Nannoniscoides hirsutus, new species
Figure 30

Synonyms: None.

Diagnosis: Nannoniscoides, with a laterally serrated pleon. Body hirsute and densely reticulate. Cephalon three times as broad as the distance between the anterior ends of the cephalic keels. Antero-lateral angles with a stout seta on second somite, none on first or third. First peraeonal somite wider than cephalon; last two peraeonal somites pointed at lateral border. Uropodal endopod slightly shorter than exopod. Antero-lateral processes of cephalon not reaching frontal border. Apex of male first pleopods with tubular lateral expansion and each apex with three setae.

Measurements: Holotype male length 1.2 mm., width pleon 0.4 mm.

Type locality: South Atlantic, L.G.O. Biotrawl No. 12, type only, cat. no. I-122.

Distribution: Known only from type locality.

Affinities: This species may be distinguished from *N. angulatus* Hansen by the fact that the first peraeonal somite is wider than the cephalon, not narrower.

Genus: NANNONISCUS G. O. Sars, 1869

Type species: Nannoniscus oblongus G. O. Sars

Synonyms: Nannoniscus G. O. Sars, 1869; — Hansen, 1916, pp. 87–89.

Diagnosis: Nannoniscidae with last two peraeonal somites incompletely fused. Pleon with a single somite. Uropoda biramous. First antenna short, with a bulbous organ attached to last article.

This genus contains 15 described species. Twelve of these were desccribed by Hansen (op. cit.); Vanhöffen (1914) described two species, and G. O. Sars described one.

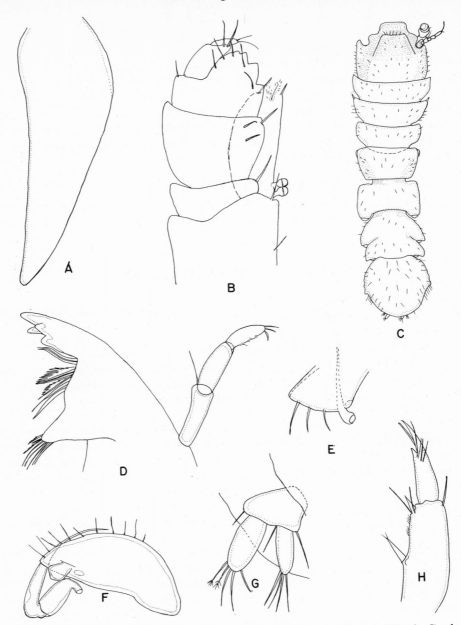

Figure 30. *Nannoniscoides hirsutus*, n. sp. A: maxillipedal epipode; B: maxilliped; C: dorsal view male holotype; D: mandible; E: first pleopod; F: male second pleopod; G: uropod and anus; H: first paraeopod.

It is impossible at this date to construct a satisfactory key to all of the species, and the reader is referred, therefore, to the following key modified from Hansen (op. cit.), in which he treats all known species except *australis* and *bidens* of Vanhöffen. The structure of the appendages of these southern species is not yet known. Here three of Hansens abyssal species, one of G. O. Sars's, and two apparently new abyssal species are described.

A KEY TO THE SPECIES OF NANNONISCUS
(Modified from Hansen, 1916)

1. Abdominal operculum of female with an acute process on lower surface 2

1. Abdominal operculum of female without tubercle or process on lower surface 6
2. Antero-lateral angles of first peraeonal somite terminating in a spine, those of second with a short fine seta . *simplex* Hansen and *australis* Vanhöffen
2. Antero-lateral angles of first peraeonal somite without a terminal spine but with or without a fine seta, those of second with a real spine 3
3. First or second peraeonal somites not one-half as broad again as sixth somite 4
3. First and second peraeonal somites more than one-half as broad again as sixth somite . *laticeps* Hansen
4. Lateral margin of pleon convex or straight . . . 5
4. Lateral margin of pleon concave just outside base of uropods . . . . *analis* Hansen
5. Antennal squama as long as the diameter of third peduncular article . . . . *oblongus* G. O. Sars

5. Antennal squama shorter than the diameter of third peduncular article . . . . *arcticus* Hansen

6. Second article of first antenna with process short, leaving the fourth article uncovered 7

6. Second article of first antenna with long process overlapping the fourth article 12

7. Posterior ventral area of peraeon without any process 8

7. Posterior ventral area of peraeon with one or two large recurved acute processes 9

8. Antennular vesicle two and a half to three times as long as broad . . . . . . *inermis* Hansen

8. Antennular vesicle pyriform not one-half as long again as broad . . . . . . *aequiremis* Hansen

9. With only one recurved process 10

9. With two processes . . . . . . *armatus* Hansen and *laevis*, n. sp.

10. Postero-lateral margin of pleon without incision or tooth 11

10. Postero-lateral margin of pleon with an incision and a conspicuous angle or tooth . . . . *minutus* Hansen and *bidens* Vanhöffen and *camayae*, n. sp.

11. First peraeopod without stout setae on inferior margin of (fifth article) propod . . . . *plebejus* Hansen

11. First peraeopod with two stout setae on inferior margin of (fifth article) propod . . . . *crassipes* Hansen

12. Anterior margin of front of cephalon nearly half as wide as cephalon width . . . . *spinicornis* Hansen

12. Anterior margin of front of cephalon less than one-half as wide as cephalon . . . . . *affinis* Hansen

LIST OF THE SPECIES OF NANNONISCUS

Species	Depth Range (Meters)	
	Least	Greatest
1. *oblongus* G. O. Sars	225	1505
2. *simplex* Hansen	1070	1505
3. *arcticus* Hansen	75	699
4. *analis* Hansen	—	2258
5. *laticeps* Hansen	—	552
6. *reticulatus* Hansen	—	552
7. *inermis* Hansen	—	2258
8. *aequiremis* Hansen	—	885
9. *plebejus* Hansen	—	1505
10. *minutus* Hansen	—	1096
11. *armatus* Hansen	—	3521
12. *spinicornis* Hansen	—	2465
13. *affinis* Hansen	—	1505
14. *australis* Vanhöffen	—	385
15. *bidens* Vanhöffen	—	385
16. *caspius* G. O. Sars	intertidal	
17. *crassipes* Hansen	?225	468

Nannoniscus inermis Hansen
Figure 31 A–C

Synonyms: *Nannoniscus inermis* Hansen, 1916, pp. 98–99, Pl. IX.

Diagnosis: *Nannoniscus* with cephalon a little more than four and a half times as broad as the distance between the anterior ends of the cephalic keels.

Antero-lateral angles of first somite of peraeon without spine; second and third with spine. Tubercle or process lacking from female operculum, which has a straight distal margin. Uropodal endopod almost twice as long as exopod. Pleon without teeth.

Measurements: Female with marsupium length 3.3 mm.

Type locality: North Atlantic, Davis Strait, *Ingolf* Station 24, latitude 63° 06′ N., longitude 56° 00′ W., 2258 meters, temperature 2.4° C. (Hansen, op. cit.).

Distribution: Known only from type locality.

Affinities: This species seems most nearly related to *N. aequiremis* Hansen, differing from it in having a more elongate antennular vesicle.

Nannoniscus armatus Hansen
Figure 31 D–E

Synonyms: *Nannoniscus armatus* Hansen, 1916, pp. 102–103, Pl. X.

Diagnosis: *Nannoniscus* with cephalon four times as broad as the distance between the anterior ends of the cephalic keels. Antero-lateral angles of first and third somites without spines on setae. Tubercle or process lacking from female operculum, which has a convex distal margin. Uropodal exopod considerably less than one-half the length of endopod. Pleon without teeth.

Measurements: Juvenile length 1.6 mm.

Type locality: North Atlantic, south of Davis Strait, *Ingolf* Station 38, latitude 59° 12′ N., longitude 51° 05′ W., 3521 meters, temperature 1.3° C. (Hansen, op. cit.).

Distribution: Known only from type locality.

Affinities: This species is closely related to *N. laevis*, n. sp., differing from it only in having a narrower frontal area on the cephalon and blunt lateral borders to the seventh peraeonal somite rather than angular ones.

Nannoniscus analis Hansen
Figure 31 F–H

Synonyms: *Nannoniscus analis* Hansen, 1916, pp. 95–96, Pl. VIII–IX.

Diagnosis: *Nannoniscus* with cephalon four times as broad as the distance between the anterior ends of the cephalic keels. Antero-lateral angles of first and third somites with no spines but frequently with a short seta; second with a distinct long spine. Operculum with a highly raised strong acute process. Uropodal endopod not twice as long as exopod. Pleon without teeth.

Measurements: Large specimen length 2.6 mm.

Type locality: North Atlantic, Davis Strait, *Ingolf* Station 24, latitude 63° 06′ N., longitude 56° 00′ W., 2258 meters, temperature 2.4° C. (Hansen, op. cit.).

Distribution: Known only from type locality.

Affinities: The concave nature of the pleonal

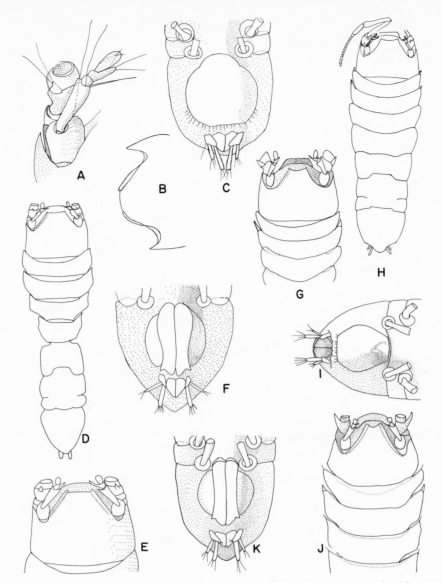

Figure 31. A–C: *Nannoniscus inermis* Hansen.   A: anterior left part of head with antennula and antenna of female; B: outline of anterior of head of female; C: abdomen and two posterior thoracic segments of female. D–E: *Nannoniscus armatus* Hansen. D: dorsal view female; E: dorsal view head of female. F–H: *Nannoniscus analis* Hansen. F: abdomen of male; G: dorsal view of male anterior; H: dorsal view of female. I–K: *Nannoniscus oblongus* G. O. Sars. I: ventral view of uropods, anus, and abdomen of female; J: dorsal view of female; K: ventral view of uropods, anus, and abdomen of male.

lateral margins distinguishes this species from the others.

Nannoniscus oblongus G. O. Sars
Figure 31 I–K

Synonyms: *Nannoniscus oblongus* G. O. Sars, 1870, p. 164; — 1897, p. 119, Pl. 50 (female only); — Hansen, 1916, pp. 92–94, Pl. VIII.

Diagnosis: *Nannoniscus* with cephalon as much as seven times as broad as the distance between the anterior ends of the cephalic keels. Antero-lateral angles with stiff spine or seta on first, second, and third somites. Operculum with a large medial spine

and with distal margin semi-circular. Uropodal exopod shorter than endopod. Pleon without teeth.

Measurements: Largest male 2.2 mm. (Hansen, op. cit.).

Type locality: Off the Lofoten Islands, at Skraaven, in depths ranging from 225 to 468 meters (Hansen, op. cit.).

Distribution: North Atlantic: Davis Strait, *Ingolf* Station 32, latitude 66° 35′ N., longitude 56° 38′ W., 599 meters, temperature 3.9° C.; west of Iceland, *Ingolf* Station 98, latitude 65° 38′ N., longitude 26° 27′ W., 260 meters, temperature 5.9° C.; southwest of Iceland, *Ingolf* Station 78, latitude 60° 37′ N.,

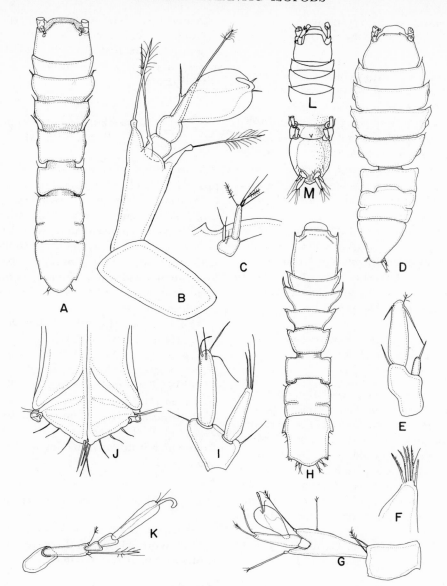

Figure 32. A–C: *Nannoniscus camayae*, n. sp. A: dorsal view female holotype; B: first antenna holotype; C: uropod. D–G: *Nannoniscus laevis*, n. sp. D: dorsal view female holotype; E: uropod; F: mandibular molar process; G: first antenna. H–K: *Nannoniscus primitivus*, n. sp. H: dorsal view male holotype; I: uropods; J: first male pleopod; K: first antenna. L–M: *Nannoniscus spinicornis*, Hansen. L: dorsal view anterior; M: Ventral view posterior.

longitude 27° 52′ W., 1505 meters, temperature 4.5° C. South Atlantic: L.G.O. Biotrawl No. 212, one female, cat. no. I-123.

Nannoniscus camayae, new species
Figure 32 A–C

Synonyms: None.

Diagnosis: *Nannoniscus* with cephalon three times as broad as the distance between the anterior ends of the cephalic keels. Antero-lateral angles of first peraeonal somite without spines or setae; second and third with setae. Operculum without projected spines but with a pair of depressions on either side of midline.

Fourth article of first antenna extending to one-third the length of vesicle. Uropodal exopod one-half the length of endopod. Pleon with a single tooth on each lateral margin.

Measurements: Female holotype length 4.1 mm., width pleon 0.7 mm.

Type locality: North Atlantic, Caribbean, L.G.O. Biotrawl No. 100, type only, cat. no. I-121.

Distribution: Known only from type locality.

Affinities: Closely related to *N. minutus* Hansen and *N. bidens* Vanhöffen. It differs from *minutus* and *bidens* in lacking the stout spine at the antero-lateral angle of the first peraeonal somite.

Nannoniscus laevis, new species
Figure 32 D–G

Synonyms: None.

Diagnosis: *Nannoniscus* with cephalon three times as broad as the distance between the anterior ends of the cephalic keels. Antero-lateral angles of first peraeonal somite with a stout seta; second and third with a fine seta. Operculum without projecting spines. Peraeon with two stout recurved spines ventrally. Fourth article of first antenna extends beyond antennal vesicle. Pleon without teeth on lateral margins.

Measurements: Holotype female length 3.2 mm., width pleon 0.6 mm.

Type locality: South Atlantic L.G.O. Biotrawl No. 53, type and three female paratypes, cat. no. I-125.

Distribution: Known only from type locality.

Affinities: The blunt lateral borders of the seventh peraeonal somite distinguish this species from its nearest relative, *N. armatus* Hansen.

Nannoniscus primitivus, new species
Figure 32 H–K

Synonyms: None.

Diagnosis: *Nannoniscus* with cephalon twice as broad as the distance between the anterior ends of the cephalic keels. Antero-lateral angles of first peraeonal somite sharply pointed but without spines; second with stout spine, third with weak seta. Second article of first antenna without distal spine-like projections and third not extending beyond start of vesicle. Uropodal exopod two-thirds the length of endopod.

Measurements: Holotype male length 1.8 mm., width pleon 0.3 mm.

Type locality: North Atlantic, Caribbean, L.G.O. Biotrawl No. 97, type only, cat. no. I-178.

Distribution: Known only from type locality.

Affinities: This species is unique in the primitive structure of the first antenna and its vesicle. The spines on the pleon are probably secondary sexual characteristics.

Nannoniscus spinicornis Hansen
Figure 32 L–M

Synonyms: *Nannoniscus spinicornis* Hansen, 1916, pp. 104–105, Pl. X, Figs. 2a–2g.

Diagnosis: *Nannoniscus* with cephalon twice as broad as the distance between the anterior ends of the cephalic keels. Antero-lateral angles of the first three peraeonal somites only slightly produced, acute, but without spines or setae. Second and third articles of first antenna with spine-like projections which extend to middle of vesicle. Uropodal exopod one-half the length of endopod.

Measurements: Length of female specimen, 1.5 mm. (Hansen, 1916, p. 104).

Type locality: North Atlantic, South of Jan Mayen, *Ingolf* Station 113, latitude 69° 31' N., longitude 7° 06' W., 2465 meters, temp. —1.0° C., one female specimen (Hansen, op. cit.).

Distribution: Known only from type locality.

Affinities: This species is close to *N. affinis* Hansen, from which it differs in having a wider frontal area to the cephalon.

Nannoniscus species indeterminable

Damaged specimens of *Nannoniscus* were taken from L.G.O. Biotrawl No. 16, three specimens, and L.G.O. Biotrawl No. 107, one female.

Family: EURYCOPIDAE

Type genus: *Eurycope*, G. O. Sars.

Diagnosis: Paraselloidea with peraeopods 5–7 inclusive paddle-like, modified for swimming and bearing dactyls. Cephalon (usually) separated from first peraeonal somite. Pleon with one or two somites. Uropoda uni-biramous; peduncle not flattened and not bearing pulmose setae.

Composition: This family contains *Eurycope*, *Storthyngura*, *Syneurycope*, *Munnopsurus*, and *Acanthocope*. The genera, except for *Munnopsurus*, are represented in the Atlantic abyss and are distinguished from one another in the following key.

A KEY TO THE GENERA OF THE EURYCOPIDAE

1. Uropoda biramous 2
1. Uropoda uniramous . . . . *Acanthocope*
2. Mandibular incisor reduced to a simple single tooth . . . . *Munnopsurus*
2. Mandibular incisor toothed, normal 3
3. Pleon with lateral spines . . . . *Storthyngura*
3. Pleon without lateral spines 4
4. Inner margin of maxillipedal palp articles with denticles . . . . *Syneurycope*
4. Inner margin of maxillipedal palp articles without denticles . . . . *Eurycope*

A LIST OF THE KNOWN ABYSSAL SPECIES OF EURYCOPE

Species	Depth Range (Meters)	
	Least	Greatest
1. *hanseni* Ohlin	520	2669
2. *incisa* Gurjanova	2380	2380
3. *abyssicola* Beddard	3886	3886
4. *complanata* Bonnier	950	2702

Species	Depth Range (Meters)	
	Least	Greatest
5. *furcata* G. O. Sars, Hansen	150	2258
6. *murrayi* Walker, Hansen	>1000	>2700
7. *nodifrons* Hansen (not Wolff, 1956)	2702	2702
8. *parva* Bonnier, Hansen	872	2702
9. *producta* G. O. Sars, Hansen, Hult	72	2087
10. *scabra* Hansen	2486	2486
11. *spinifrons* Gurjanova	308	3000
12. *ovalis* Vanhöffen	3423	3423
13. *galatheae* Wolff	6960	7000
14. *vicarius* Vanhöffen		3423
15. *sarsii* Beddard		2514
16. *madseni* Wolff	6960	7000

Genus: EURYCOPE G. O. Sars

Type species: *Eurycope cornuta* G. O. Sars, 1864, p. 5; — 1897, pp. 145–146, Pl. 64; — Richardson, 1905, p. 491 and references.

Diagnosis: Eurycopidae without spines on body or spine-like extensions on pleon. Frontal area of cephalon with pronounced keels dorsally. Uropoda biramous. Mandibular incisor and lacinia toothed, molar strong, normal, truncate at apex. Pleon with one somite only. Maxillipedal palp articles without denticles on inner margin.

Composition: This genus contains 41 species, about half of which are abyssal, but the exact number of species is uncertain. Some of the earlier species have been transferred to *Storthyngura*, *Acanthocope*, and *Munnopsurus*, Key characteristics for many of the species are not known, and the construction of a functional key is therefore impossible at present. The majority of the species live in relatively shallow water only.

Additionally, three new species are described herein and *E. antarctica* Vanhöffen is added to the abyssal fauna. Beddard's species, *sarsii*, *abyssicola*, and *spinosa*, are too imperfectly known to be included in this key, and this comment applies also to *E. galatheae* Wolff. It is highly doubtful that *E. nodifrons* Hansen occurs in the Pacific hadal depths as reported by Wolff (1956). Differences are clear in the maxilliped, shape of the posterior peraeonal somites, and the pleon. The specimen should be reexamined.

A KEY TO THE ABYSSAL SPECIES OF EURYCOPE

1. With peraeonal somites 5–6 fused along midline   2
1. With peraeonal somites 5–6 entirely separated . .   5
2. Discrete frontal area lacking from cephalon . . . . *antarctica* Vanhöffen
2. Discrete frontal area present on cephalon   3
3. Frontal area very broad, close to one-half the width of cephalon   4
3. Frontal area narrow, less than one-fifth the width of cephalon . . . . . . *furcata* G. O. Sars
4. Female operculum with recurved spine directed toward apex of pleon   . . . *ovaloides*, n. sp.

4. Female operculum with recurved spine directed toward head . . . . *parva* Bonnier
5. Pleon incised medially at apex . . . . *incisa* Gurjanova
5. Pleon not incised medially   6
6. Frons of cephalon well defined   8
6. Frons of cephalon not well defined   7
7. Pleon ovoid longer than wide . . . . *scabra* Hansen
7. Pleon shield-shaped, as wide as long . . . . *nodifrons* Hansen
8. Uropodal exopod one-seventh the length of endopod . . . . *murrayi* (Walker)
8. Uropodal exopod one-third to one-half or more than the length of endopod   9
9. Frons of cephalon with stout spines or seta on margin   10
9. Frons of cephalon without stout setae . . . . . 13[a]
10. Pleon with a spine on each postero-lateral border . . . . *spinifrons* Gurjanova
10. Pleon without spines at postero-lateral border . .   11
11. Frontal area with three to five stout setae on each side of apex   12
11. Frontal area with one stout seta on each side at apex . . . . *nodosa*, n. sp.
12. Frontal area with three spines on each side of apex . . . . *gaussi* Wolff
12. Frontal area with five spines on each side of apex . . . . *producta* G. O. Sars
13. Antero-lateral angles of pleon spine-like and projecting . . . . *acutitelson*, n. sp.
13. Antero-lateral angles of pleon not spine-like and projecting   14
14. Apex of frontal area of cephalon around one-fifteenth the width of the cephalon   15
14. Apex of frontal area of cephalon around one-third the width of the cephalon   16
15. Apex of frontal area deeply incised with medial part concave . . . . *complanata* Bonnier
15. Apex of frontal area incised but with distal part (apical incision) straight . . . . *vicarius* Vanhöffen, *hanseni* Ohlin
16. Apex of pleon blunt . . . . *madseni* Wolff
16. Apex of pleon rounded . . . . . *ovalis* Vanhöffen

[a] *Ovalis* is placed here due to Wolff's (1956) redescription in which setae are not mentioned, even though Vanhöffen (1914) showed setae.

Eurycope antartica Vanhöffen
Figure 33 A–B

Synonyms: *Eurycope antarctica* Vanhöffen, 1914, pp. 589–590.

Diagnosis: *Eurycope* with apex of frontal area rounded, around one-third the width of cephalon, lacking stout setae. Apex of pleon pointed. Inner distal margin of male second pleopod without vermiform appendage. Peraeonal somites 5–6 fused along midline. Uropodal exopod about one-half the length of endopod.

Measurements: Mature female 3.0 mm. long (Vanhöffen, op. cit.).

Type locality: Antarctic *Gauss* station, 66° 15′ S., 80° 19′ E., 385 meters, 135 specimens (Vanhöffen, op. cit.).

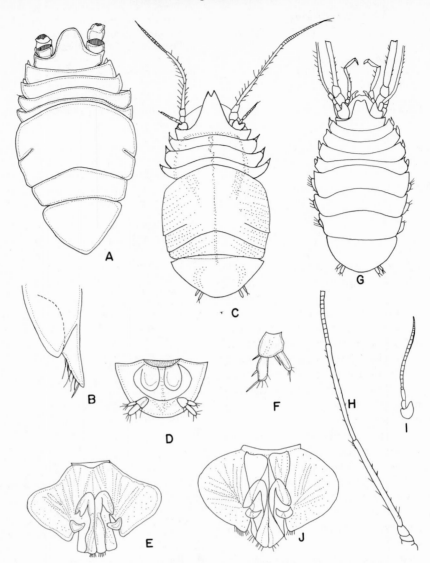

Figure 33. A–B: *Eurycope antarctica* Vanhöffen. A: dorsal view male length 1.8 mm., width 0.6 mm.; B: apex of first male pleopod. C–F: *Eurycope furcata* G. O. Sars. C: dorsal view female; D: ventral view uropods; E: first and second male pleopods; F: uropods female. G–J: *Eurycope producta* G. O. Sars. G: dorsal view female; H: second antenna; I: first antenna; J: first and second male pleopods.

Distribution: Also taken from South Atlantic Ocean, L.G.O. Biotrawl No. 201, three males, three females, cat. no. I-233.

Eurycope furcata G. O. Sars
Figure 33 C–F

Synonyms (incomplete): *Eurycope furcata* G. O. Sars, 1870, p. 165; — 1898, p. 148; — Gurjanova, 1933, p. 425; — Hansen, 1916, p. 151; — Hult, 1941, pp. 109–110.

Diagnosis: Eurycope with apex of frontal area deeply incised without stout setae, about one-tenth the width of cephalon. Pleon with acute antero-lateral angles, apex evenly rounded, without postero-lateral spines. Inner distal margin of male second pleopod without vermiform appendage. Peraeonal somites 5–6 fused along midline. Uropodal exopod slightly shorter than endopod.

Measurements: Adult female scarcely attaining 2 mm., (G. O. Sars, 1898, p. 149).

Type locality: Lofoten Islands at Skraaven, 100–200 fathoms, sandy clay (G. O. Sars, 1898, p. 149).

Distribution: West coast of Norway to Davis Strait and off west coast of Greenland from c. 150 meters to 2258 meters (Hult, 1941, p. 109). It was taken by the *Ingolf* at two stations (Hansen, 1916, p. 151): Station 24, Davis Strait, latitude 63° 06′ N., longitude 56° 00′ W., 2258 meters, temperature 2.4° C., one specimen; Station 78, southwest of Iceland, latitude 60° 37′ N., longitude 27° 52′ W., 1505 meters, temperature 4.5° C., two specimens. It was not collected by *Vema*.

Eurycope producta G. O. Sars
Figure 33 G–J

Synonyms (incomplete): *Eurycope producta* G. O. Sars, 1868, p. 113; — 1898, p. 146; — Gurjanova, 1933; p. 424; — 1938, p. 334; — Hansen, 1916, p. 147; — Stephensen, 1917, p. 298; — Tattersall, 1905, p. 75; — Hult, 1941, pp. 107–109.

Diagnosis: *Eurycope* with apex of frontal area convex, without stout setae, about one-fifth the width of cephalon. Pleon without spines or incisions, apex broadly rounded. Inner distal margin of male second pleopod without vermiform appendage. Peraeonal somites 5–6 entirely separated. Uropodal rami nearly equal in length.

Measurements: Adult female 3 mm. length (G. O. Sars, 1898, p. 146).

Type locality: Norwegian coast from Christiania Fjord to Vadsö (G. O. Sars, 1898, p. 146).

Distribution: Eurybathial arctic-boreal Norway, south and east of Greenland, south and southwest of Iceland (Hult, op. cit., pp. 108–109). *The Ingolf* collected the species from three stations: Station 25, Davis Strait, latitude 63° 30′ N., longitude 54° 25′ W., 1096 meters, temperature 3.3° C., two specimens; Station 78, southwest of Iceland, latitude 60° 37′ N., longitude 27° 52′ W., 1505 meters, temperature 4.5° C., three specimens; Station 138, northwest of the Faeroes, latitude 63° 26′ N., longitude 7° 56′ W., 887 meters, temperature −0.6° C., one specimen. The maximum depth, according to Hult (op. cit.), is 2087 meters and the minimum 72 meters. It was not collected by *Vema*.

Eurycope vicarius Vanhöffen
Figure 34 A–G

Synonyms: *Eurycope vicarius* Vanhöffen, 1914, pp. 586–587, Figs. 116–117; — Wolff, 1956, pp. 130–132.

Diagnosis: *Eurycope* with apex of frontal area convex, without stout setae, around one-tenth the width of cephalon. Pleon without spines or incisions, apex rounded. Inner distal margin of male second pleopod without vermiform appendage. Peraeonal somites 5–6 entirely separated. Uropodal exopod about one-third the length of endopod.

Measurements: 1.6 mm., 2.5 mm., 3 mm., 3.5 mm., 4.5 mm., and 9 mm. length of six specimens (Vanhöffen, op. cit., p. 587). Wolff's (op. cit.) female lectotype was 8.8 mm. long and 2.8 mm. wide.

Type locality: Antarctic continent, 3423 meters, 3 April 1903, *Gauss* (Vanhöffen, op. cit.).

Distribution: Antarctic 3423 meters (Vanhöffen) and taken by *Vema* from the South Atlantic, L.G.O. Biotrawl No. 201, seven females, cat. no. I-234. The specimen from *Gauss* Station at 385 meters has been subsequently described as *E. gausii* by Wolff (1956, op. cit.).

Eurycope complanata Bonnier
Figure 34 H–L

Synonyms: *Eurycope complanata* Bonnier, 1896, p. 601, Pl. 34; — Hansen, 1916, pp. 145–146, Pl. 13.

Diagnosis: *Eurycope* with apex of frontal area lacking spines, apex sharply concave, around one-eleventh the width of cephalon. Pleon without spines or incisions, apex pointed. Inner distal margin of male second pleopod with pronounced vermiform appendage. Peraeonal somites 5–6 entirely separated. Uropodal exopod one-third shorter than endopod.

Measurements: Male 5 mm. long (Bonnier, op. cit.)

Type locality: North Atlantic, Bay of Biscay, latitude 44° 17′ N., longitude 4° 38′ W., 950 meters (Hansen, op. cit.).

Distribution: North Atlantic. Taken by *Ingolf* at Station 24, Davis Strait, latitude 63° 06′ N., longitude 56° 00′ W., 2258 meters, temperature 2.4° C., four specimens, and Station 36, Davis Strait, latitude 61° 50′ N., longitude 56° 21′ W., 2702 meters, temperature 1.5° C., two specimens; and by *Vema* from L.G.O Biotrawl No. 7, one male and four fragments, cat. no. 135.

Eurycope murrayi Walker
Figure 34 M

Synonyms (incomplete): *Munnopsis*(?) *murrayi* Walker, 1903, p. 227, Pl. 18; — Tattersall, 1905, pp. 27, 73; — 1911, p. 190 (ref. Hansen, 1916). *Munneurycope tjalfiensis* Stephensen, 1913, p. 99, Figs. 6–8; — 1915, p. 23, Figs. 12–13. *Eurycope murrayi* Walker, Hansen, 1916, pp. 137–140, Pl. 12.

Diagnosis: *Eurycope* with frontal area probably obsolete. Pleon without projecting spines or incisions, apex rounded. Peraeonal somites 5–6 entirely separated. Uropodal exopod around one-tenth the length of the endopod.

Measurements: Length varies from about 7 mm. to a little over 8 mm., male (Stephensen, 1915, p. 24).

Type locality: West of Ireland between 350 and 1710 fathoms (Hansen, 1916, p. 139).

Distribution: Taken in the North Atlantic from the following places: West of Cape Farewell: *Tjalfe*, latitude 60° 07′ N., longitude 48° 26′ W., 2000 meters wire out, one specimen (Stephensen, 1915).

South of Iceland: *Thor* latitude 61° 34′ N., longitude 19° 05′ W., 1800 meters wire out, four specimens, *Thor*, latitude 61° 30′ N., longitude 17° 08′ W., 1800 meters wire out, fourteen specimens; *Thor*, latitude 62° 47′ N., longitude 10° 03′ W., 1500 meters wire out, two specimens.

Southwest of the Faeroes: *Thor*, latitude 60° 00′ N., longitude 10° 35′ W., 1000 meters wire out, three specimens; *Thor*, latitude 59° 52′ N., longitude 9° 53′ W., 1500 meters wire out, five and a half

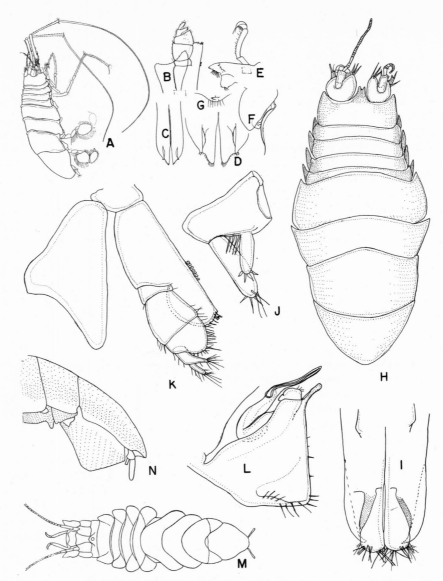

Figure 34. A–G: *Eurycope vicarius* Vanhöffen. A: lateral view; B: maxilliped; C: first pleopod; D: first pleopod. E: mandible; F: second male pleopod; G: apex of female operculum. H–L: *Eurycope complanata* Bonnier. H: dorsal view male; I: first male pleopod; J: uropod; K: maxilliped and maxillipedal epipod; L: second pleopod. M: *Eurycope murrayi* Walker, dorsal view. N: *Eurycope parva* Bonnier, ventro-lateral view of abdomen.

specimen (Hansen, 1916, p. 139). Hansen (1916) cites other finds.

This species was not collected by *Vema*.

Eurycope parva Bonnier
Figure 34 N

Synonyms: *Eurycope parva* Bonnier, 1896, p. 60, Pl. 33; — Hansen, 1916, pp. 149–150, Pl. 13.

Diagnosis: *Eurycope* with a broad blunt frontal area apex lacking spines and about one-half the width of cephalon. Pleon without spine incisions or projections. Peraeonal somites 5–6 fused along midline. Female operculum with recurved spine directed toward

cephalon and located at distal end of operculum. Uropodal exopod scarcely one-third as long as endopod. (After Hansen, op. cit.).

Measurements: Male 3 mm. long (Hansen, op. cit.).

Type locality: North Atlantic, Bay of Biscay, latitude 44° 17′ N., longitude 4° 38′ W., 950 meters (Hansen, op. cit.).

Distribution: Taken by *Ingolf* at Station 36, Davis Strait, latitude 61° 50′ N., longitude 56° 21′ W., 2702 meters, temperature 1.5° C., two specimens; and by *Thor* from southwest of the Faeroes, latitude 61° 15′ N., longitude 9° 35′ W., 872–970 meters, one female (Hansen, op. cit.). This species was not captured by the *Vema*.

Eurycope nodifrons Hansen
Figure 35 A–C

Synonyms: *Eurycope nodifrons* Hansen, 1916, pp. 140–141, Pl. 13. ? Wolff, 1956, pp. 123–125.

Diagnosis: Eurycope with obsolete frontal area. Pleon without spines or incisions, apex broadly rounded. Peraeonal somites 5–6 entirely separated (uropoda missing).

Measurements: Length 5 mm. (Hansen, op. cit. p. 140).

Type locality: North Atlantic, *Ingolf* Station 36, Davis Strait, latitude 61° 50′ N., longitude 56° 21′ W., 2702 meters, temperature 1.5° C., one specimen (Hansen, op. cit.).

Distribution: Known only from type locality.

Eurycope hanseni Ohlin
Figure 35 D–E

Synonyms: *Eurycope hanseni* Ohlin, 1901, p. 34, Fig. 7; — Hansen, 1916, pp. 144–145, Pl. 13.

Diagnosis: *Eurycope* with frontal area having an indented margin, setae lacking, and only about one-fifteenth the width of cephalon. Pleon without spines or incisions, apex broadly rounded. Inner distal margin of male second pleopod without vermiform appendage. Peraeonal somites 5–6 entirely separated. Uropodal exopod almost as long as endopod.

Measurements: Female length 10 mm. (Hansen, op. cit.).

Type locality: (Probably) North Atlantic, latitude 77° 52′ N., longitude 3° 5′ W., 2669 meters: and latitude 76° 36′ N., longitude 12° 10′ E., 1708 meters (Hansen, op. cit.).

Distribution: Also taken by *Ingolf* from Station 105, east of Iceland, latitude 65° 34′ N., longitude 7° 31′ W., 1435 meters, temperature —0.8° C., three speci-mens, small; Station 102, east of Iceland, latitude 66° 23′ N., longitude 10° 26′ W., 1412 meters, tempera-ture —0 9° C., one specimen; Station 113, south of Jan Mayen, latitude 69° 31′ N., longitude 7° 06′ W., 2465 meters, temperature —1 0° C , four specimens; Station 118, south of Jan Mayen, latitude 68° 27′ N., longitude 8° 20′ W., 1996 meters, temperature —0.1° C., one specimen (Hansen, op. cit.). This species was not captured by the *Vema*. Gurjanova (1946) and Gorbunov (1946) record it from many Arctic positions to 2500 meters.

Eurycope incisa Gurjanova
Figure 35 F–L

Synonyms: *Eurycope incisa* Gurjanova, 1946a, pp. 278–280, 295, Fig. 10.

Diagnosis: *Eurycope* with obsolete frontal area. Pleon with deep concave medial incision. Peraeonal

somites 5–6 entirely separated. Uropodal exopod one-third the length of endopod.

Measurements: Length 10 mm. (?) (Gurjanova, op. cit., p. 279).

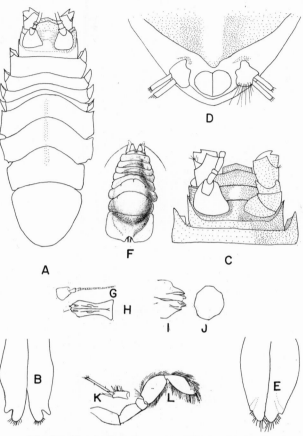

Figure 35. A–C: *Eurycope nodifrons* Hansen. A: dorsal view; B: first pleopod; C: dorsal view cephalon. D–E: *Eurycope hanseni* Ohlin. D: ventral view uropods and anus; E: first pleopod. F–L: *Eurycope incisa* Gurjanova. F: dorsal view; G: first antenna; H: pleo-pod; I: male operculum; J: female oper-culum; K: uropod; L: peraeopod.

Type locality: Arctic Ocean, *Sadko* Station 10, latitude 80° 02′ N., longitude 3° 19′ E., 2380 meters (Gurjanova, op. cit. p. 293).

Distribution: Known only from type locality. This species was not taken by *Vema*.

Eurycope acutitelson, new species
Figure 36 A–E

Synonyms: None.

Diagnosis: *Eurycope* with apex of frontal area devoid of spines, about one-sixth the width of cepha-lon. Pleon with antero-lateral angles sharp, spine-like, projecting, apex evenly rounded. Inner distal angle of male second pleopod without vermiform appendage. Peraeonal somites 5–6 entirely separated. Uropodal exopod one-half the length of endopod.

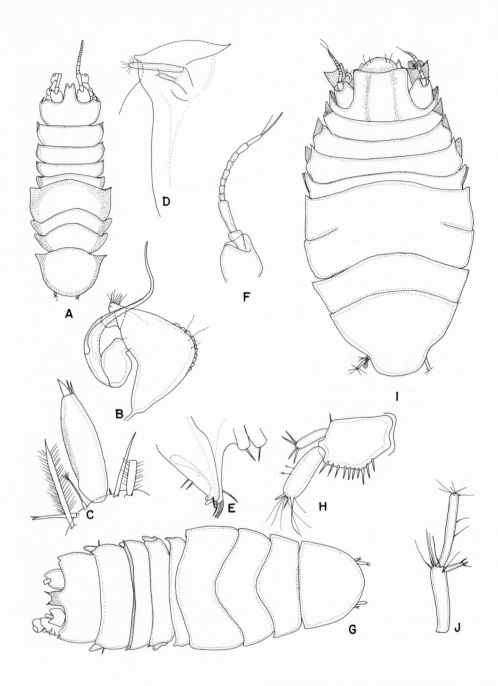

Figure 36. A–E: *Eurycope acutitelson*, n. sp. A: dorsal view male holotype; B second pleopod; C: sixth peraeopod; D: lateral view pleotelson; E: male pleopod. F–H: *Eurycope nodosa*, n. sp. F: first antenna; G: dorsal view female holotype; H: uropod. I–J: *Eurycope ovaloides*, n. sp. I: dorsal view gravid female holotype; J: uropod.

Measurements: Holotype male length 3.4 mm., width pleon 1.0 mm., allotype length 3.2 mm., width pleon 0.9 mm.

Type locality: South Atlantic, L.G.O. Biotrawl No. 52, types plus six male and six female paratypes, cat. no. I-138.

Distribution: Known only from type locality.

Affinities: This species is unique in its sharp pleonal antero-lateral borders.

Eurycope nodosa, new species
Figure 36 F–H

Synonyms: None.

Diagnosis: *Eurycope* with broad frontal apex bearing a stout seta on each side and being around one-seventh the width of cephalon. Pleon shield-shaped, apex evenly rounded, lacking spines or incisions. Peraeonal somites 5–6 completely separated. Uropodal exopod about one-half the length of endopod.

Measurements: Female holotype length 4.6 mm., width pleon 1.4 mm.

Type locality: South Atlantic, L.G.O. Biotrawl No. 53, type and one female paratype, cat. no. I-137.

Distribution: Known only from type locality.

Affinities: This species is allied to *gaussi* Wolff from the Antarctic, from which it differs in having fewer setae on the frontal area.

Eurycope ovaloides, new species
Figure 36 I–J

Synonyms: None.

Diagnosis: *Eurycope* with broad frontal area bearing three spines on each side and being around one-half the width of cephalon. Pleon without spines or projections, apex rounded. Peraeonal somites 5–6 fused on midline. Uropodal exopod about one-third the length of endopod.

Measurements: Gravid female holotype length 4.3 mm., width pleon 1.9 mm.

Type locality: South Atlantic, L.G.O. Biotrawl No. 14, type and one female paratype, cat. no. I-127.

Distribution: Known only from type locality.

Affinities: This species is allied to *ovalis* Vanhöffen, from which it differs in having only three spines on either side of the frontal area and in having the frontal margin of the frontal area nearly straight and not deeply incised.

Eurycope species indeterminable

Fragments of *Eurycope* were common and were taken from L.G.O. Biotrawl No. 1, ten fragments; no. 9, one female fragment; no. 12, three fragments; no. 16, several fragments; no. 49, three fragments; no. 51, two fragments of two species; no. 52, fourteen miscellaneous fragments; no. 53, fifty-two fragments; no. 94, two fragments; no. 101, one fragment; no. 201, four fragments; no. 218, three fragments; no. 231, four fragments; no. 233, one fragment; no. 234, six fragments; no. 237, one female fragment.

Genus: STORTHYNGURA Vanhöffen

Synonyms: *Storthyngura* Vanhöffen, 1914, p. 583; — Hansen, 1916, p. 132; — Wolff, 1956, p. 112.

Diagnosis: Eurycopidae with biramous uropoda. Dorsum of body provided with spines. Pleon laterally with spine-like projections. Front of cephalon well defined. Last three peraeonal somites immovable but usually with indications of separation. Coxal plates visible in dorsal view on peraeonal somites 2–4 inclusive. Pleon separated from peraeon.

Type species: *Storthyngura elegans* Vanhöffen, 1914, p. 584, Fig. 114. Unfortunately, Vanhöffen (op. cit.) did not select a type, and not all of the species cited by him actually belong to the genus.

Composition: Of the 13 species cited by Wolff (1956) one does not belong to *Storthyngura* but belongs instead to *Acanthocope*—viz., *A. atlantica* (Beddard). This error was continued by Birstein (1957). The 18 known species are shown in the accompanying list.

Prior to this monograph only two species, *S. magnispina* (Richardson) and *S. truncata* (Richardson), were known from the abyss of the Atlantic. Six new species from the Atlantic abyss are described herein. The species range in depth from 400 to 7000 meters.

A LIST OF THE DESCRIBED SPECIES OF STORTHYNGURA

Species	Depth Range (Meters)	
	Least	Greatest
1. *elegans* Vanhöffen	3423	3423
2. *pulchra* Hansen	2490	2690
3. *novaezelandiae* (Beddard)	2012	2012
4. *magnispinis* (Richardson)	2258	2702
5. *truncata* (Richardson)	2788	3225
6. *fragilis* (Beddard)	2305	2305
7. *benti* Wolff	5230	7000
8. *furcata* Wolff	5850	6770
9. *caribbea* (Benedict)	1256	1256
10. *herculea* Birstein	6475	8100
11. *tenuispinis tenuispinis* Birstein	7246	7246
12. *tenuispinis kurilica* Birstein	7210	7230
13. *brachycephala* Birstein	5670	5680
14. *chelata* Birstein	5345	6860
15. *bicornis* Birstein	6156	6207
16. *vitjazi* Birstein	7305	8430
17. *robustissima* Monod, Stephensen 1947	400	750
18. *intermedia* (Beddard)	5670	5670

A KEY TO THE SPECIES OF STORTHYNGURA

1. Pleon with pointed apex 2
1. Pleon with truncated, rounded, or indented apex 9

2. Dorsum of cephalon with spines 3
2. Dorsum of cephalon without spines 7
3. Dorsum of pleon with spines 4
3. Dorsum of pleon without spines 5
4. Second peraeonal somite dorsally with a transverse
   row of three spines . . . . *triplispinosa*, n. sp.
4. Dorsum of second peraeonal somite with one
   medial spine 20
5. Cephalon with three dorsal spines 6
5. Cephalon with two dorsal spines . . *bicornis* Birstein'
6. Second peraeonal somite with two spines
   in row at midline . . . . *pulchra* (Hansen)
6. Second peraeonal somite with one
   medial spine . . . . *chelata* Birstein
7. Dorsum of pleon with spine 8
7. Dorsum of pleon without
   spine . . . . *novaezelandiae* (Beddard)
8. Dorsum of 3–4 peraeonal somites each with
   one medial spine . . . . *symmetrica*, n. sp.
8. Dorsum of 3–4 peraeonal somites each
   with two spines in longitudinal
   row . . . . *caribbea* (Benedict)
9. Dorsum of cephalon with spines 10
9. Dorsum of cephalon without spines 11
10. Apex of pleon indented . . . . . . *vemae*, n. sp.
10. Apex of pleon rounded . . . . . . *digitata*, n. sp.
11. Apex of pleon incised medially 12
11. Apex of pleon truncated or rounded, not incised
    medially 14
12. Dorsum of pleon without spines . . *elegans* Vanhöffen
12. Dorsum of pleon with spines 13
13. With one spine . . . . *furcata* Wolff
13. With three spines 21
14. Dorsum of pleon with spines 15
14. Dorsum of pleon without spines 17
15. With three or more spines 16
15. With one or two spines 18
16. With three spines . . . . *tenuispinis kurillica* Birstein
16. With four spines . . . . *tenuispinis tenuispinis* Birstein
17. Lateral spines peraeon longer than wide 22
17. Lateral spines peraeon broader
    than long . . . . *herculea* Birstein
18. With two spines on pleon dorsum 19
18. With one spine on pleon dorsum . . *birsteini*, n. sp.
19. Apex of pleon rounded . . . . *snanoi*, n. sp.
19. Apex of pleon straight . . . . *truncata* (Richardson)
20. Dorsum of pleon with three spines in
    longitudinal row . . . . *robustissima* Monod
20. Dorsum of pleon with two spines in
    longitudinal row . . . . *benti* Wolff
21. Spines at pleonal apex sharp . . *brachycephala* Birstein
21. Spines at pleonal apex
    blunt . . . . *magnispinis* (Richardson)
22. Apex of pleon straight . . . . . . *vitjazi* Birstein
22. Apex of pleon evenly
    rounded . . . . *intermedia* (Beddard)

Storthyngura digitata, new species
Figure 37 A–C

Synonyms: None.

Diagnosis: Storthyngura with spines on dorsum of
cephalon and pleon. Cephalon with four spines, two
on each side of midline. Peraeonal somites 1–4 each
with a transverse row of three spines, somites 5–7 with
transverse row of two spines. Pleon with four spines;

lateral border spinulate, apical border rounded,
spinulate. Uropodal exopod one-half the width of
endopod and two-thirds as long as endopod. Endopod longer than peduncle. Spine of body not tapering,
as wide at distal as proximal end.

Measurements: Female holotype length 5.8 mm.,
width pleotelson 1.2 mm.

Type locality: South Atlantic, L.G.O. Biotrawl
No. 212, type only, cat. no. I-143.

Distribution: Known only from type locality.

Affinities: This species is related to *S. vemae*, but the
blunt nature of the body spines makes it distinctive.

Storthyngura truncata (Richardson)
Figure 37 D

Synonyms: Eurycope truncata Richardson, 1908a,
pp. 67–69, Fig. 1; — Richardson, 1908b, p. 84, Fig.
20, *Storthyngura truncata* (Richardson), Vanhöffen,
1914.

Description: "Body oblong-ovate, a little more than
twice as long as wide. Dorsal surface smooth.

"The head is wider than long, and is produced
anteriorly in a truncate process which extends between
the basal articles of the first pair of antennae. On
either side of the median process there is a slight
double emargination. The eyes are wanting. The
first pair of antennae have the basal article large and
dilated. There is a large and conspicuous spine on the
inner margin. The second and third articles are small
and feeble, and of equal length. The flagellum extends to the end of the fourth article of the peduncle of
the second antennae, and is composed of about
seven articles. The second antennae have the basal
article short and furnished with a long, conspicuous
spine on the outer margin. The second article is about
twice as long as the first, and is furnished on the
anterior margin with one long spine. The third
article is about as long as the second, and has two
spines, one on the outer and one on the inner margin.
The fourth article is short, and is not furnished with
any spines. The last two articles of the peduncle and
the flagellum are missing. The mandibles have a well
developed palp and molar process.

"The first four segments of the thorax are about
equal in length. The antero-lateral angles of the
first segment are drawn out on either side in one long,
sharp epimeral spine. The lateral margins of the
second segment are drawn out on either side in one
long, sharp spine and one small spine just back of it,
both epimeral. The lateral margins of the third and
fourth segments are produced on either side in three
spines, two small spines and one long, sharp median
one, a little curved anteriorly. The last two spines are
epimeral. The last three segments have the lateral
margins produced on either side in one long, sharp
spine directed anteriorly. The fifth and sixth segments

are of nearly equal length in the median dorsal line. The seventh segment is nearly twice as long as either of the preceding segments.

"The abdomen is composed of one segment. Near the base of the segment the lateral margin is produced on either side in one long, sharp spine directed anteriorly. Below these spines the lateral margins are almost straight to about the middle of the segment, where there is an abrupt indentation on either side. This indentation is followed by two long, sharp spines, one on either side, directed posteriorly. Below these two spines the lateral margins slightly converge to a truncate extremity. Just within the two indentations of the lateral margin are indications of two tiny tubercles on the dorsal surface. The uropods are placed on either side of the truncate extremity just below the second lateral spine. They are small and feeble and consist of a basal article and two branches of nearly equal length.

"All the four anterior pairs of legs are missing. The three posterior pairs are similar, natatory, with the merus much enlarged and both the merus and propodus furnished with long, plumose hairs.

"The operculum of the female is furnished with a small spine about the middle." (Richardson, 1908a.)

Measurements: None available.

Type locality: North Atlantic, off Martha's Vineyard, U.S. Bureau Fish. *Albatross*, 1525 fathoms (2788 meters) (Richardson, *op. cit.*).

Distribution: North Atlantic, off Martha's Vineyard, 2788 meters (Richardson, 1908a, p. 69); southeast of Georges Bank (Richardson, 1908a); and *Albatross* Station 2572, off Georges Bank, 3225 meters (Richardson, 1908b, p. 84).

Affinities: This species is most closely related to the Atlantic *S. snanoi* described later, but it differs in having the pleonal apex markedly produced beyond the postero-lateral angles.

Storthyngura magnispinis (Richardson)
Figure 37 E

Synonyms: Eurycope magnispinis Richardson, 1908b, pp. 84–86, Fig. 21; — Hansen, 1916, pp. 132–134, Pl. 12, Figs. 3a–n.

Description: "Body oblong-ovate, about twice as long as wide. Head with the front produced in the middle in a rostrum with the extremity truncate and the sides incurved; on either side of the rostrum the frontal margin has a double excavation; the antero-lateral angles are acute. The eyes are absent. The first pair of antennae have the basal article large and armed with one long spine; the two following articles are subequal in length and are small; the flagellum is lost in the only specimen. The first article of the peduncle of the second antennae is short, and is furnished on the outer margin with a single spine;

the second article is a little longer than the first and is unarmed; the third article is a little longer than the second and is armed with two spines, one on the outer and one on the inner margin; the antennae are broken at the end of the fourth article.

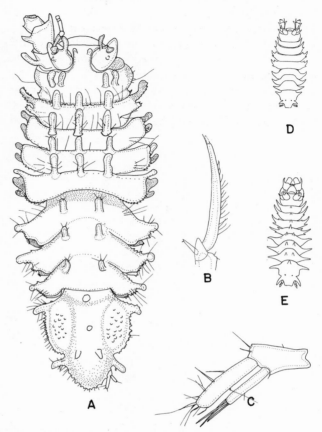

Figure 37. A–C: *Storthyngura digitata*, n. sp. A: dorsal view female holotype; B: sixth peraeopod; C: uropod. D: *Storthyngura truncata* (Richardson), dorsal view. E: *Storthyngura magnispinis* (Richardson), dorsal view.

"The first segment of the thorax has the antero-lateral angles produced in one long spine on either side, directed anteriorly; the second segment has the lateral margin produced in one long anterior spine directed anteriorly and one small posterior one on either side; the third and fourth segments have the lateral margin produced on either side in three spines, two small ones on either side of one long one directed anteriorly; the last three segments have the lateral margins produced on either side in a single long spine, directed anteriorly in the fifth and sixth segments and a little posteriorly in the seventh segment.

"The abdomen has the lateral margin produced on either side at the base in one long spine directed a little posteriorly; below these spines, the lateral margins are nearly parallel to about the middle of the segment, where there is an abrupt incision; below this incision is a single long spine, directed posteriorly;

below these spines the lateral margins of the segment converge slightly to a truncate extremity. The uropoda have the basal article short; the inner branch is about twice as long as the basal article; the outer branch is a little more than half the length of the inner branch.

"The first four segments of the thorax are each armed on the dorsal surface in the median longitudinal line with a single spine on the anterior margin, the spine on the fourth segment being the longest and very prominent; on the three following segments there are two long spines, one on each side of the median longitudinal line on each segment, those on the sixth and seventh segments being nearer the middle transverse line of the segment. The abdomen has one long median spine near the base, and two rudimentary spines or tubercles on the dorsal surface, just opposite the incisions in the lateral margins." (Richardson, 1908b.)

Measurements: None available.

Type locality: Off Nantucket Shoals, U.S. Bureau Fish. *Albatross*, Station 2043, 2680 meters.

Distribution: North Atlantic, off Nantucket Shoals (Richardson, 1908b). *Ingolf* Station 24, 2258 meters. See also Hanson (1916).

Affinities: This species appears to be related to the Pacific species *S. brachycephala* Birstein, from which it differs in having the apical pleonal spines blunt (almost not spines at all) rather than sharp.

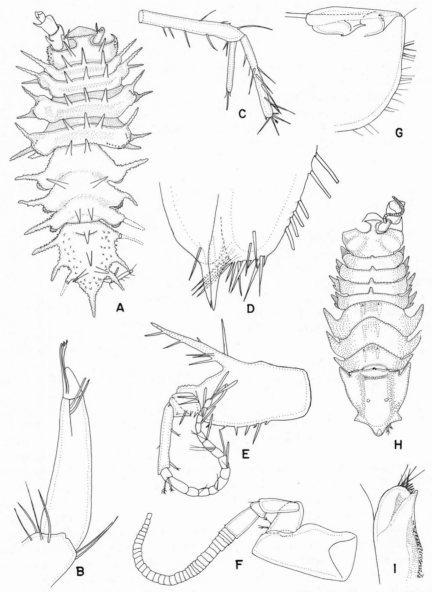

Figure 38. A–E: *Storthyngura triplispinosa*, n. sp. A: dorsal view female holotype; B: first peraeopod; C: uropod; D: apex of male pleopod; E: first antenna. F–I: *Storthyngura symmetrica*, n. sp. F: first antenna; G second male pleopod; H: dorsal view male holotype; I: first male pleopod.

Storthyngura triplispinosa, new species
Figure 38 A–E

Synonyms: None.

Diagnosis: *Storthyngura* with spines on dorsum of cephalon and pleon. Cephalon with two spines, one on either side of midline. Peraeonal somites 1–4 with three spines in transverse row, somites 5–7 each with two spines in transverse row. Pleon with four dorsal spines and six lateral spines, apex pointed, terminating in a long spine. Uropodal exopod as wide as endopod and two-thirds its length, peduncle as long as endopod. Spines of body tapering to a point.

Measurements: Holotype female length 14.5 mm., width pleon 4.0 mm.

Type locality: South Atlantic, L.G.O. Biotrawl No. 51, type only, cat. no. I-149.

Distribution: Also found in L.G.O. Biotrawl No. 14, one female, cat. no. I-240; L.G.O. Biotrawl No. 53, fourteen females, one male, cat. no. I-150; and L.G.O. Biotrawl No. 212, one male, one female, cat. no. I-144.

Affinities: The transverse row of three spines on the dorsum of the second peraeonal somite distinguishes this species from the others.

Storthyngura symmetrica, new species
Figure 38 F–I

Synonyms: None.

Diagnosis: *Storthyngura* without spines on dorsum of cephalon but with spines on dorsum of pleon. Pleonal somites 1–4 each with an antero-medial spine, somites 5–7 each with a pair of spines. Pleon with three spines, lateral border with four spines, apex pointed and recurved under pleon; postero-lateral spines broader than long, antero-lateral spines directed toward cephalon.

Measurements: Holotype male length 6.5 mm., width pleon 2.0 mm., allotype length 18.5 mm., width pleon 5.5 mm.

Type locality: South Atlantic, L.G.O. Biotrawl No. 53, types plus two male and five female paratypes, cat. no. I-146.

Distribution: Known only from type locality.

Affinities: The short wide postero-lateral spines on the pleon distinguish this species from the group of species bearing spines on the body and pleon.

Storthyngura vemae, new species
Figure 39

Synonyms: None.

Diagnosis: *Storthyngura* with spines on dorsum of cephalon and pleon. Dorsum of cephalon with a spine on either side of midline. Dorsum of pleon with

three spines. Peraeonal somites 1–4 each with a single spine antero-medially, somites 5–7 each with a pair of spines medially. Pleon with four lateral blunt spines, apex bilobed and spinulate at margin. Uropodal endopod widest at distal end and longer than peduncle. Lateral projections of body blunt.

Measurements: Male holotype length 3.5 mm., width pleon 0.8 mm.

Type locality: North Atlantic, L.G.O. Biotrawl No. 9, type plus one fragmentary paratype, cat. no. I-148.

Distribution: Known only from type locality.

Affinities: This species resembles *S. digitata*, but has pointed rather than blunt spines and the apex of the pleon is convex rather than rounded.

Storthyngura birsteini, new species
Figure 40 A–B

Synonyms: None.

Diagnosis: *Storthyngura* with spines on dorsum of peraeon and pleon, none on cephalon. Peraeonal somites 2–4 each with a single dorsal spine at midline of anterior margin; somites 5–7 each with a pair of dorsal spines at midline. Pleon with a single spine on mid-dorsal line of anterior part. Apex of pleon broadly rounded, not produced beyond the sharp postero-lateral angles. Uropodal exopod and endopod about equal in width, exopod one-third shorter than endopod, which is equal to peduncle in length.

Measurements: Female holotype length 21.5 mm., width pleon 7.8 mm., and one juvenile female paratype and three fragments.

Type locality: South Atlantic, L.G.O. Biotrawl No. 202, types only, cat. no I-230.

Distribution: Known only from type locality.

Affinities: The absence of spines from the dorsum of the cephalon and the rounded pleonal apex ally this species to *S. truncata* Richardson, from which it differs significantly in the presence of dorsal spines on the body and of one dorsal spine not two, on the pleon.

Storthyngura snanoi, new species
Figure 40 C–E

Synonyms: None.

Diagnosis: *Storthyngura* without spines on dorsum of cephalon and with a pair of spines on dorsum of pleon. Peraeonal somites 1–4 each with an antero-medial spine, somite 5 with a pair of spines, somites 6–7 without spines. Pleon with four lateral projections, apex evenly rounded, not extending beyond uropods. Uropodal endopod widest at distal end; it is twice the length of exopod and is longer than peduncle.

Measurements: Female holotype length 3.2 mm., width pleon 0.6 mm.

Type locality: North Atlantic, Caribbean, L.G.O. Biotrawl No. 95, type only, cat. no. I-145.

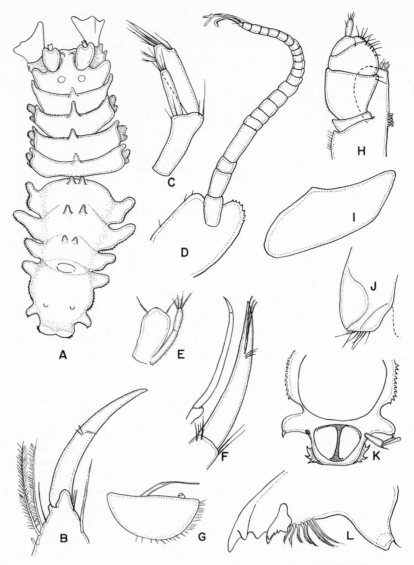

Figure 39. *Storthyngura vemae*, n. sp. A: dorsal view male holotype; B: sixth peraeopod; C: uropod; D: first antenna; E: third pleopod; F: first peraeopod; G: second pleopod; H: maxilliped; I: maxillipedal epipod; J: first pleopod; K: ventral view anus and uropod; L: mandible.

Distribution: Known only from type locality.

Affinities: This species is close to *S. truncata* Richardson, from which it differs in having the pleonal apex rounded, not straight.

Storthyngura species indeterminable

Fragments of *Storthyngura* were taken from L.G.O. Biotrawl No. 47, one female fragment, and L.G.O. Biotrawl No. 214 one juvenile related to *S. symmetrica*.

Genus: SYNEURYCOPE Hansen

Synonyms: Syneurycope Hansen, 1916, pp. 130–131; — Menzies, 1956a, pp. 5–6; *Ilychthonos* Barnard, 1920, pp. 414–415.

Diagnosis: Eurycopidae with pleon consisting of (one? or) two somites. Last three peraeonal somites fused into a solid piece. Uropoda biramous. Coxal plates visible in dorsal view on peraeonal somites 2–4 inclusive. Third article of maxillipedal palp with characteristic denticles along inner margin. Lateral border of pleon without spine-like extensions. (Modified from Menzies, 1956a, p. 5, with corrections.)

Type species: Syneurycope parallela Hansen, 1916, pp. 131–132.

Composition: The species belonging to this genus are all markedly attenuate. Three described species are known from bathyal to abyssal depths.

parallela Hansen	3474 meters
hanseni Menzies	5104–5122 meters
capensis Barnard	1280 meters

Here two additional new abyssal species are described from the South Atlantic abyss.

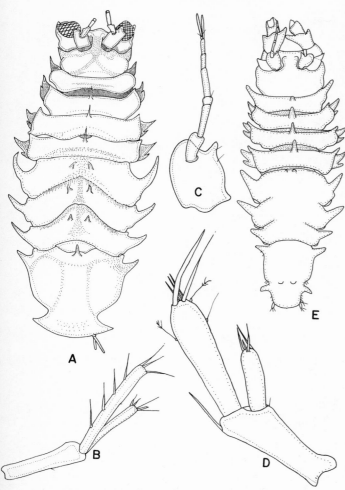

Figure 40. A–B: *Storthyngura birsteini*, n. sp. A: dorsal view female holotype; B: uropod. C–E: *Storthyngura snanoi*, n. sp. C: first antenna; D: uropod; E: dorsal view female holotype.

A KEY TO THE SPECIES OF SYNEURYCOPE
(Modified from Menzies, 1956a, p. 6)

1. Dorsum of cephalon with spines . . . *multispina*, n. sp.
1. Dorsum of cephalon without spines 2
2. Mandibular palp small, unarmed 4
2. Mandibular palp well developed with 3–4 setae on apical article 3
3. Maxilliped with coupling hooks . . *parallela* Hansen
3. Maxilliped without coupling hooks . . . . *hanseni* Menzies
4. First peraeonal somite fused with cephalon . . . . *heezeni*, n. sp.
4. First peraeonal somite separated from cephalon . . . . *capensis* (Barnard)

Syneurycope heezeni, new species
Figure 41 A–E

Synonyms: None.
Diagnosis: *Syneurycope* with cephalon and first peraeonal somite fused. Dorsum of cephalon smooth, frontal margin between first antennae concave. Maxilliped without coupling hooks. Mandibular palp without setae on apical article. Fifth peraeopods with paddle-shaped terminal articles. Exopod of uropod one-fourth as long as endopod. First pleonal somite completely separated from pleon.

Measurements: Holotype female length 4.5 mm., width pleon 0.7 mm.

Type locality: South Atlantic, L.G.O. Biotrawl No. 200, types and one female paratype, cat. no. I-227.

Distribution: Found also at L.G.O. Biotrawl No. 201, two females, two fragments, cat. no. I-229, and L.G.O. Biotrawl No. 220, one female, cat. no. I-228.

Affinities: This species is unique in having the cephalon fused with the first peraeonal somite.

Syneurycope parallela Hansen
Figure 41 F

Synonyms: *Syneurycope parallela* Hansen, 1916, pp. 131–132, Pl. 12.

Diagnosis: *Syneurycope* without spines on dorsum of head. First pleonal somite clearly separated from pleotelson. Maxilliped with three coupling hooks. Uropodal exopod one-fifth the length of endopod.

Measurements: Length female 3.7 mm. (Hansen, op. cit. p. 131).

Type locality: North Atlantic, southwest of Cape Farewell, *Ingolf* Station 22, latitude 58° 10′ N., longitude 48° 25′ W., 3474 meters, temperature 1.4° C., one specimen (Hansen, op. cit.).

Distribution: Known only from type locality.

Affinities: Related to *S. hanseni* Menzies but with coupling hooks on the maxilliped.

Syneurycope hanseni Menzies
Figure 42 A–D

Synonyms: *Syneurycope hanseni* Menzies, 1956a, pp. 6–7, Fig. 2.

Diagnosis: *Syneurycope* without spines on dorsum of cephalon. First pleonal somite incompletely separated from pleon. Maxilliped without coupling hooks. Uropodal exopod one-third the length of endopod. Mandibular palp well developed, terminal article setiferous. Outer lobe at apex of male first pleopod longer than inner lobe.

Measurements: Male length 3.75 mm., width second peraeonal somite 0.65 mm.

Type locality: North Atlantic, L.G.O. Biotrawl No. 1, type only, cat. no. 11758 A.M.N.H.

Distribution: Known only from type locality.

Affinities: This species is related to *S. parallela* Hansen, from which it differs in lacking coupling hooks.

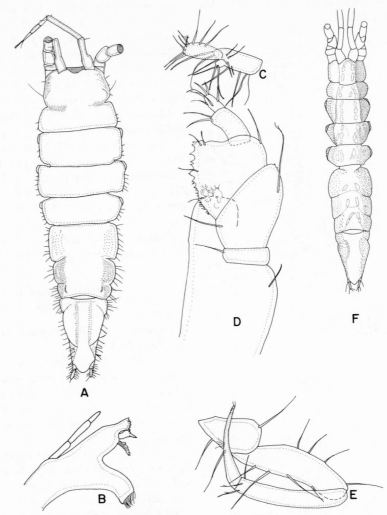

Figure 41. A–E: *Syneurycope heezeni*, n. sp. A: dorsal view female holotype; B: mandible; C: uropod; D: maxilliped; E: gnathopod. F: *Syneurycope parallela* Hansen, dorsal view male.

Syneurycope multispina, new species

Figure 42 E–K

Synonyms: None.

Diagnosis: *Syneurycope* with a row of four to six spines in longitudinal row on either side of midline of dorsum of cephalon. First pleonal somite completely separated from pleotelson. Maxilliped without coupling hooks. Mandibular palp well developed, apical article setiferous. Outer lobe at apex of male first pleopod shorter than inner lobe.

Measurements: Holotype male length 4.3 mm., width pleon 0.6 mm., female allotype length 4.2 mm., width pleon 0.6 mm.

Type locality: South Atlantic, L.G.O. Biotrawl No. 52, types plus one female paratype.

Distribution: Known only from type locality.

Affinities: This species is unique in having spines on the dorsum of the cephalon.

Genus: ACANTHOCOPE Beddard

Synonyms: *Acanthocope* Beddard, 1885, p. 922; — Beddard, 1886, pp. 78–79; — Menzies, 1956a, p. 2.

Diagnosis: Eurycopidae with uniramous uropoda. Dorsum of body spinous. Pleon with lateral spine-like projections. Front of cephalon well defined. Last three peraeonal somites immovable. Pleon with a single somite. Coxal plates not visible in dorsal view on peraeonal somites 2–4 inclusive. Pleon completely fused with peraeon.

Type species: *Acanthocope spinicauda* Beddard.

Composition: Four species are known from *Acanthocope*. These are as follows:

Species	Depth Range (Meters)	
	Least	*Greatest*
1. *spinicauda* Beddard	3290	3290
2. *acutispina* Beddard	2650	2650
3. *atlantica* (Beddard)	1646	1646
4. *spinosissima* Menzies	1169	1169

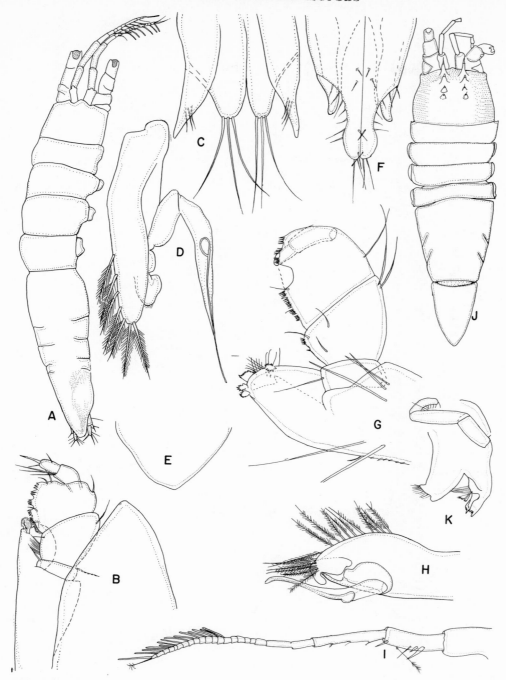

Figure 42. A–D: *Syneurycope hanseni* Menzies. A: dorsal view male; B: maxilliped; C: first pleopod; D: second pleopod. E–K: *Syneurycope multispina*, n. sp. E: apex of pleotelson; F: apex of first male pleopod; G: maxilliped; H: second pleopod; I: first antenna; J: dorsal view male holotype; K: mandible.

The genus ranges from 1169 meters to 3290 meters. Only two species were known previously from the Atlantic; none was abyssal. Here three additional new species are described.

A KEY TO THE SPECIES OF ACANTHOCOPE

1. Body with dorsal spines 2
1. Body without dorsal spines . . . . *acutispina* Beddard

2. Pleon with dorsal spine(s) 3
2. Pleon without dorsal spine(s) 4
3. Pleon with one dorsal spine . . . *spinicauda* Beddard
3. Pleon with two dorsal spines . . . *atlantica* (Beddard)
4. First three peraeonal somites dorsally each with a median spine 5
4. First three peraeonal somites dorsally without spines 6
5. Flagellum of first antenna with over 20 articles. Frons of cephalon convex . . . . *annulatus*, n. sp.

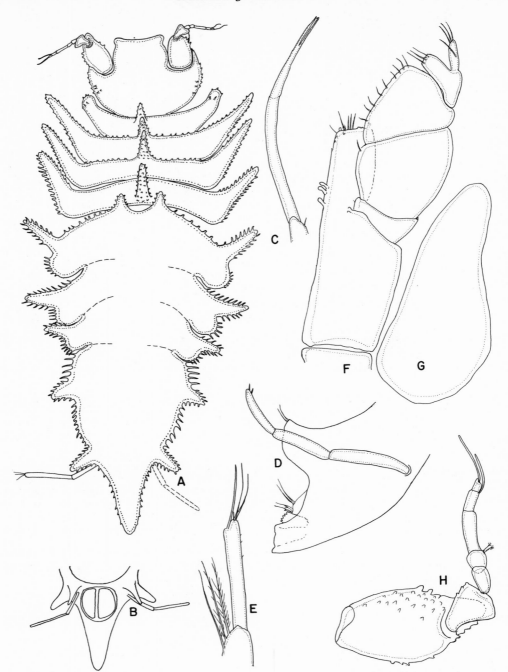

Figure 43. *Acanthocope argentinae*, n. sp. A: dorsal view female holotype; B: anus and uropods; C: second peraeopod; D: mandible; E: seventh peraeopod; F: maxilliped; G: maxillipedal epipod; H: first antenna.

5. Flagellum of first antenna with six
   articles. Frons of cephalon concave on
   margin . . . . *argentinae*, n. sp.
6. Fourth peraeonal somite dorsally with long
   medial spine . . . . *unicornis*, n. sp.
6. Fourth peraeonal somite dorsally
   without spine . . . . *spinosissima* Menzies

Acanthocope argentinae, new species
Figure 43

Synonyms: None.

Diagnosis: Cephalon and pleon lacking dorsal spines. Single short medial spine on dorsum peraeonal somites 1–4 inclusive, fifth with a pair of spines. Flagellum of first antenna with five articles only.

Measurements: Female holotype length 3.6 mm., width pleotelson 1.5 mm.

Type locality: South Atlantic, L.G.O. Biotrawl No. 12, type only, cat. no. I-155.

Distribution: Known only from type locality.

Affinities: This species is closest to *A. annulatus*,

from which it differs in having the frons of the cephalon concave.

Acanthocope unicornis, new species
Figure 44 A

Synonyms: None.

Diagnosis: *Acanthocope* without spines on dorsum of cephalon or pleon. Only fourth peraeonal somite with dorsal spine at midline extending as far as the frons of cephalon. Flagellum of first antenna with four articles only.

Measurements: Female holotype length 5.4 mm., width pleotelson 1.8 mm.

Type locality: South Atlantic, L.G.O. Biotrawl No. 18, type only, cat. no. I-152.

Distribution: Known only from type locality.

Affinities: Related to *A. spinosissima*, from which it differs in having a long spine on the fourth peraeonal somite.

Acanthocope annulatus, new species
Figure 44 B–C

Synonyms: None.

Diagnosis: *Acanthocope* lacking spines from dorsum of cephalon and pleon. First four peraeonal somites each with a short medial spine dorsally, fifth with a pair of spines dorsally at midline. Flagellum of first antenna with over 20 articles. Lateral border of cephalon sharply spinulate.

Measurements: Female holotype length 3.2 mm., width pleotelson 1.0 mm.

Type locality: South Atlantic, L.G.O. Biotrawl No. 53, type only, cat. no. I-156.

Distribution: Known only from type locality.

Affinities: Closest to *A. argentinae*, from which it differs in having the frons of the cephalon convex.

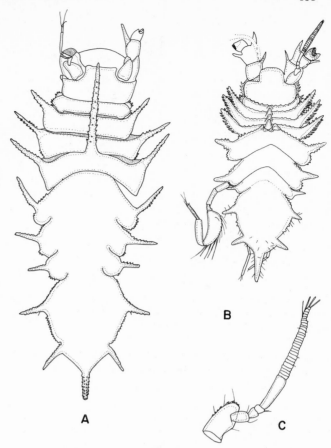

Figure 44. A: *Acanthocope unicornis*, n. sp., dorsal view female holotype. B–C: *Acanthocope annulatus*, n. sp. B: dorsal view female holotype; C: first antenna.

Acanthocope species indeterminable

Fragments of *Acanthocope* were collected from L.G.O. Biotrawl No. 18, two females; No. 94, two females; and No. 96, one female.

Family: ILYARACHNIDAE

Type genus: *Ilyarachna* G. O. Sars.

Synonyms: *Mesostenus* G. O. Sars, 1864, p. 211. *Ilyarachna* G. O. Sars, 1869, p. 44; — 1899, p. 134; — Hansen, 1916, p. 121; — Hult, 1936, p. 12, — Wolff, 1956, p. 106. *Aspidarachna* G. O. Sars, 1899, p. 140; — Hansen, 1916, p. 121; — Hult, 1936, p. 12. *Echinozone* G. O. Sars, 1899, p. 139; — Hansen, 1916, p. 128; — Hult, 1936, p. 12. (incomplete list).

Diagnosis: Paraselloidea with only peraeopods 5–6 inclusive paddle-like. Peraeopods 7 walking legs. Pleon with one or two somites. Cephalon with first antennae not separated by a pronounced frontal area. Mandible with reduced setiferous molar; incisor reduced to a simple lobe. Uropoda with flattened peduncle bearing plumose setae. Uropoda uni-biramous.

Composition: The family contains two presently recognized genera, *Ilyarachna* G. O. Sars and *Pseudarachna* G. O. Sars.

In *Pseudarachna* the mandible lacks a palp and the uropoda are uniramous and only the fifth pair of peraeopods is paddle-like (Vanhöffen, 1914, p. 593); no abyssal species are known. In *Ilyarachna* a mandibular palp is present, the uropoda are uni-biramous, and the 5–6 pair of peraeopods are paddle-like; there are several abyssal species.

Because so many species of *Ilyarachna* are imperfectly known, it is impossible at present to draw up a key

LIST OF ILYARACHNA SPECIES

	Depth Range (Meters)	
Species	Least	Greatest
1. *abyssorum* Richardson	4060	4165
2. *affinis* Barnard	1280	1280
3. *crassiceps* Barnard	1280	1280
4. *antarctica* Vanhöffen	252	3423
5. *aries* (Vanhöffen)	385	385
6. *magnifica* (Vanhöffen)	350	385
7. *arctica* (Hansen)	103	103
8. *bicornis* Hansen	2702	2702
9. *dubia* Hansen	1666	1902
10. *spinosissima* Hansen	2702	3521
11. *bergendali* Ohlin	21	698
12. *longicornis* G. O. Sars, Hult	18	2788
13. *clypeata* G. O. Sars	216	450
14. *coronata* G. O. Sars	188	1505
15. *quadrispinosa* Beddard	22	360
16. *starokadmoskii* Gurjanova	130	780
17. *zachsi* Gurjanova	105	780
18. *fusiformis* (Barnard)	1280	1280
19. *derjugini* Gurjanova	2500	2500
20. *acarina* Menzies and Barnard	73	1118

to the species. Nevertheless, it may be useful to provide the following groupings of species on the basis of uropodal structure.

A. Uropoda uniramous	B. Uropoda biramous	C. Structure of uropoda unknown
1. *longicornis*	1. *coronata*	1. *crassiceps*
2. *denticulata*	2. *clypeata*	2. *affinis*
3. *spinosissima*	3. *arctica*	3. *bergendali*
4. *antarctica*	4. *magnifica*	4. *starokadmoskii*
5. *bicornis*	5. *aries*	5. *derjugini*
6. *dubia*	6. *quadrispinosa*	
7. *zachsi*	7. *abyssorum*	

Only five of the species were known from abyssal depths of the Atlantic and Arctic:

1. *abyssorum*
2. *bicornis*
3. *spinosissima*
4. *longicornis* (auct. *hirticeps?*)
5. *derjugini*

Genus: ILYARACHNA G. O. Sars

Ilyarachna abyssorum Richardson, 1911
Figure: None available

Synonyms: None.

Diagnosis: *Ilyarachna* with "corps oblong-ovale environ trois fois plus long que large, 4 millim. 5 × 13 millimètres.

"Tête trois fois plus large que longue, 1 millimètre × 3 millimètres; ses angles antérieurs latéraux sont arrondis et ne forment pas saillie; les parties latérales de la tête ne sont pas dilatées. Yeux absents. Les antennes de la première paire ont l'article basal large et dilaté, avec le bord externe latéral recourbé en

dehors et l'angle externe antéro-latéral saillant au delà de l'angle interne; les second et troisième articles sont petits et étroits, le deuxième étant un peu plus court que le troisième; le flagellum se compose de onze articles. Les antennes de la deuxième paire sont cassées au bout du quatrième article. Les mandibules n'ont pas de palpe.

"Les quatre premiers segments du thorax sont courts et subégaux comme longueur, chacun d'eux ayant environ 1 millimètre; les trois segments qui suivent sont plus larges et croissent graduellement en longueur; le cinquième a 1 millim. 5 de long, le sixième 1 millim. 7⁵ et le septième 2 millimètres. Les épimères sont présents sur les quatre premiers segments; ils s'étendent sur l'entière longueur du bord latéral dans les trois premiers; leurs extrémités antérieures sont très aiguës et forment des processus qui dèpassent le bord antérieur des segments; ils semblent partagés en deux parts dont l'une est antérieure et l'autre postérieure. Les épimères du quatrième segment occupent les deux tiers postérieurs du bord latéral; ils sont aigus à leurs extrémités antérieures.

"L'abdomen se compose de deux segments, l'un antérieur court, l'autre terminal large, de forme triangulaire, avec l'apex arrondi. L'abdomen mesure 3 millimètres de long et 3 millimètres de large à la base. Les uropodes consistent en un article basilaire et en deux branches placées près du bord externe latéral du pédoncule; ces dernières sont situées à quelque distance de l'extrémité; la branche interne est postérieure à la branche externe et plus grande quoique ne dépassant pas l'extrémité du pédoncule; la branche externe est menue." (Richardson, 1911, pp. 533–4).

Three specimens collected by *Talisman*, 25 August 1883, Station 135, 4165 meters; two fragments, 24 August 1883, Station 134, 4060 meters, Azores. Not collected by *Vema*.

Ilyarachna bicornis Hansen
Figure 45 A

Synonyms: *Ilyarachna bicornis* Hansen, 1916, p. 125, Pl. 11.

Diagnosis: *Ilyarachna* with uniramous uropoda. Cephalon with a pair of dorsal spines. Proximal margins of peraeonal somites 1–4 inclusive spinulate. Pleon with two somites. (From Hansen, op. cit.)

Measurements: Largest specimen 8.7 mm. (Hansen, op. cit.).

Type locality: North Atlantic, Davis Strait, *Ingolf* Station 36, latitude 61° 50′ N., longitude 56° 21′ W., 2702 meters, temperature 1.5° C., two specimens.

Distribution: Known only from type locality.

Affinities: Hansen (op. cit.) indicated that this species was close to *I. hirticeps* but differed in head spines.

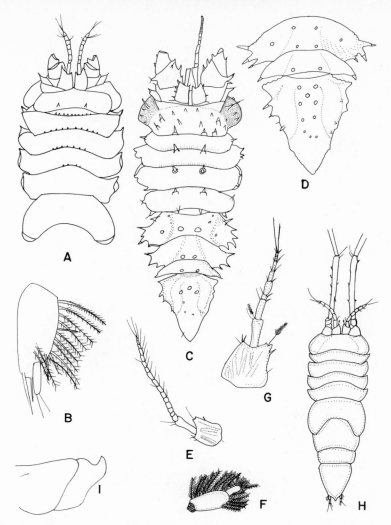

Figure 45. A: *Ilyarachna bicornis* Hansen, dorsal view female anterior. B–D: *Ilyarachna spinosissima* Hansen. B: female uropod; C: dorsal view male; D: dorsal view posterior. E–H: *Ilyarachna longicornis* G. O. Sars. E: male first antenna; F: uropod; G: female first antenna; H: dorsal view female. I: *Ilyarachna derjugini* Gurjanova, second peraeonal somite lateral margin (after Gurjanova, 1946a).

Ilyarachna spinosissima Hansen
Figure 45 B–D

Synonyms: *Ilyarachna spinosissima* Hansen, 1916, pp. 127–128, Pls. 11, 12.

Diagnosis: *Ilyarachna* with uniramous uropods. Cephalon with about 14 spines dorsally. Peraeonal somites 1–4 inclusive with denticles on distal margin, dorsum with a pair of stout spines on somites 1–3 inclusive, with four spines on fourth somite. Lateral borders of somites 5–7 with stout spines; pleon with lateral and dorsal spines; pleon with two somites.

Type locality: North Atlantic, Davis Strait, *Ingolf* Station 36, latitude 61° 50′ N., longitude 56° 21′ W., 2702 meters, temperature 1.5° C., one male, one female (Hansen, op. cit.).

Distribution: Taken also from *Ingolf* Station 38, south of Davis Strait, latitude 59° 12′ N., longitude 51° 05′ W., 3521 meters, temperature 1.3° C.

Affinities: This species is close to *I. multispinosa*, from which it differs in having fewer spines on the pleon and at the lateral peraeonal margins.

Ilyarachna longicornis G. O. Sars
Figure 45 E–H

Synonyms: *Ilyarachna longicornis* G. O. Sars, 1864, p. 212; — 1897, p. 136, Pl. LIX; — Hult, 1941, pp. 97–100 and references. *Ilyarachna hirticeps* G. O. Sars; — Hult, 1941, p. 97 and references.

Diagnosis: *Ilyarachna* with uniramous uropods. Cephalon and peraeon smooth, without dorsal spines. Mandibular palp triarticulate. First antenna with nine articles in female and 13 articles in male. Apex of pleon pointed. Frontal margin of cephalon almost straight, width of basal article of first antenna equal to one-seventh the width of cephalon. Pleon with one somite.

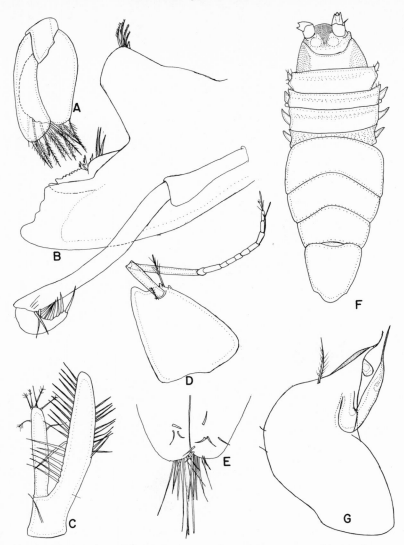

Figure 46. *Ilyarachna nodifronoides*, n. sp. A: third pleopod; B: mandible female allotype;
C: uropod female allotype; D: first antenna; E: first pleopod; F: dorsal view male holotype;
G: second male pleopod.

Measurements: Adult female length about 3 mm. (Sars, 1897).

Type locality: Skager Rak, Norway (?).

Distribution: Subarctic and Arctic seas, and North Atlantic, panarctic boreal, eurybathic (Hult, op. cit., p. 100). It was taken by the *Ingolf* from 14 stations (Hansen, 1916, p. 124) and by the *Thor* from four stations (Hansen, op. cit.). One *Ingolf* station was abyssal: Station 113, latitude 69° 31′ N., longitude 7° 06′ W., 2465 meters, temperature −1.0° C., one specimen. The species was not captured by the *Vema*.

Ilyarachna derjugini Gurjanova
Figure 45 I

Synonyms: *Ilyarachna derjugini* Gurjanova, 1946a, pp. 275–276, 294, Fig. 6.

Diagnosis: *Ilyarachna* with uropodal structure unknown. Cephalon and peraeon devoid of dorsal

spines. Apex of pleon pointed. Coxal plates of second peraeonal somite strongly recurved and pointed. Pleon with one somite (otherwise as in *hirticeps*). (After Gurjanova, op. cit.)

Measurements: Length 4 mm.

Type locality: Arctic Ocean, *Sedov* Station 100, 1938, latitude 81° 10′ N., longitude 137° 17′ E., 2500 meters (Gurjanova, op. cit. p. 293).

Distribution: Known only from type locality.

Affinities: Closely related to and possibly identical with *I. longicornis* G. O. Sars, as judged from Gurjanova's illustration and the statements by Hult, 1941, p. 97.

Ilyarachna nodifronoides, new species
Figure 46

Synonyms: None.

Diagnosis: *Ilyarachna* with two pleonal somites. Cephalon and peraeon without dorsal spines. Uropod

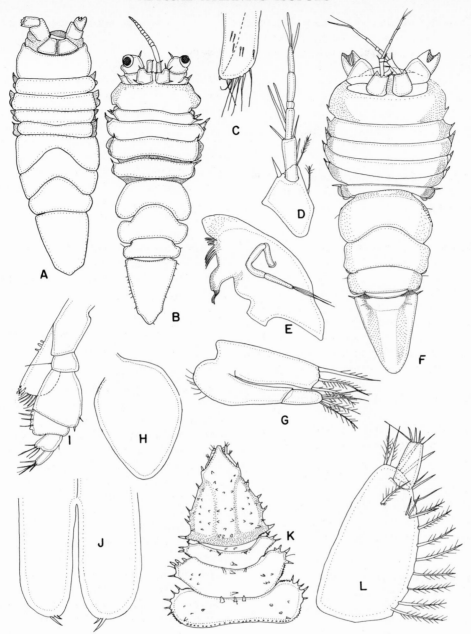

Figure 47. A: *Ilyarachna africana*, n. sp., dorsal view female holotype. B–C: *Ilyarachna spinoafricana*, n. sp. B: dorsal view male holotype; C: first male pleopod. D–I: *Ilyarachna simplex*, n. sp. D: first antenna; E: mandible; F: dorsal view female holotype; G: third pleopod; H: maxillipedal epipod; I: maxilliped. J–L: *Ilyarachna multispinosa*, n. sp. J: male first pleopod; K: dorsal view holotype male fragment; L: uropod.

with single ramus, peduncle produced into a process extending beyond the length of the uropodal ramus. Width of basal article of first antenna about one-fifth the width of cephalon. Apex of pleon evenly rounded.

Measurements: Male holotype length 4.5 mm., width pleon 0.8 mm., allotype female length 7.0 mm., width pleon 1.4 mm.

Type locality: South Atlantic, L.G.O. Biotrawl No. 52, types and 13 female, four male paratypes, cat. no. I-52.

Distribution: Known only from type locality.

Affinities: In general shape this species is similar to *Eurycope nodifrons* Hansen, from which it differs in lacking the incisions at the apex of the male first pleopods. The uropoda are *Ilyarachna* type, not *Eurycope*.

Ilyarachna africana, new species
Figure 47 A

Synonyms: None.

Diagnosis: *Ilyarachna* with one pleonal somite. Cephalon, peraeon, and pleon without spines dorsal or lateral. Uropoda missing. Pleon shield-shaped, apex triangulate. First article of first antenna one-third to one-fourth the width of cephalon. Coxal plate of second somite not curved like a hook.

Measurements: Female holotype length 3.6 mm., width pleon 0.7 mm.

Type locality: South Atlantic, L.G.O. Biotrawl No. 14, type and one female paratype, cat. no. I-159.

Distribution: Known only from type locality.

Affinities: This species belongs to the smooth body group of *Ilyarachna*. Its wide triangulate basal article of the first antenna is distinctive.

Ilyarachna spinoafricana, new species
Figure 47 B–C

Synonyms: None.

Diagnosis: *Ilyarachna* with two pleonal somites. Cephalon, peraeon, and pleon without dorsal spines. First peraeonal somite laterally with a pair of stout spines. Epimera of second somite not curved and hook-like but bearing a stout seta. Pleon shield-like, apex triangulate. First article of first antenna one-fifth the width of cephalon. Uropodal structure not known.

Measurements: Male holotype length 2.7 mm., width pleon 0.5 mm., allotype length 3.5 mm., width pleon 0.7 mm.

Type locality: South Atlantic, L.G.O. Biotrawl No. 55, types only, cat. no. I-169.

Distribution: Known only from type locality.

Affinities: Related to *africana* but having stout coxal plate spines lacking from *africana*.

Ilyarachna simplex, new species
Figure 47 D–I

Synonyms: None.

Diagnosis: *Ilyarachna* with pleon of two somites. Dorsum of cephalon, peraeon, and pleon without spines. Antero-lateral angles of pleon with a stout spine, apex of pleon narrowly rounded. Structure of uropod not known. Width of basal article of first antenna about one-fifth the width of cephalon. Cephalon with a spine on each lateral margin. Coxal plates of second peraeonal somite not curved and hook-like.

Measurements: Female holotype length 2.9 mm., width pleon 0.6 mm.

Type locality: South Atlantic, L.G.O. Biotrawl No. 53, type only, cat. no. I-53.

Distribution: Known only from type locality.

Affinities: Related to *africana* and *spinoafricana* but with stout seta at antero-lateral angle of pleon.

Ilyarachna multispinosa, new species
Figure 47 J–L

Synonyms: None.

Diagnosis: *Ilyarachna* with two pleonal somites. Peraeon and pleon with dorsal spines. Each lateral border of pleon with five stout two-pointed setae, apex pointed, triangulate, and spinulate. Uropod with a single ramus only, extending beyond apex of peduncle. Seventh peraeonal somite with three to four spines at lateral border and only five on dorsum.

Measurements: Holotype male fragment length 2.4 mm., width pleon 0.9 mm.

Type locality: South Atlantic, L.G.O. Biotrawl No. 52, type only, cat. no. I-164.

Distribution: Known only from type locality.

Affinities: This species is related to *I. argentinae* and *I. spinosissima*, from which it differs in the arrangement of the spines on the pleon and peraeon.

Ilyarachna argentinae, new species
Figure 48 A–D

Synonyms: None.

Diagnosis: *Ilyarachna* with pleon of two somites. Peraeon and pleon with many stout two-pointed setae or spines on dorsum and at lateral borders. Each lateral border of pleon with five stout two-pointed setae, apex pointed, triangulate, and spinulate. Uropod with single ramus only extending beyond apex of peduncle. Seventh peraeonal somite with three spines at lateral border and eight on dorsum.

Measurements: Intersex fragment length not known width pleon 0.6 mm.

Type locality: South Atlantic, L.G.O. Biotrawl No. 12, type only, cat. no. I-92.

Distribution: Known only from type locality.

Affinities: This species is close to *I. multispinosa*, from which it differs in having more spines on pleon and at lateral borders of the peraeonal somites.

Ilyarachna gurjanovae, new species
Figure 48 E

Synonyms: None.

Diagnosis: *Ilyarachna* with two pleonal somites. Cephalon, peraeon, and pleon with dorsal spines. Uropod with one branch. Each lateral border of pleon with seven stout setae. Dorsum of seventh peraeonal somite with six stout setae, lateral borders with two stout setae. Apex of pleon triangulate, smooth.

Measurements: Female allotype length 3.2 mm., width pleon 0.7 mm.

Type locality: South Atlantic, L.G.O. Biotrawl No. 53, type and one female paratype, cat. no. I-163.

Distribution: Known only from type locality.

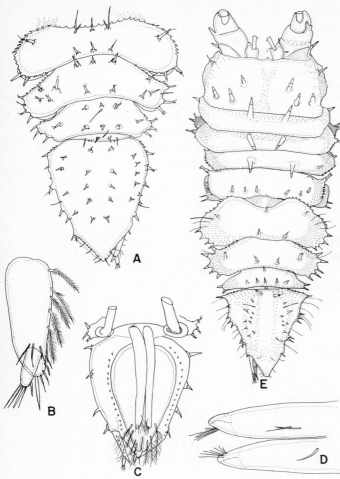

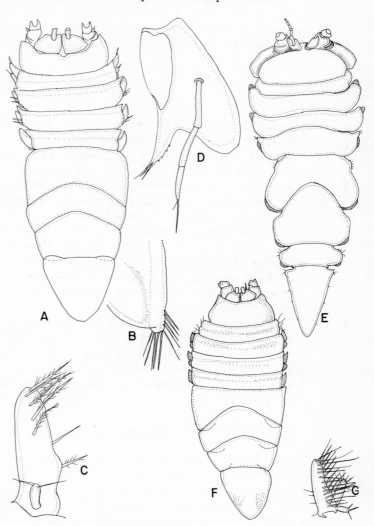

Affinities: This species is a smooth body form, distinguished from the others by its uniramous uropods, by the lack of spines at the antero-lateral border of the pleon, and by the very broad first article of the first antenna.

Ilyarachna triangulata, new species
Figure 49 D–E

Synonyms: None.

Diagnosis: *Ilyarachna* with one pleonal somite. Cephalon, peraeon, and pleon without dorsal spines. Coxal plates at peraeonal somite 2 not recurved and hook-like. Pleon shield-like with acute antero-lateral angles bearing several fine setae. Apex of pleon pointed. Basal article of first antenna about one-fifteenth the width of cephalon. Uropods lost.

Figure 48. A–D: *Ilyarachna argentinae*, n. sp. A: intersex fragment; B: uropod; C: ventral view of pleon; D: first male pleopod. E: *Ilyarachna gurjanovae*, n. sp., dorsal view female allotype.

Affinities: This species is related to *I. argentinae* and *I. multispinosa*, from which it differs in the spines on the dorsum of the pleon and the last peraeonal somite.

Ilyarachna indentifrons, new species
Figure 49 A–C

Synonyms: None.

Diagnosis: *Ilyarachna* with one pleonal somite. Cephalon, peraeon, and pleon devoid of dorsal spines. Uropod with a minute ramus which does not extend to end of peduncle. First article of first antenna one-fourth the width of cephalon. Antero-lateral angles of pleon evenly rounded, apex evenly rounded.

Measurements: Holotype female length 4.4 mm., width pleon 1.0 mm.

Type locality: South atlantic, L.G.O. Biotrawl No. 53, type and 20 fragment paratypes.

Distribution: Known only from type locality.

Figure 49. A–C: *Ilyarachna indentifrons*, n. sp. A: dorsal view female holotype; B: first male pleopod; C: uropod. D–E: *Ilyarachna triangulata*, n. sp. D: mandible; E: dorsal view female holotype. F–G: *Ilyarachna scotia*, n. sp. F: dorsal view female holotype; G: uropod.

Measurements: Holotype female length 4.4 mm., width pleon 0.7 mm.

Type locality: South Atlantic, L.G.O. Biotrawl No. 14, type and one fragment, cat. no. I-160.

Distribution: Known only from type locality.

Affinities: This species is somewhat similar to *africana*, but has more acute antero-lateral angles to the pleon and proportionally much narrower basal articles to the first antenna; in these respects it also differs from *simplex*. The mandible shows reduction of structure.

Ilyarachna scotia, new species
Figure 49 F–G

Synonyms: None.

Diagnosis: Ilyarachna with one pleonal somite. Uropoda biramous, exopod one-third the length of endopod and both much shorter than the peduncle. Cephalon, peraeon, and pleon devoid of dorsal spines or setae. Coxal plates of second peraeonal somite not hook-like and recurved. Pleon shield-shaped without sharp angles, apex rounded. Basal article of first antenna about one-fifth the width of cephalon.

Measurements: Holotype female length 3.2 mm., width pleon 0.6 mm.

Type locality: South Atlantic, L.G.O. Biotrawl No. 200, type only, cat. no. I-200.

Distribution: Known only from type locality.

Affinities: Related to *I. indentifrons* but differing in having biramous instead of uniramous uropods.

Ilyarachna species indeterminable

Fragments of Ilyarachna were taken at L.G.O. Biotrawl no. 14, one female fragment; no. 54, two fragments; no. 98, one cephalon; no. 107, one crushed; no. 201, four damaged; no. 212, four fragments; no. 218, three fragments; no. 231, five fragments.

Family : DESMOSOMIDAE

Diagnosis: Paraselloidea with cephalon free. All peraeopods except the first modified for swimming, not paddle-like, provided with plumose marginal setae. Mandibles with toothed incisor, lacinia, and setal row, palp triarticulate or lacking, molar reduced to setiferous lobe. First four peraeonal somites with large coxal plates visible in dorsal view. Last three peraeonal somites without coxal plates visible in dorsal view. Pleon with one or two somites. Uropoda unibiramous, with quadrate, ventral peduncle. Flagellum of first antenna pauciarticulate, without specialized vesicle or bladder. Frontal region of cephalon well developed.

Composition: The family contains only two genera, *Echinopleura* G. O. Sars and *Desmosoma* G. O. Sars. Only *Desmosoma* contains abyssal species. In *Echinopleura* the fifth peraeonal somite is constricted and longer than wide, whereas it is not constricted in *Desmosoma*.

Genus: DESMOSOMA G. O. Sars

Type species: *Desmosoma lineare* G. O. Sars, 1864, p. 215; — 1899, pp. 125–126.

Synonyms: *Desmosoma* Sars, 1863; — Meinert, 1890; — Bonnier, 1896; — Sars, 1899; — Stephensen, 1915; — Hansen, 1916; — Monod, 1926b; — Nordenstam, 1933; — Hult, 1941. *Eugerda* Meinert, 1890; — Vanhöffen, 1914; — Hult, 1941.

Diagnosis: Desmosomidae with fifth peraeonal somite not constricted and elongated.

Composition: This genus now contains around 25 species and is well represented in polar, shallow water,

and deep sea regions. The known species are shown in the accompanying list. All species except *D. elongatum* Bonnier (illustration not available) and a proposed new one are included in the key. It has been assumed that the uropoda of *D. falklandicum* Nordenstam were biramous. This assumption may have been incorrect, in which case its position in the key would have to be changed.

LIST OF SPECIES OF DESMOSOMA

		Depth Range (Meters)	
	Species	Least	Greatest
1.	*tenuimanum* G. O. Sars	11	698
2.	*latipes* Hansen	1094	1094
3.	*lineare* G. O. Sars	50	697
4.	*elongatum* Bonnier	950	950
5.	*longispinum* Hansen	3521	3521
6.	*simile* Hansen	2258	2258
7.	*gracilipes* Hansen	2258	2702
8.	*politum* Hansen	1070	1505
9.	*coarctatum* (Hansen) G.O.S.	24	2702
10.	*laterale* (Hansen)	50	1096
11.	*armatum* G. O. Sars	25	478
12.	*angustum* Hansen, G.O.S.	50	680
13.	*chelatum* Stephensen	25	25
14.	*insigne* Hansen	2702	2702
15.	*plebejum* Hansen	1412	1666
16.	*australis* Nordenstam	64	148
17.	*brevipes* Nordenstam	64	148
18.	*modestum* Nordenstam	125	250
19.	*falklandicum* Nordenstam	16	16
20.	*polaris* Gurjanova	40	510
21.	*zenkewitschi* Gurjanova	65	65
22.	*reticulata* Gurjanova	698	698
23.	*longimanum* (Vanhöffen)	2735	2735
24.	*filipes* Hult	34	1000
25.	*intermedium* Hult	30	2258

A KEY TO THE SPECIES OF DESMOSOMA

1. Uropoda biramous 2
1. Uropoda uniramous 11
2. Pleon with postero-lateral spines 3
2. Pleon without postero-lateral spines, rounded . . 8
3. First peraeopod stout, with long stout setae . . . 4
3. First peraeopod weak, without long
stout setae . . . . *filipes* Hult
4. Fifth peraeonal somite with a stout seta at
antero-lateral angles. . . . . . *coarctatum* (Hansen)
4. Fifth peraeonal somite without a stout seta at
antero-lateral angles 5
5. Antero-lateral angles of fifth peraeonal
somite sharp . . . . *reticulata* Gurjanova
5. Antero-lateral angles of fifth peraeonal somite
rounded 6
6. First peraeopod with only one long stout setae on
carpus . . . . *longimana* (Vanhöffen)
6. First peraeopod with two or more stout setae on
carpus 7
7. With two stout setae . . . . *laterale* (Hansen)
7. With five stout setae . . . . *politum* Hansen
8. First peraeopod stout with four stout
setae . . . . *zenkewitschi* Gurjanova
8. First peraeopod weak, with no setae or five
stout setae 9
9. Lateral border of pleon
serrated . . . . *intermedium* Hult
9. Lateral border of pleon not serrated 10
10. Coxal plate of second peraeonal somite
triangulate . . . . *tenuimanum* G. O. Sars
10. Coxal plate of second peraeonal somite
rounded . . . . *latipes* Hansen
11. Pleon with spine or tooth at postero-lateral
angle 12
11. Pleon rounded at postero-lateral margin, no tooth
present 17
12. First peraeopod stout, with stout setae 13
12. First peraeopod weak, without stout setae . . . 14
13. First antenna with six articles . . . . *birsteini*, n. sp.
13. First antenna with five articles . *armatum* G. O. Sars
14. Coxal plates elongate, much longer than wide . . 15
14. Coxal plates short, about as wide as long 16
15. Lateral borders 6-7 peraeonal somites
subcircular . . . . *magnispinum*, n. sp.
15. Lateral borders 6-7 peraeonal somites
almost straight . . . . *longispinum* Hansen
16. Antero-lateral angles of fifth peraeonal somite
sharply pointed . . . . *simile* Hansen
16. Antero-lateral angles of fifth peraeonal
somite rounded . . . . *gracilipes* Hansen
17. First peraeopod stout, with stout setae 18
17. First peraeopod weak, without stout setae . . . 22
18. Fourth peraeonal somite with pronounced spine at
antero-lateral angle . . . . *insigne* Hansen
18. Fourth peraeonal somite without spine at antero-
lateral angle 19
19. Fifth peraeonal somite not longer than wide . . 21
19. Fifth peraeonal somite longer than wide 20
20. Frons of cephalon straight . . . . . *plebejum* Hansen
20. Frons of cephalon convex . . . . *angustum* Hansen[a]
21. Postero-lateral angles of peraeonal somites
5-6 rounded . . . . *chelatum* Stephensen
21. Postero-lateral angles of peraeonal somites
5-6 sharp . . . . *polaris* Gurjanova
22. Fifth peraeonal somite longer than wide 25
22. Fifth peraeonal somite not longer than wide . . . 23

23. Coxal plates elongated and pointed, produced
forward at apex . . . . *lineare* G. O. Sars
23. Coxal plates rectangular, or not elongate and
pointed 24
24. First peraeonal somite much shorter than
second . . . . *brevipes* Nordenstam
24. First peraeonal somite as long as
second . . . . *falklandicum* Nordenstam
25. First peraeonal somite one-half as long as
second . . . . *modestum* Nordenstam
25. First peraeonal somite one-third as long as
second . . . . *australis* Nordenstam

[a] Ref. G. O. Sars, 1899, suppl. Pl. II, fig. 2.

Desmosoma gracilipes Hansen
Figure 50 A–B

Synonyms: *Desmosoma gracilipes* Hansen, 1916, pp. 113–114, Pl. 11.

Diagnosis: *Desmosoma* with a spine at each postero-lateral angle of the pleon. Frons of cephalon transverse at apex. Coxal plates bilobed and quadrate. First peraeonal somite and second subequal in length. First peraeopod weak, without stout setae. Uropoda uniramous.

Measurements: Female with marsupium length 3.2 mm., male 2.7 mm.

Type locality: North Atlantic, Davis Strait, *Ingolf* Station 24, latitude 63° 06′ N., longitude 56° 00′ W., 2258 meters, temperature 2.4° C., five specimens (one male).

Distribution: Also from *Ingolf* Station 36, Davis Strait, latitude 61° 50′ N., longitude 56° 21′ W., 2702 meters, temperature 1.5° C., one specimen (Hansen, op. cit.).

Affinities: This species is close to *D. simile* Hansen, but has the antero-lateral angle of the fifth peraeonal somite rounded, not sharply pointed.

Desmosoma insigne Hansen
Figure 50 C–E

Synonyms: *Desmosoma insigne* Hansen, 1916, pp. 118–120, Pl. 11.

Diagnosis: *Desmosoma* without a spine at each postero-lateral angle of pleon. Frons of cephalon blunt at apex. Coxal plates bilobed and quadrate. First peraeonal somite longer than second. Fourth peraeonal somite as long as wide, with acute antero-lateral angles. First peraeopod stout and with a stout seta on merus. Uropoda uniramous.

Measurements: Female with marsupium length 3.1 mm., male 1.85 mm. (Hansen, op. cit.).

Type locality: North Atlantic, Davis Strait, *Ingolf* Station 36, latitude 61° 50′ N., longitude 56° 21′ W., 2702 meters, temperature 1.5° C., six specimens (Hansen, op. cit.).

Distribution: Known only from type locality.

Affinities: The spines at the antero-lateral margins of the peraeonal somites are distinctive.

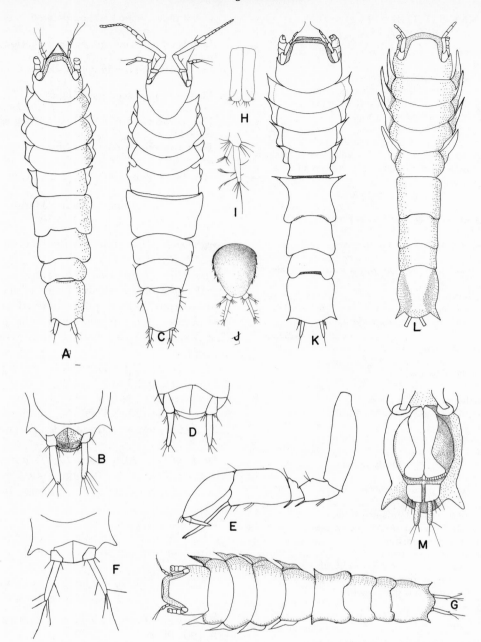

Figure 50. A–B: *Desmosoma gracilipes* Hansen. A: dorsal view ovigerous female; B: uropods of subadult female. C–E: *Desmosoma insigne* Hansen. C: dorsal view of female with marsupium; D: uropods and abdomen of female. E: first peraeopod. F–G: *Desmosoma simile* Hansen. F: uropods and abdomen of female; G: dorsal view of ovigerous female. H–J: *Desmosoma intermedium* Hult. H: first male pleopod; I: uropod; J: male pleotelson. K: *Desmosoma coarctatum* (G. O. Sars), after Hansen, *natator*, dorsal view male. L–M: *Desmosoma longispinum* Hansen. L: dorsal view of male; M: abdomen and uropods of male.

Desmosoma simile Hansen

Figure 50 F–G

Synonyms: *Desmosoma simile* Hansen, 1916, pp. 112–113.

Diagnosis: *Desmosoma* with a long spine at each postero-lateral angle of the pleon. Frons of cephalon transverse at apex. Coxal plates slightly elongate, bilobed. First and second peraeonal somites subequal in length; fifth with projecting spine-like antero-lateral angles. First peraeopod weak, without stout setae. Uropods uniramous.

Measurements: Ovigerous female length 2.2 mm. (Hansen, op. cit.).

Type locality: North Atlantic, Davis Strait, *Ingolf* Station 24, latitude 63° 06′ N., longitude 56° 00′ W., 2258 meters, temperature 2.4° C., five specimens (Hansen, op. cit.).

Distribution: Known only from type locality.

Affinities: Close to *gracilipes* but with the antero-lateral angle of the fifth peraeonal somite pointed rather than rounded.

Desmosoma intermedium Hult
Figure 50 H–J

Synonyms: *Desmosoma intermedium* Hult, 1936, pp. 2–6, Figs. 1–21; — 1941, pp. 80–84.

Diagnosis: *Desmosoma* without a spine at each postero-lateral angle of the pleon but with lateral margins serrated. Frons of cephalon concave at apex. Coxal plates triangular and minute, not strongly produced. First peraeonal somite slightly shorter than second. First peraeopod weak without stout setae. Uropoda biramous.

Measurements: None available.

Type locality: Koster Fjord, off Vattenholm, 206 meters, temperature 6.2° C. (Hult, 1936).

Distribution: North Atlantic, Norway, Kattegat, 100 meters to 2258 meters, and *Ingolf* Station 24, latitude 63° 06′ N., longitude 56° 00′ W., 2258 meters.

Affinities: Looking much like *D. elongatum* Bonnier but with uniramous uropods.

Desmosoma coarctatum (Hansen) G. O. S.
Figure 50 K

Synonyms: *Eugerda coarctata* G. O. Sars, 1899, p. 253, *Desmosoma natator* Hansen, 1916, p. 115; — Gurjanova 1933, p. 418. *Desmosoma coarctatum* (G. O. Sars), Hult 1936, p. 10; — 1941, pp. 86–88 and references.

Diagnosis: *Desmosoma* with a spine at each postero-lateral angle of pleon. Frons of cephalon straight at apex. Coxal plates slightly produced, bilobed. First and second peraeonal somites subequal in length. Fifth with a long spine at each antero-lateral angle. First peraeopod stout, with stout seta. Uropoda uniramous.

Measurements: Female length 2.0 mm., male 1.5 mm. (G. O. Sars, op. cit., p. 253).

Type locality: North Atlantic, Skager Rak, north of Skagen, 125 fathoms (G. O. Sars, op. cit., p. 250).

Distribution: Besides the Skager Rak (Hult, 1941) the species was found at Davis Strait, *Ingolf* Station 36, latitude 61° 50′ N., longitude 56° 21′ W., 2702 meters, temperature 1.5° C., one specimen (Hansen, op. cit., p. 116).

Affinities: This species is unique in having the stout spines at the antero-lateral angles of the fifth peraeonal somite.

Desmosoma longispinum Hansen
Figure 50 L–M

Synonyms: *Desmosoma longispinum* Hansen, 1916, pp. 111–112, Pl. 10.

Diagnosis: *Desmosoma* with a long spine at each postero-lateral angle of the pleon. Frons of cephalon rounded slightly at apex. Coxal plates elongated, strongly produced forward, over twice as long as wide, and pointed at apex. First and second peraeonal somites subequal in length. First peraeopods weak; without stout setae. Uropods uniramous.

Measurements: Female length 2.1 mm., male 1.8 mm. (Hansen, op. cit.).

Type locality: North Atlantic, south of Davis Strait, *Ingolf* Station 38, latitude 59° 12′ N., longitude 51° 05′ W., 3521 meters, 4 specimens (Hansen, op cit.).

Distribution: Known only from type locality.

Affinities: This species is close to *magnispinum* but has the lateral borders of the peraeonal somites 6–7 straight rather than rounded.

Desmosoma striata, new species
Figure 51 A–F

Synonyms: None.

Diagnosis: *Desmosoma* without spines at each postero-lateral border of pleon. Pleon evenly rounded, lacking serrations. Coxal plates bilobed. First and second peraeonal somites subequal in length. First with stout spines at antero-lateral angle. Fifth without spines at antero-lateral angles. Structure of first peraeopod not known. Uropods uniramous.

Measurements: Female with oostegites length 1.4 mm., width pleon 0.2 mm.

Type locality: North Atlantic, L.G.O. Biotrawl No. 17, type only, cat. no. I-179.

Distribution: Known only from type locality.

Affinities: Because of the absence of the first peraeopods it is difficult to determine the affinities of this species. The stout spines at the first peraeonal somite are distinctive.

Desmosoma magnispinum, new species
Figure 51 G–J

Synonyms: None.

Diagnosis: *Desmosoma* with a pronounced long spine at postero-lateral angle of pleon. Coxal plates much elongated, pointed. First and second peraeonal somites subequal in length. Fifth without spines at antero-lateral angles. Lateral borders of sixth and seventh semicircular. First peraeopod weak, without stout setae. Uropods uniramous.

Measurements: Holotype male length 2.1 mm., width pleon 0.25 mm.

Type locality: North Atlantic, Bay of Panama, L.G.O. Biotrawl No. 103, type only, cat. no. I-176.

Distribution: Known only from type locality.

Affinities: This species is similar to *D. longispinum* Hansen, from which it differs in having semicircular lateral borders to peraeonal somites 6–7.

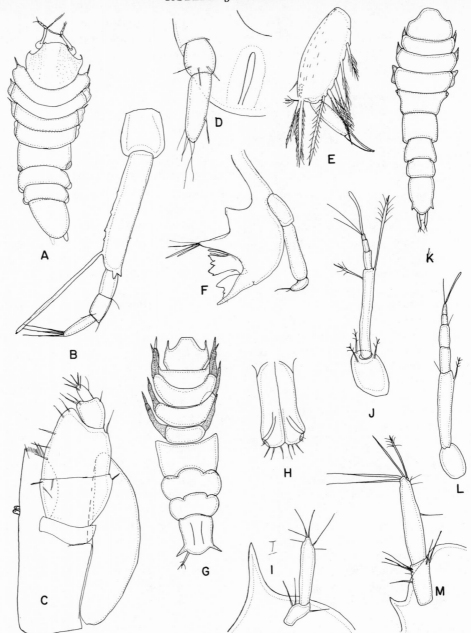

Figure 51. A–F: *Desmosoma striata*, n. sp. A: dorsal view female with oostegites; B: first antenna; C: maxilliped; D: uropod; E: third peraeopod; F: mandible. G–J: *Desmosoma magnispinum*, n. sp. G: dorsal view male holotype; H: pleopod ventral view; I: uropod; J: first antenna. K–M: *Desmosoma birsteini*, n. sp. K: dorsal view gravid female holotype; L: first antenna; M: uropod.

Desmosoma birsteini, new species
Figure 51 K–M

Synonyms: None.

Diagnosis: *Desmosoma* with a stout spine at each postero-lateral angle. Coxal plates triangulate and bilobed. First peraeonal somite slightly shorter than second. Fifth without spines at antero-lateral angles. First peraeopod stout with long stout seta. Uropods uniramous.

Measurements: Gravid female holotype length 2.3 mm., width pleon 0.3 mm.

Type locality: North Atlantic, L.G.O. Biotrawl No. 9, holotype only, cat. no. I-170.

Distribution: Known only from type locality.

Affinities: This species is close to *D. armatum* G. O. Sars, from which it differs in having six articles to the first antenna instead of five. The pleonal spines are also more pronounced on *birsteini*.

Desmosoma species indeterminable

Fragments of *Desmosoma* were found at: L.G.O. Biotrawl No. 16, one female; No. 18, one multilated; No. 49, one fragment; No. 231, one fragment.

Family: DENDROTIONIIDAE

Synonyms: Dendrotioniidae Vanhöffen, 1914; — *Dendrotiini* Nordenstam, 1933, pp. 198–199.

Diagnosis: Paraselloidea with free cephalon. All peraeopods ambulatory. Mandibular incisor with teeth, lacinia with teeth, molar expanded, truncated. Maxillipedal palp with narrow subsimilar articles, all less than one-half the width of endite. Uropods with long peduncle, biramous.

Composition: This family contains *Dendrotion* G. O. Sars, a shallow water genus, and the new abyssal genus described herein. I have transferred *Mormomunna* Vanhöffen and *Pseudomunna* Hansen to the Munnidae (p. 172–173.)

A KEY TO THE GENERA OF THE DENDROTIONIIDAE

1. Mandible with palp . . . . . *Dendrotion* G. O. Sars
1. Mandible without palp . . . . *Dendromunna*, n. gen.

DENDROMUNNA, new genus

Type species: *Dendromunna spinipes*, new species.

Diagnosis: Dendrotioniidae with one pleonal somite. Mandible lacking palp. Coxal plates visible in dorsal view on peraeonal somites 2–6 inclusive. Lateral borders of peraeonal somites expanded into spine-like processes, each process with an apical cluster of spines. Dorsum of body with similar projections. Uropoda biramous, rami shorter than peduncle.

Composition: This genus contains only the type.

Dendromunna spinipes, new species
Figure 52 A–B

Synonyms: None.

Diagnosis: *Dendromunna* with a pair of stout apically spinous spine-like processes on dorsum of peraeonal somites 2–4 inclusive. Uropoda with rami one-sixth the length of the stout peduncle. Eyes

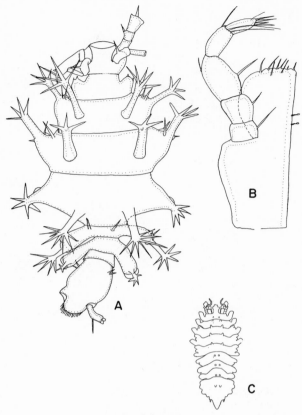

Figure 52. A–B: *Dendromunna spinipes*, n. sp. A: dorsal view female holotype; B: maxilliped. C: *Ianirella lobata* Richardson, dorsal view intersex.

lacking. Frons of cephalon concave. Apex of pleon convex and fringed with setae.

Measurements: Female holotype length 2.0 mm., width pleotelson 0.3 mm.

Type locality: South Atlantic, L.G.O. Biotrawl No. 54, type only, cat. no. I-182.

Distribution: Known only from type locality.

Affinities: Unique.

Family: IANIRELLIDAE

Diagnosis: Paraselloidea with free head, eyes lacking, mandibles normal, molar process well developed, expanded at truncated apex. Antennae shorter than body. First antenna much shorter than second antenna. All peraeopods simple, last six walking legs. Dactyls of last six peraeopods with two claws. Pleon with one somite only. Uropoda uniramous or biramous, peduncle present. Maxillipedal palp with first three articles expanded, as wide as endite. Anus contained in branchial chambers. (Modified from Menzies, 1956a, p. 11.)

Composition: This family contains at least two related genera, *Ianirella* and *Spinianirella*, and possibly *Rhacura*. The species *Ianirella pusilla* type of *Ianirella* Sayce, being a homonym, deserved a new name, which Richardson (1904, p. 6) suggested as *Heterias*. It does not belong to *Ianirella* Bonnier.

Genus: IANIRELLA Bonnier, 1896

Synonym: *Ianirella* Bonnier, 1896, p. 587; *not* *Ianirella* Sayce, 1900, p. 124.

Type species: *Ianirella nanseni* Bonnier, 1896, p. 587, Pl. 33.

Diagnosis: Same as for the family; coxal plates visible in dorsal view on peraeonal somites 5–7 inclusive. Uropoda with peduncle uniramous.

Composition: The genus contains eight species, all from the Atlantic Ocean. Three are known from abyssal depths, the remainder from bathyal depths. Two additional new abyssal species are described here.

LIST OF THE SPECIES OF IANIRELLA

| | Depth Range (Meters) | |
Species	Least	Greatest
1. *nanseni* Bonnier	950	950
2. *lobata* Richardson	2480	3225
3. *spongicola* Hansen	913	913
4. *laevis* Hansen	2258	2702
5. *glabra* Richardson	946	946
6. *vemae* Menzies	5104	5122
7. *abyssicola* Richardson	1205	1205
8. *bonnieri* Stephensen	1227	1227
9. *caribbica* Menzies	1169	1169

A KEY TO THE SPECIES OF IANIRELLA

1. Lateral processes on peraeonites rounded . . . . *lobata* Richardson
1. Lateral processes on peraeonites pointed 2
2. Body with dorsal spines 8
2. Body without dorsal spines 3
3. Lateral borders of pleon each with five major projections . . . . *abyssicola* Richardson
3. Lateral borders of pleon each with three projections 4
4. Rostrum lacking 5
4. Rostrum present 6
5. Frons of cephalon rounded . . . . . *vemae* Menzies
5. Frons of cephalon bifid . . . . . . *bifida*, n. sp.
6. Rostrum with apical spines 7
6. Rostrum without apical spines . . *magnifrons*, n. sp.
7. Rostrum with four apical spines . . . . *laevis* Hansen
7. Rostrum with three spines . . . . *glabra* Richardson
8. Submedian spines of 3–4 peraeonal somite shorter than medial spine 9
8. Submedian spines of 3–4 peraeonal somite longer than medial spine . . . . . . *nanseni* Bonnier
9. Medial spine at front of cephalon as wide as long . . . . *spongicola* Hansen
9. Medial spine at front of cephalon much longer than wide 10
10. Pleon with dorsal spines . . . . . *caribbica* Menzies
10. Pleon without dorsal spines . . . *bonnieri* Stephensen

Ianirella lobata Richardson
Figure 52 C

Synonyms: *Ianirella lobata* Richardson, 1908, pp. 78–79, Figs. 8–11.

Diagnosis: *Ianirella* with lateral borders of peraeonal extensions blunt and rounded. Dorsum of cepha-lon with a pair of spines. Each peraeonal somite and pleon with a pair of dorsal spines. Three lateral projections on each side of pleon; each is rounded, not pointed. Cephalon with rostrum, but spines are lacking from it.

Measurements: None given.

Type locality: North Atlantic, southeast of Georges Bank, *Albatross* Station 2571, 2480 meters, three speci-mens, cat. no. 38967, U.S.N.M.

Distribution: Southeast of Georges Bank, *Albatross* Station 2572, 3225 meters, and *Albatross* Station 2573, 3186 meters.

Affinities: This species is unique in having rounded lateral borders of the somites.

Ianirella bifida, new species
Figure 53 A–D

Synonyms: None.

Diagnosis: *Ianirella* with lateral borders of peraeo-nal extensions sharply pointed. Dorsum of cephalon, peraeon, and pleon without spines. Lateral borders of pleon each with three stout apically spined pro-jections. Apex of pleon bluntly pointed. Cephalon lacks rostrum, but frons has a medial pair of spined projections.

Measurements: Holotype, intersex, length 3.8 mm., width pleon 1.2 mm.

Type locality: South Atlantic, L.G.O. Biotrawl No. 53, type, cat. no. I-183.

Distribution: Known only from type locality.

Affinities: Related to *vemae* but with a bifid frons on the cephalon.

Ianirella laevis Hansen
Figure 53 E–G

Synonyms: *Ianirella laevis* Hansen, 1916, p. 26, Pl. I.

Diagnosis: *Ianirella* with lateral borders of peraeo-nal extensions sharply pointed. Dorsum of cephalon, peraeon, and pleon smooth. Lateral borders of pleon each with two stout apically spined projections, apex of pleon pointed. Cephalon with rostrum bearing four stout spines.

Measurements: Largest female length 4.0 mm. (Hansen, op. cit.).

Type locality: North Atlantic, *Ingolf* Station 24, latitude 63° 06′ N., longitude 56° 00′ W., 2258 meters, temperature 2.4° C., seven specimens.

Distribution: Also known from *Ingolf* Station no. 36, latitude 61° 50′ N., longitude 56° 21′ W., 2702 meters, temperature 1.5° C., four specimens (Hansen, op. cit.).

Affinities: This species is allied to *I. glabra* Richard-son, from which it differs in having four spines, not three, on the apex of the cephalic rostrum.

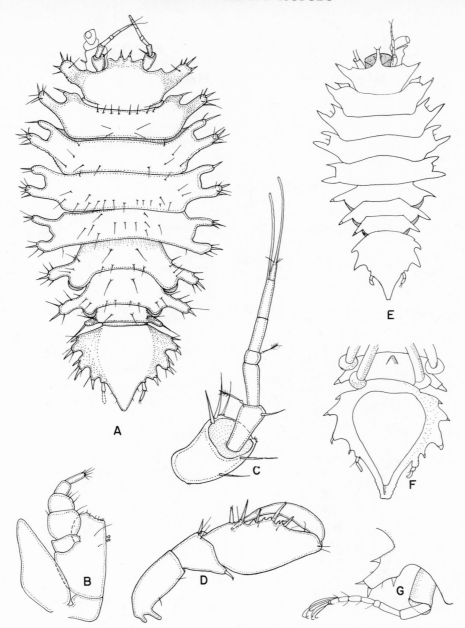

Figure 53. A–D: *Ianirella bifida*, n. sp. A: dorsal view holotype intersex; B: maxilliped; C: first antenna; D: first peraeopod. E–G: *Ianirella laevis* Hansen. E: dorsal view female; F: ventral view abdomen; G: anterior of cephalon.

Ianirella vemae Menzies
Figure 54 A–B

Synonyms: *Ianirella vemae* Menzies, 1956a, p. 12, Fig. 5.

Diagnosis: *Ianirella* with lateral borders of peraeonal extensions sharply pointed. Dorsum of cephalon peraeon and pleon without spines. Lateral borders of pleon each with three stout apically spined projections. Apex of pleon blunt, setiferous. Cephalon lacks rostrum.

Measurements: Holotype, intersex, length 3.3 mm., width at second peraeonal somite 1.8 mm. (Menzies, op. cit.).

Type locality: North Atlantic, near Puerto Rico trench, L.G.O. Biotrawl No. 1, 5104–5122 meters, type only, cat. no. 11761, A.M.N.H.

Distribution: Known only from type locality.

Affinities: This species is related to *bifida*, from which it differs in having the frons of the cephalon rounded and not bifid.

Ianirella magnifrons, new species
Figure 54 C–D

Synonyms: None.

Diagnosis: *Ianirella* with lateral borders of peraeonal projections pointed. Dorsum of cephalon, peraeon

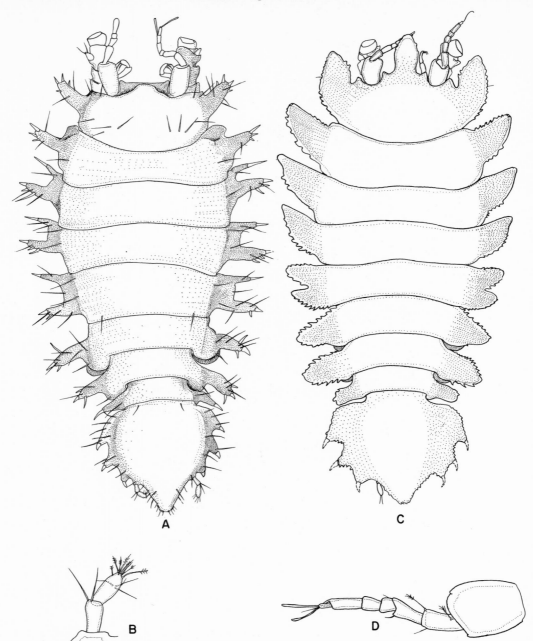

Figure 54. A–B: *Ianirella vemae* Menzies. A: dorsal view holotype intersex; B: uropod.
C–D: *Ianirella magnifrons*, n. sp. C: dorsal view female intersex; D: first antenna.

and pleon without spines. Lateral borders of pleon each with three stout apically spined projections. Apex of pleon blunt. Cephalon with spatulate-shaped rostrum. Lateral margins of body and pleon spinulate.

Measurements: Female intersex length 3.2 mm., width pleon 1.0 mm.

Type locality: South Atlantic, L.G.O. Biotrawl No. 51, type only, cat. no. I-184.

Distribution: Known only from type locality.

Affinities: The absence of apical spines on the rostrum distinguishes this species from *laevis* and *glabra*.

SPINIANIRELLA, new genus

Synonyms: None.

Type species: *Spinianirella walfishensis*, new species.

Diagnosis: Ianirellidae with coxal plates visible in dorsal view on peraeonal somites 3–7 inclusive. Spinous expansions at lateral border of cephalon and peraeonal somites 1–6 inclusive. Mandibular palp triarticulate. Second from last article of prehensile first peraeopod longer by one-half than the propodal article and with many stout spines and setae along inferior margin. Pleon with serrated lateral margins, spiniform extensions lacking.

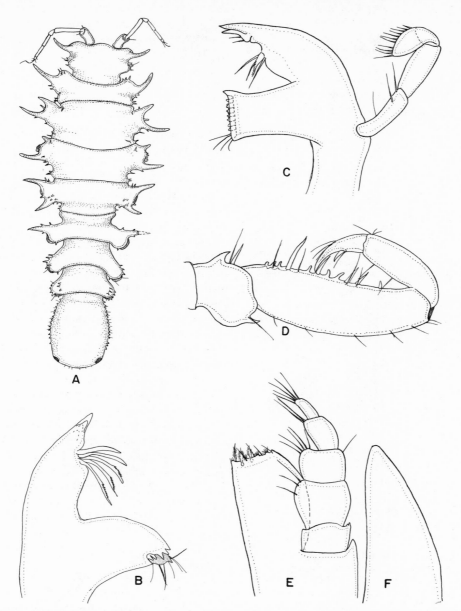

Figure 55. *Spinianirella walfishensis*, n. sp. A: dorsal view female holotype; B: right mandible; C: left mandible of paratype; D: first peraeopod; E: maxilliped; F: maxillipedal epipod.

Spinianirella walfishensis, new species
Figure 55

Synonyms: None.

Diagnosis: *Spinianirella* with 13 spines on either side of pleon, apex rounded and smooth. Frons of cephalon evenly convex. Dorsum of body and pleon without spines. First antenna with six articles. Maxilliped without coupling hooks.

Measurements: Holotype female length 5.2 mm., width pleon 0.8 mm.

Type locality: South Atlantic Ocean, L.G.O. Biotrawl No. 16, holotype and one paratype, cat. no. I-192.

Distribution: Found also at L.G.O. Biotrawl No. 54, one female, cat. no. I-199.

Affinities: Unique.

Genus: RHACURA Richardson

Synonyms: *Rhacura* Richardson 1908a, pp. 72–74.

Type species: *Rhacura pulchra* Richardson.

Diagnosis: Ianirellidae (?) with eyes, without coxal plates visible in dorsal view. Cephalon incised laterally. Pleon laterally with several deep incisions. Last two articles of maxillipedal palp narrow; others as wide as endite. Structure of mandibles not known.

Rhacura pulchra Richardson
Figure 56 F

Synonyms: *Rhacura pulchra* Richardson, 1908a, pp. 74–75.

Description: "Body oblong-ovate, about twice as long as wide. Dorsal surface covered with granulations. Head much wider than long, with the front

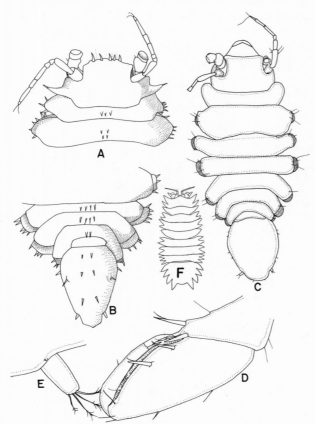

Figure 56. A–B: *Munna (Munna) acanthifera* Hansen. A: dorsal view head; B: dorsal view posterior. C–E: *Munna (Munna) argentinae*, n. sp. C: dorsal view female holotype; D: first peraeopod; E: uropod. F: *Rhacura pulchra* Richardson, dorsal view female (from Richardson, 1906).

produced in the middle in an obtuse triangular process, which does not extend as far as the antero-lateral processes; the lateral margins are drawn out on either side in two acute triangular processes, both

directed anteriorly; the posterior one is slightly narrower than the anterior process. The eyes are minute and are situated closer to the posterior margin than to the anterior margin. The first pair of antennae have the first article of the peduncle largest; the second and third are subequal and are a little shorter than the first; the flagellum is composed of eighteen articles. The second pair of antennae are broken at the fourth article of the peduncle in the only specimen; the third article is furnished with an antennal scale. The maxillipeds have the first three articles of the palp expanded and dilated. The first segment of the thorax has the lateral margins drawn out on either side in one triangular expansion, acute at the extremity and directly anteriorly; the second and third segments have the lateral margins drawn out on either side in two triangular expensions [*sic*], about equal in width, one anterior and the other posterior; the fourth segment has one triangular expansion to the lateral margin on either side; the fifth and sixth segments have the lateral margins drawn out on either side in two triangular expansions of about equal size; the seventh and last segment of the thorax has the lateral margins drawn out in three triangular processes on either side, all of equal size.

"The abdomen has the lateral margins drawn out on either side in four triangular expansions, the last expansion corresponding to the post-lateral expansion in the species of the genus *Iolella*; between the post-lateral expansions is a small rounded lobe. The uropoda are lost in the only specimen.

"The first pair of legs are prehensile, the other six ambulatory in character and furnished with biunguiculate dactyli. The margins of the entire body are armed with minute acute spinules.

"The only specimen, a female, was found at Station 2572, steamer *Albatross*, southeast of Georges Bank, at a depth of 1,769 fathoms.

"The type is in the U.S. National Museum, Cat. no. 38964." (Richardson, 1908a, pp. 74–75.)

Measurements: None given.

Type locality: North Atlantic, southeast of Georges Bank, *Albatross* Station 2572, 3225 meters, type only, cat. no. 38964 U.S.N.M.

Distribution: Known only from type locality.

Affinities: Unique. Not collected by *Vema*.

Family: MUNNIDAE

Synonyms: *Munnidae* G. O. Sars, 1899; — Vanhöffen, 1914. *Munnini* Hansen, 1916; —Nordenstam, 1933, pp. 197–198.

Diagnosis: Paraselloidea with cephalon free from peraeon. All peraeopods ambulatory. Mandibles with expanded, truncated molar process. Maxillipedal palp with first three articles as broad as endite. Pleon with two somites

Composition: According to Nordenstam, 1933, p. 198, this family (or subgroup, as he called it) contained the following genera: *Munna* Krøyer, 1839; *Paramunna* G. O. Sars, 1866; *Coulmania* Hodgson,

1910; *Notoxenus* Hodgson, 1910; *Austrosignum* Hodgson, 1910; and *Echinomunna* Vanhöffen, 1914. He was uncertain of the status of *Austrurus* Beddard, 1885. These genera, except for *Munna* (one species only), contain only shallow water species. It is probable that the genus *Acanthomunna* Beddard, 1885, also belongs to this family. Here one additional new species is described in *Acanthomunna* and a new genus is described.

A KEY TO THE GENERA OF THE MUNNIDAE
(Modified after Menzies, in press)

1. Coxal plates of peraeon not visible in dorsal view . . 2
1. Coxal plates of peraeon visible in dorsal view . . 3
2. Mandible with triarticulate palp 4
2. Mandible lacks palp . . . . *Coulmania*
3. Coxal plates visible in dorsal view on peraeonal
   somites 2–7 inclusive 5
3. Coxal plates visible in dorsal view only on peraeonal
   somites 5–7 inclusive 6
4. Each somite of peraeon with single spine
   on dorsal surface . . . . *Notoxenus*
4. Peraeonal somites lack spines . . . . . *Paramunna*
5. Body strongly spinous 7
5. Body lacks spines (may have stout setae) . . . *Munna*
6. Ocular peduncles short, with ocelli . . . *Austrosignum*
6. Ocular peduncles narrow, long, directed
   out from head as spine-like projections,
   ocelli lacking . . . . *Notoxenoides*, n. genus
7. Uropoda insert dorsally, with stout peduncle
   and stout rami . . . . *Acanthomunna*
7. Uropoda insert laterally, with rami small
   and leaf-like . . . . *Echinomunna*

Genus: MUNNA Krøyer

Synonyms: *Haliacris* Pfeffer, 1889. *Caecimunna* Richardson, 1908a, p. 79.

Type species: *Munna boecki* Krøyer, 1839.

Diagnosis: Munnidae with coxal plates visible in dorsal view on peraeonal somites 2–7 inclusive. Body lacking spines. Eyes on short immovable peduncle, preocular lobes generally present. Uropoda lacking peduncle.

Subgenus: MUNNA

Reference: Menzies, in press.

Type species: *Munna boecki* Krøyer, 1839.

Diagnosis: *Munna* with inferior uropodal ramus rounded in cross-section, lacking recurved apical spines.

Composition: This subgenus contains 14 species (Menzies, op. cit.). Only one species, *Munna* (*M*) *acanthifera* Hansen, 1916, is known mainly from below shelf depth (viz., below 200 meters). The subgenus was represented in L.G.O. collections by a single blind abyssal species from the South Atlantic.

Munna (*Munna*) *acanthifera* Hansen
Figure 56 A–B

Synonyms: *Munna acanthifera* Hansen, 1916, pp. 40–42, Pl. III.

Diagnosis: *Munna* (*sensu stricto*) without eyes, cephalon with a triangulate lateral expansion, frons with five stout marginal spines. Epimeral areas strongly spinous. Pleon and peraeon with some stout spines.

Measurements: Length female 3.1 mm., male 2.8 mm.

Type locality: North Atlantic, from the following stations by the *Ingolf* and the *Thor*:

Davis Strait: *Ingolf* Station 32, latitude 66° 35′ N., longitude 56° 38′ W., 599 meters, temperature 3.9° C., 16 specimens; *Ingolf* Station 35, latitude 65° 16′ N., longitude 55° 05′ W., 682 meters, temperature 3.6° C., numerous specimens; *Ingolf* Station 27, latitude 64° 54′ N., longitude 55° 10′ W., 740 meters, temperature 3.8° C., two specimens; *Ingolf* Station 25, latitude 63° 30′ N., longitude 54° 25′ W., 1096 meters, temperature 3.3° C., ten specimens; *Ingolf* Station 24, latitude 63° 06′ N., longitude 56° 00′ W., 2258 meters, temperature 2.4° C., about 28 specimens.

West of Iceland: *Ingolf* Station 89, latitude 64° 45′ N., longitude 27° 20′ W., 584 meters, temperature 8.4° C., one specimen.

Southwest of Iceland: *Ingolf* Station 81, latitude 61° 44′ N., longitude 27° 00′ W., 913 meters, temperature 6.1° C., one specimen; *Ingolf* Station 78, latitude 60° 37′ N., longitude 27° 52′ W., 1505 meters, temperature 4.5° C., seven specimens.

East of Iceland: *Ingolf* Station 105, latitude 65° 34′ N., longitude 7° 31′ W., 1435 meters, temperature −0.8° C., two specimens.

North of Iceland: *Ingolf* Station 126, latitude 67° 19′ N., longitude 15° 52′ W., 552 meters, temperature −0.5° C. eight specimens; *Ingolf* Station 124, latitude 67° 40′ N., longitude 15° 40′ W., 932 meters, temperature −0.6° C., one specimen.

South of Iceland, *Thor*, latitude 62° 11′ N., longitude 19° 36′ W., 1899 to 2144 meters, temperature not recorded, three specimens (Hansen, 1916, pp. 41–42).

Affinities: The lateral cephalic spines are unique to this and to *Caecimunna truncata* Richardson, known from 80–390 fathoms off New England.

Munna (*Munna*) *argentinae*, new species
Figure 56 C–E

Synonyms: None.

Diagnosis: *Munna* (*Munna*) without eyes. First antenna with seven articles, last article one-half the length of prior article. Second antenna slightly longer than the body, flagellum with 20 articles. Cephalon as wide as long, preocular lobes absent, frontal margin convex, entire, without setae or spines. Maxilliped with three coupling hooks. Pleotelson pyriform, lateral margins smooth, lacking large setae or spines, a few minute setae along lateral margin. Uropoda inferior ramus small, superior ramus lacking. Mandibular palp missing.

Measurements: Holotype female length 2.0 mm., width pleotelson 0.45 mm.

Type locality: South Atlantic, L.G.O. Biotrawl No. 201, holotype only, cat. no. I–217.

Distribution: Known only from type locality.

Affinities: This is the first blind abyssal species of *Munna* known from the South Atlantic. It differs from *M.* (*M.*) *acanthifera* Hansen in lacking tri-angulate expansions at the lateral margin of the cephalon.

Genus: ACANTHOMUNNA Beddard

Synonyms: Acanthomunna Beddard, 1886, pp. 102–103; — *Mormomunna* Vanhöffen, 1914, pp. 569–571. *Pseudomunna* Hansen, 1916, pp. 47–48.

Type species: Acanthomunna proteus Beddard, 1886, pp. 47–50.

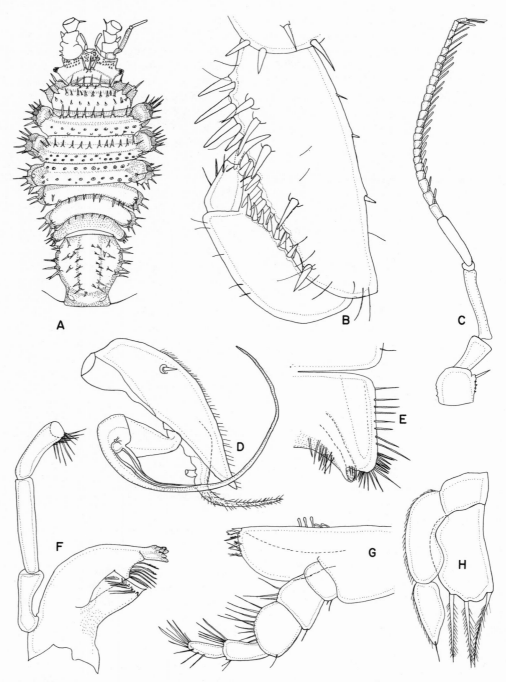

Figure 57. *Acanthomunna beddardi*, n. sp. A: dorsal view male holotype; B: gnathopod; C: first antenna; D: second pleopod; E: first pleopod; F: mandible; G: maxilliped; H: third pleopod.

Diagnosis: Munnidae with eyes. Body covered densely with stout spines. Mandibular palp present, Coxal plates visible in dorsal view on peraeonal somites 2–7. Endite of second male pleopod curved, appendage pointed and hirsute. Lateral expansion lacking from apex of male first pleopods. First peraeopod stout, dactyl with two claws, other articles with many stout setae on inferior margin. Uropoda massive, with peduncle and biramous and dorsal insertion.

Composition: The dorsal insertion of the massive uropods characterizes this genus, and it is therefore highly probable that *Mormomunna* Vanhöffen and *Pseudomunna* Hansen are synonyms. Hansen did not think so on the basis of the male first pleopods, but even within *Munna* the male first pleopods differ rather markedly. In the species which I have been able to examine I did not find the maxillipedal palp articles as narrow as indicated by Hansen for *hystrix*;

they are nevertheless narrower than other Munnidae. The species range from bathyal to abyssal depths.

LIST OF THE SPECIES OF ACANTHOMUNNA

Species	Depth Range (Meters)	
---	Least	Greatest
1. *proteus*	1281	2011
2. *spinipes*	385	385
3. *hystrix*	1505	1505

A KEY TO THE SPECIES OF ACANTHOMUNNA

1. Cephalon with spines on dorsum 2
1. Cephalon without spines on dorsum 3
2. With a central cluster of three spines . *beddardi*, n. sp.
2. With one spine near each lateral border . . . . *proteus* Beddard
3. First peraeonal somite with only four spines . . . . *spinipes* (Vanhöffen)
3. First peraeonal somite with more than six spines . . . . *hystrix* (Hansen)

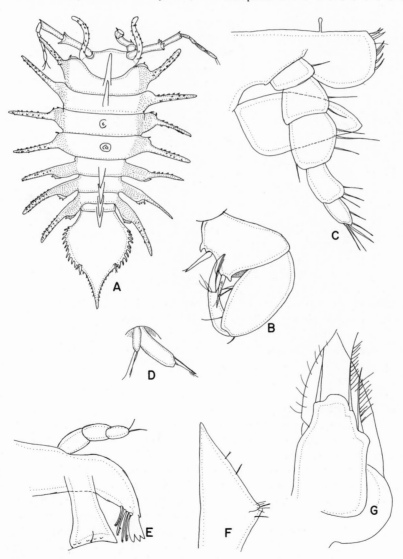

Figure 58. *Notoxenoides abyssi*, n. sp. A: dorsal view male holotype; B: gnathopod; C: maxilliped; D: uropod; E: mandible; F: first pleopod; G: third pleopod.

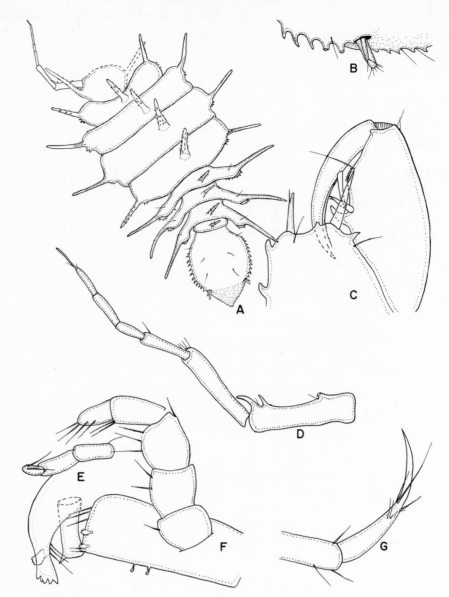

Figure 59. *Notoxenoides vemae*, n. sp. A: dorsal view female holotype; B: dorsal view uropod; C: first peraeopod; D: first antenna; E: mandible; F: maxilliped; G: third peracopod.

Acanthomunna beddardi, new species
Figure 57

Synonyms: None.

Diagnosis: *Acanthomunna* with bifurcated frons of cephalon and three stout spines in a cluster at midline of dorsum of cephalon. Three transverse rows of stout spines on dorsum of first three peraeonal somites and one row on somites 5 and 6. Pleon irregularly spinous. Propod with seven stout spines along inferior margin.

Measurements: Male holotype length 5.4 mm., width pleon 1.5 mm.

Type locality: South Atlantic, L.G.O. Biotrawl No. 53, type only, cat. no. I-180.

Distribution: Known only from type locality.

Affinities: This species is distinct in having the central cluster of three spines in the dorsum of cephalon.

NOTOXENOIDES, new genus

Type species: *Notoxenoides abyssi,* new species.

Synonyms: None.

Diagnosis: Munnidae with coxal plates evident in dorsal view on peraeonal somites 5–7 inclusive. Uropoda biramous small, leaf-like, peduncle lacking, insertion lateral. Lateral borders of peraeonal somites 1–7 inclusive produced into spine-like process, dorsum at midline of each somite with a long spine. Maxillipedal palp narrower than endite. Mandibular palp triarticulate; molar expanded and truncated at apex. Apex of male first pleopods triangulate. Ocular peduncles narrow and curved forward in front of cephalon, ocelli lacking.

Composition: Known from type species and the one other new species described herein. *Pleurogonium pulchrum* Hansen possibly belongs to this genus.

Notoxenoides abyssi, new species
Figure 58

Synonyms: None.

Diagnosis: Notoxenoides with a produced, pointed, spinulate pleon. Flagellum of first antenna with four articles. Dorsum of pleon without spines, lateral border spinulate. Propod with only a stout seta on inferior margin. Ocular peduncles projecting in front of cephalon. Second article of peduncle of first antenna with a spine at distal outer margin.

Measurements: Length holotype male 1.9 mm., width pleotelson 0.44 mm., length gravid allotype 2.0 mm., width pleotelson 0.5 mm.

Type locality: South Atlantic, L.G.O. Biotrawl No. 54, types plus two male and one female paratypes, cat. no. I-181.

Distribution: Known only from type locality.

Affinities: The species resembles *Pleurogonium pul-*

chrum Hansen, 1916, in having the dorsal spines on the body. The mandibles would obviously distinguish the two, but Hansen did not describe them for *pulchrum*. Its nearest abyssal relative is the following new species.

Notoxenoides vemae, new species
Figure 59

Synonyms: None.

Diagnosis: Notoxenoides with apex of pleon pointed but not strongly produced. Flagellum of first antenna with four articles. Dorsum of pleon without spines, lateral border spinulate. Propod with a curved spine and one stout seta on inferior margin. Ocular peduncles (?) directed laterally. Second article of peduncle of first antenna without spines.

Measurements: Female holotype length 1.8 mm, width at widest point 0.8 mm.

Type locality: South Atlantic, L.G.O. Biotrawl No. 18, type only, cat. no. I-174.

Distribution: Known only from type locality.

Affinities: Related to *N. abyssi* Menzies and *P. pulchrum* Hansen, but with sharp laterally directed ocular peduncles.

ACANTHASPIDIDAE, new family

Diagnosis: Paraselloidea with free cephalon. Eyes lacking, mandible with tapering yet blunt molar, palp present. Uropod with long peduncle. None of the peraeopods modified for swimming; dactyl of sixth with two claws. Last two articles of maxillipedal palp one-half the width of first three; second $\frac{1}{2}$ the width of endite. Somites of peraeon much wider than long. Pleon with two somites.

Composition: The family probably contains *Jolanthe* Beddard, *Microprotus* Richardson, and *Katianira* Richardson. *Janthopsis* and *Rhacura* probably belong to the Ianirellidae (Menzies, in press). The family is related to the Ianirellidae, but the maxillipedal palp articles are too narrow and it has two somites to the pleon instead of only one. The very long uropodal peduncle characterizes members of the family.

Genus: ACANTHASPIDIA Stebbing

Type species: Acanthoniscus typhlops G. O. Sars, 1879, p. 434.

Synonym: Acanthoniscus G. O. Sars, 1879, p. 434, — 1885, p. 119, Pl. X. *Acanthaspidia* Stebbing, 1893, p. 378.

Diagnosis: Acanthaspididae with mandible having triarticulate palp and lacinia and setal row. Uropoda biramous, with long peduncle, insertion terminal. Maxillipedal palp with expanded first three articles all

less than one-half the width of endite. Cephalon without eyes or eye stalks. Peraeonal somites provided with spine-like lateral expansions. Coxal plates visible in dorsal view on somites 5–7 inclusive. Pleonal lateral margin with many spine-like projections.

Composition: The genus contains three species besides the new one described here:

| Species | Depth Range (Meters) | |
	Least	Greatest
1. *typhlops* (G. O. Sars)	823	1354
2. *decorata* (Hansen, 1895)	4000	4000
3. *drygalskii* Vanhöffen	350	385

A KEY TO THE SPECIES OF ACANTHASPIDIA

1. Body with a single median row of single spines . . 2
1. Body with a pair of spines on midline . . . . *drygalskii* Vanhöffen
2. Frons bifid 3
2. Frons with single frontal horn . . . . *decorata* Hansen
3. Lateral border fifth peraeonal somite trifid . . . . *typhlops* (G. O. Sars)
3. Lateral border of fifth peraeonal somite with one large spine and a small one . *bifurcata*, n.sp.

Acanthaspidia bifurcata, new species
Figure 60

Synonyms: None.

Diagnosis: Acanthaspidia with bifurcating rostrum,

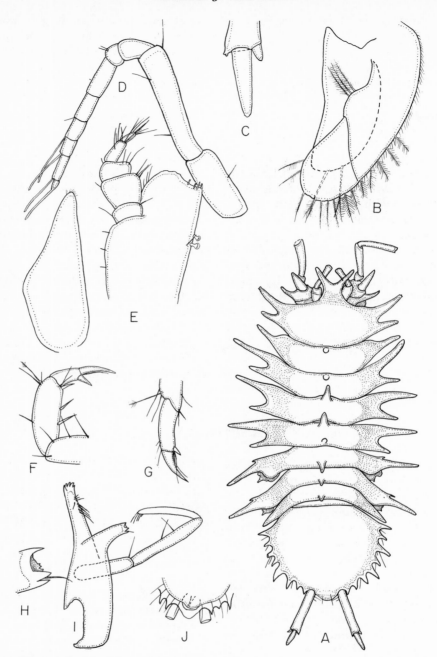

Figure 60. *Acanthaspida bifurcata*, n. sp. A: in toto, type; B: third pleopod of female; C: uropodal rami; D: first antenna; E: maxilliped; F: first peraeopod; G: fifth perae-opod; H: apex of molar of right mandible; I: right mandible; J: ventral surface of pleotelson.

first six peraeonal somites each with a mid-dorsal spine. Last three peraeonal somites with one spine-like lateral expansion and smaller tooth. Each lateral border of pleon with seven spine-like projections alternating in size. Maxilliped with two coupling hooks. Flagellum of first antenna with eight articles.

Measurements: Holotype female length 4.2 mm., width pleotelson 1.5 mm., and one fragmentary female paratype.

Type locality: South Atlantic, L.G.O. Biotrawl No. 16, types only, cat. no. I-216.

Distribution: Known only from type locality.

Affinities: Related to *typhlops* but with fewer peraeonal spine-like lateral extensions.

Acanthaspidia decorata Hansen
Figure 61 A

Synonyms: *Acanthaspidia decorata* Hansen, 1895, pp. 6–7, Pl. I.

Diagnosis: *Acanthaspidia* with mid-frontal pro-jection a simple spine. Each peraeonal somite with a single mid-dorsal spine except fourth, which has two. Each lateral border of pleon with eight spines; apex concave. Lateral borders of somites 5–7 with only one large spine-like extension. Flagellum of first antenna with ten or more articles.

Measurements: Male length 9.7 mm. (Hansen, op. cit.).

Type locality: Plankton Expedition, North Atlantic, Station 158, latitude 7.5° N., longitude 21.3° W., 4000 meters.

Distribution: Known only from type locality. It was not collected by *Vema*.

Affinities: The simple spine at the frons of the cephalon and the concave apical margin on the pleon distinguish this species.

Family: ABYSSIANIRIDAE Menzies

Synonyms: Abyssianiridae Menzies, 1956a, pp. 12–13.

Diagnosis: Paraselloidea with free head. Mandibles normal, molar process expanded and truncated at apex. First antenna shorter than body. Peraeonal somites all of similar length, none fused. Peraeopods 2–7 simple walking legs, two claws on dactyls, not three, no legs modified for swimming. First peraeopod prehensile. Coxal plates rounded, not spiniform, visible in dorsal view. Pleon with two somites. Uropoda biramous, inserting dorsally with short peduncle. Maxillipedal palp with first three articles as wide as endite. (Modified after Menzies, 1956a.)

Composition: Formerly this family contained only the type genus. It is now possible to add one new genus, *Xostylus*, with a single new species. The family is closely allied to the Munnidae through the genus *Austrosignum*, which may ultimately have to be transferred to the Abyssianiridae.

Genus: ABYSSIANIRA Menzies

Synonyms: Abyssianira Menzies, 1956a, p. 14.

Type species: Abyssianira dentifrons Menzies, 1956a, p. 15.

Diagnosis: Abyssianiridae with coxal plates visible in dorsal view on peraeonal somites 2–7 inclusive. Lateral margins of cephalon flattened and expanded.

Abyssianira dentifrons Menzies
Figure 61 B–H

Synonyms: Abyssianira dentifrons Menzies, 1956a, p. 15.

Diagnosis: *Abyssianira* with denticulate body margins. Cephalon expanded, flattened rostrum, and lateral horns. Pleotelson lateral border denticulate, apex rounded. First antenna with six articles, last about one-third shorter than penultimate article. Male first pleopod with three setae at each angle on either side of sympod. Maxilliped with two coupling hooks. Mandible with triarticulate palp, last article with two apical setae. Uropodal exopod one-half the length of endopod.

Measurements: Holotype male length 2.75 mm., width at second peraeonal somite 0.85 mm.

Type locality: North Atlantic, L.G.O. Biotrawl No. 1, type only, cat. no. 11762 A.M.N.H.

Distribution: Also found at South Atlantic, L.G.O. Biotrawl No. 214, one female, cat. no. I-203; L.G.O. Biotrawl No. 12, one male, two females, cat. no. I-90.; L.G.O. Biotrawl No. 51, one fragment, cat. no. I-185.

Affinities: This species is closely allied to *A. argentenensis*, from which it differs in having the apex of the pleon smooth, not spinulate.

Abyssianira argentenensis, new species
Figure 61 I–L

Synonyms: None.

Diagnosis: *Abyssianira* with quadrate pleotelson. First antenna with six articles, last article subequal in length to penultimate article. Propod of first peraeopod with only one stout two-pointed seta. Apex of pleon spinulate. Uropodal exopod two-thirds the length of endopod.

Measurements: Holotype female length 1.5 mm., pleon 0.5 mm.

Type locality: North Atlantic, holotype, L.G.O. Biotrawl No. 207, cat no. I-218.

Distribution: Known only from type locality.

Affinities: Closely related to *A. dentifrons*, from which it differs in having the apex of the pleon spinulate.

XOSTYLUS, new genus

Type species: Xostylus parallelus, new species.

Diagnosis: Abyssianiridae with coxal plates visible in dorsal view on last three peraeonal somites only. Lateral margins of cephalon not flattened and expanded.

Composition: Monotypic.

Affinities: Closely related to *Abyssianira* but resembling the Nannoniscidae in general body shape. The peraeopods are ambulatory and none is modified for swimming; the mandibular molar is stout and truncated at the end.

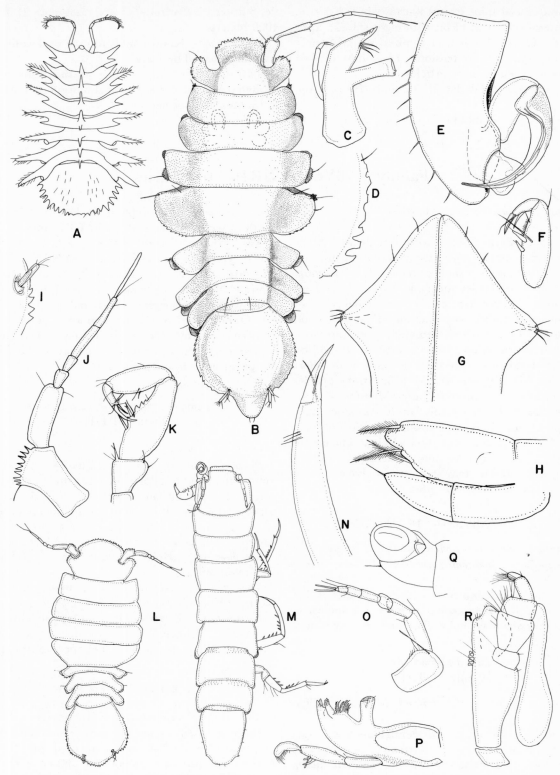

Figure 61. A: *Acanthaspida decorata* Hansen, dorsal view. B–H: *Abyssianira dentifrons* Menzies. B: dorsal view male holotype; C: mandible; D: lateral border of pleotelson; E: second pleopod; F: first peraeopod; G: first pleopod; H: third pleopod. I–L: *Abyssianira argentenensis*, n. sp. I: uropod dorsal view; J: first antenna; K: first peraeopod; L: dorsal view female holotype. M–R: *Xostylus parallelus*, n. sp. M: dorsal view female holotype; N: sixth peraeopod; O: first antenna; P: mandible; Q: second antenna; R: maxilliped.

Xostylus parallelus, new species
Figure 61 M–R

Synonyms: None.

Diagnosis: *Xostylus* with lateral border of pleon smooth, apex curved evenly rounded, devoid of spines. Frons of cephalon straight. Flagellum of first antenna with six articles. Second article of mandibular palp with three characteristic stout spines.

Epipod of maxilliped bottle-shaped; endite with four coupling hooks.

Measurements: Holotype female length 8.1 mm., width pleotelson 1.0 mm.

Type locality: South Atlantic, L.G.O. Biotrawl No. 12, type cat. no. I-200.

Distribution: Known only from type locality.

Affinities: Unique.

Family: IANIRIDAE

Diagnosis: Paraselloidea with cephalon free. Dactyls of peraeopods 2–7 inclusive with three claws (two major ones and an accessory one). Palp of maxilliped with last two articles narrow, others twice as wide and about equal to width of endite. Peraeopods all ambulatory, first often prehensile, none modified for swimming. Uropoda terminal biramous and with peduncle. Peraeonal somites all of similar length.

Composition: This major heterogeneous family of the Paraselloidea is represented in the main by shallow water genera, viz.: *Ianira, Ianiropsis, Jaera, Caecijaera, Janiralata, Iathrippa,* etc. Two genera contain abyssal species, *Ianira* (one species only) and a new one described herein.

Genus: IANIRA Leach

Synonyms: *Ianira* Leach, 1814, p. 434; — Sars, 1897, p. 99. *Henopomus* Krøyer, 1847, p. 366.

Type species: *Ianira maculosa* Leach.

Diagnosis: Ianiridae with two-jointed pleon. Coxal plates visible in dorsal view on peraeonal somites 2–7 inclusive. Mandible with expanded truncated molar, lacinia and setae row present, palp triarticulate. Exopod of third pleopod narrower than endopod. Apex of male first pleopod without lateral expansions. Second antenna with pronounced scale. First antenna shorter than second. Cephalon and pleon without pronounced lateral spine-like projections.

Composition: Only one species in this genus is from the abyss. This is *Ianira maculosa* Leach of Hansen, 1916, which is here described as a new species.

Ianira hanseni, new species
Figure 62 A–B

Synonyms: *Ianira maculosa* Leach, 1814, Hansen, 1916, pp. 14–16, Pl. I.

Diagnosis: *Ianira* with a quadrate cephalon. Eyes removed from lateral border of cephalon. Apex of male first pleopod trilobed. Postero-lateral margin of pleon spinulate.

Measurements: Female length 6.5 mm., male length 7.0 mm. (Hansen).

Type locality: North Atlantic, south of Iceland, *Thor*, latitude 60° 11' N., longitude 19° 36' W., 1899 to 2143 meters, two specimens (Hansen, op. cit., p.16).

Distribution: Known only from type locality.

Affinities: This species, an eye-bearing abyssal species, shows a close resemblance to *I. maculosa* Leach from the shallow water. It is based only on Hansen's description and not on specimens examined by me. It differs markedly from *maculosa* in having the apex of the male first pleopod trilobed and not simply bilobed (viz., G. O. Sars, 1897, Pl. 40). It was not captured by *Vema*.

ABYSSIJAERA, new genus

Type species: *Abyssijaera acarina,* new species.

Diagnosis: Ianiridae with pleon consisting of one somite only. Eyes lacking; mandibular molar reduced to a short spine; palp triarticulate; toothed incisor and lacinia present. Maxillipedal palp with first two articles expanded and as wide as endite. Coxal plates not visible in dorsal view on peraeonal somites.

Composition: Monotypic. Most of the peraeopods were lacking from the single specimen. I am assuming, on the other characteristics and the basis of general similarity of the species to *Jaera*, that most the dactyls of peraeopods 2–7 are triunguiculate. Otherwise I should have to establish a new family for the animal. The genus is closely related to *Jaera*, differing mainly in having one pleonal somite, not two, and in having a much reduced mandibular molar process.

Abyssijaera acarina, new species
Figure 62 C–I

Synonyms: None.

Diagnosis: *Abyssijaera* with lateral margins of pleon each with nine setae, apex rounded, with nine setae. Apex of male first pleopod rounded each with nine setae. Maxilliped with two coupling hooks (uropoda missing).

Measurements: Holotype male length 1.6 mm., width pleon 0.32 mm.

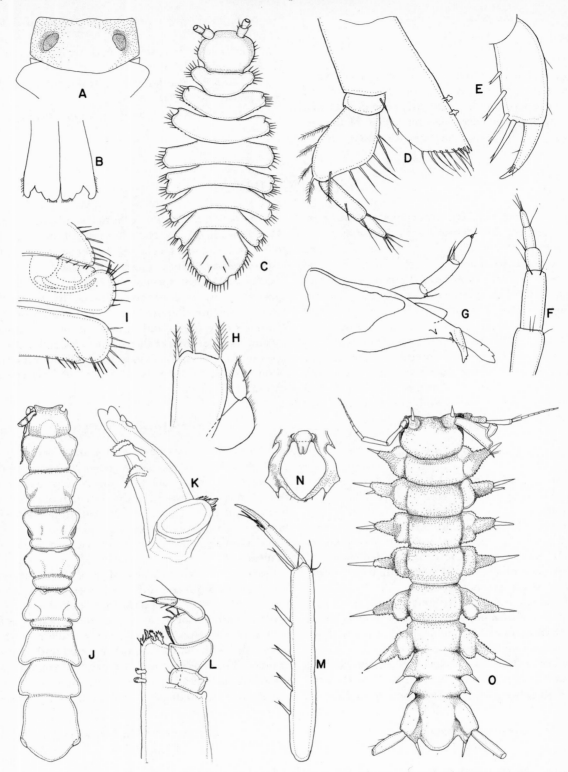

Figure 62. A–B: *Ianira hanseni*, n. sp. A: dorsal view female from latitude 62° 11′ N., longitude 19° 36′ W., after Hansen; B: distal part of medium lamella of abdomen operculum of male from same location, after Hansen. C–I: *Abyssijaera acarina*, n. sp. C: dorsal view male holotype; D: maxilliped; E: first peraeopod; F: second antenna; G: mandible; H: third pleopod; I: first pleopod. J–M: *Vemathambema elongata*, n. sp. J: dorsal view female holotype; K: mandible; L: maxilliped; M: third peraeopod. N–O: *Echinothambema ophiuroides* Menzies. N: ventral view pleon; O: dorsal view ambisexual holotype.

Type locality: North Atlantic, L.G.O. Biotrawl No. 7, type only, cat. no. I-191.

margin with a pair of swellings, each bearing a stout seta. Mandibles without a palp.

Measurements: Holotype ambisexual 5.00 mm. long, 1.5 mm. wide.

Type locality: North Atlantic, L.G.O. Biotrawl No. 1, type only, cat. no. 11760 A.M.N.H.

Distribution: Known only from type locality.

Affinities: Unique.

Family: ECHINOTHAMBEMIDAE Menzies

Synonyms: Echinothambemidae Menzies, 1956a, pp. 9–10.

Diagnosis: Paraselloidea with fused or free head, eyes lacking. Mandibles normal, molar process well developed and expanded a truncated apex. Antennae shorter than body, about twice the length of cephalon. All peraeopods simple, 2–7 simple walking legs; dactyl with two terminal claws. Uropoda terminal with peduncle. Last one or two peraeonal somites fused with pleon. First three articles of maxillipedal palp expanded, as wide as endite. Coxal plates lacking. First peduncular article of first antenna much expanded. Anus contained within the branchial chamber.

Composition: Formerly monotypic (Menzies, 1956a, p. 10). A new genus is added here and the diagnosis has accordingly been altered to allow its inclusion.

Genus: ECHINOTHAMBEMA Menzies

Type species: Echinothambema ophiuroides Menzies 1956a, p. 11.

Synonyms: Echinothambema Menzies, 1956a, pp. 10–11.

Diagnosis: Same as for family. Mandible without palp.

Composition: One abyssal Atlantic species.

Echinothambema ophiuroides Menzies
Figure 62 N–O

Synonyms: Echinothambema ophiuroides Menzies, 1956a, p. 11.

Diagnosis: Echinothambema with first antenna with six articles, last one-third longer than penultimate article. Lateral borders of peraeonal somites each with expanded and pronounced margin bearing a single stout seta. Body sharply granulate. Maxilliped with two coupling hooks. Cephalon at antero-lateral

Distribution: Known only from type locality.

Affinities: Unique.

VEMATHAMBEMA, new genus

Type species: Vemathambema elongata, new species.

Synonyms: None.

Diagnosis: Echinothambemidae with cephalon fused to first peraeonal somite and last somite of peraeon fused to pleon. First article of first antenna not expanded but stout and elongated as long as second.

Composition: Monotypic abyssal.

Affinities: Related to *Echinothambema* in the absence of coxal plates and the fusion of peraeonal somite 7 with the pleon and in the absence of a mandibular palp. Uropoda (missing) probably with peduncle.

Vemathambema elongata, new species
Figure 62 J–M

Synonyms: None.

Diagnosis: Vemathambema with smooth pleon, apex rounded, body without spines or setae. Frons of cephalon concave, devoid of spines or setae

Measurements: Holotype female length 5.2 mm width pleon 0.9 mm.

Type locality: South Atlantic, L.G.O. Biotrawl No. 15, type only, cat. no. I-112.

Distribution: Known only from type locality.

Affinities: Unique.

Family: THAMBEMATIDAE

Diagnosis: Paraselloidea with cephalon free, eyes lacking. Mandibles normal, molar process well developed and expanded at truncated apex. Antennae shorter than body. All peraeopods simple walking legs, dactyls with two terminal claws. Uropod absent. Pleon with one somite only. All peraeonal somites distinct. First three articles of maxillipedal palp as wide as endite. Coxal plates lacking.

Composition: Monotypic. The family resembles the Jaeropsidae in many significant respects, notably in the details of the structure of the maxillipeds and the shape of the front of the head and the antennae structure. The mandibular structure, however, clearly indicates its distinctiveness.

Genus: THAMBEMA Stebbing

Type species: *Thambema amicorum* Stebbing, 1912, p. 42; 1913, p. 237.

Synonyms: *Thambema* Stebbing, 1912, p. 42; — 1913, pp. 237–239.

Diagnosis: Same as for the family.

Composition: Monotypic.

Thambema amicorum Stebbing
Figure 63

Synonyms: *Thambema amicorum* Stebbing, 1912, p. 42; — 1913, pp. 237–239, Pl. 26.

Diagnosis: *Thambema* with frons of cephalon convex and even, pleon without spines or serrations, apex evenly rounded. Apex of male first pleopod pointed without lateral expansions. Second article maxillipedal palp wider than third, fourth and fifth very narrow.

Measurements: About 8 mm. (Stebbing, 1913, p. 239).

Type locality: North Atlantic, west of Donegal, *Porcupine* Station 19, latitude 54° 53′ N., longitude 10° 56′ W., 2486 meters.

Distribution: Known only from type locality. Not captured by *Vema*.

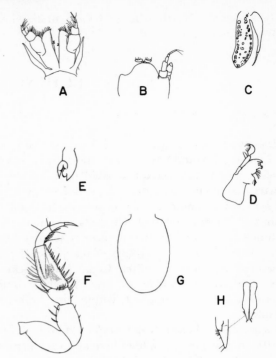

Figure 63. *Thambema amicorum* Stebbing. A: maxillipeds; B: dorsal view cephalon; C: third pleopod; D: mandible; E: second pleopod; F: first gnathopod; G: dorsal view pleon; H: first pleopod.

INCERTAE SEDIS

Genus: MESOSIGNUM, new genus

Synonyms: None.

Type species: *Mesosignum kohleri*, new species.

Diagnosis: Paraselloidea with free cephalon. All peraeopods ambulatory. Mandible with a triarticulate palp and a toothed incisor, setal row present, lacinia present, molar tapering to a flat setiferous point. Uropods uniramous, with peduncle, insertion lateral. Maxillipedal palp with narrow articles all of similar width and one-half the width of endite. First male pleopod rounded at apex. Cephalon without eyes or eye stalks. First antenna about twice the length of cephalon. Peraeonal somites, except first provided with spine-like lateral expansions. Coxal plates visible in dorsal view only on somites 5–7 inclusive. Anus separated from branchial cavity.

Remarks: The mandibles of this genus resemble *Pleurosignum* (Pleurogonidae), whereas the maxillipedal palp is like the Dendrotioniidae. The epimeral plates are like *Austrosignum* (Pleurogonidae); whereas the uropods are unique. Assignments of the genus to an existing family is impossible and the establishment of a new one seems not warranted at this time.

Composition: The genus *Mesosignum* contains two species, both abyssal and bathyal; both are new and from the Caribbean.

A KEY TO THE SPECIES OF MESOSIGNUM

1. Apex of pleon rounded . . . . *kohleri*, n. sp.
2. Apex of pleon bifurcated by stout spine-like projections . . . . *usheri*, n. sp.

Mesosignum kohleri, new species
Figure 64 A–G

Synonyms: None.

Diagnosis: *Mesosignum* with apex of pleon evenly rounded, postero-lateral projections lacking. Frons of cephalon pointed. Antero-lateral spine of second somite only twice the length of postero-lateral spine and not extending forward beyond peduncle of first antenna. Apex of male first pleopod rounded with ten marginal setae.

Measurements: Male holotype length 2.5 mm., width pleotelson 0.35 mm., allotype gravid length 2.3 mm., width pleotelson 0.30 mm.

Type locality: North Atlantic, Caribbean, L.G.O. Biotrawl No. 96, types plus one male, three female paratypes, cat. no. I-82.

Distribution: L.G.O. Biotrawl No. 94, three males, two females, two juveniles, one fragment, cat. no. I-84; No. 95, three males, cat. no. I-83; No. 97, one female, cat. no. I-85; No. 98, two males, cat. no. I-86.

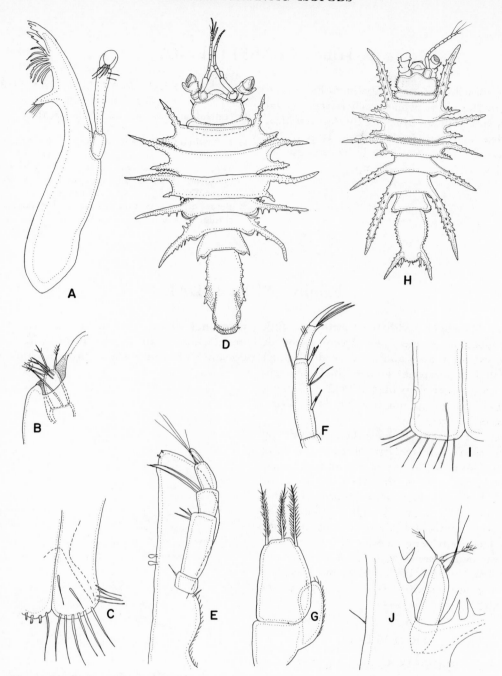

Figure 64. A–G: *Mesosignum kohleri*, n. sp. A: mandible; B: uropod; C: first pleopod; D: dorsal view male holotype; E: maxilliped; F: first peraeopod; G: third pleopod. H–J: *Mesosignum usheri*, n. sp. H: dorsal view male holotype; I: first pleopod; J: uropod.

Affinities: Near to *usheri* but without stout spine at postero-lateral angle of pleon.

Mesosignum usheri, new species
Figure 64 H–J

Synonyms: None.

Diagnosis: *Mesosignum* with stout spinulate postero-lateral spines at apex of pleon. Frons of cephalon evenly rounded. Antero-lateral spine of second peraeonal somite five times the length of postero-lateral spine and extending forward beyond peduncle of first antenna. Apex of male first pleopod straight, with eight marginal setae.

Measurements: Holotype male length 2.0 mm., width pleotelson 0.3 mm., allotype length 2.1 mm., width pleotelson 0.4 mm.

Type locality: North Atlantic, Caribbean, L.G.O. Biotrawl No. 98, types plus one female, cat. no. I-87–88.

Distribution: Known only from type locality.

Affinities: Near to *kohleri* but with stout spine at postero-lateral angles of pleon.

Tribe : FLABELLIFERA

The three subtribes of the Flabellifera have been reported from the abyss, where each is represented by several species. The subtribes are the Anthuroidea, the Seroloidea, and the Cirolanoidea. It is highly probable that the records of the latter are due to pelagic species caught on the way up.

A KEY TO THE FLABELLIFERAN SUBTRIBES
(From Menzies, in press)

1. Individual peraeonal somites longer than wide . . . . *Anthuroidea*
1. Individual peraeonal somites much wider than long 2
2. Peraeon with first somite fused medially with cephalon. First to third pleopoda smaller than operculiform fourth and fifth pairs . . . . . *Seroloidea*
2. Peraeon and cephalon not fused. Pleopods all similar in size . . . . *Cirolanoidea*

Family : SEROLIDAE

Diagnosis: Flabellifera with the fourth and fifth pairs of pleopoda large and operculiform, pleopods 1–3 normal, smaller than 4 and 5. Cephalon united medially with first peraeonal somite. Body strongly depressed, much wider than high (thick). Uropoda small, normal, subapical, not arching over pleon. (From Menzies, in press.)

Composition: The serolids have been revised by Nordenstam (1933). The majority of the species have been recovered from shallow water, and although a few abyssal species have been described, only one— *Serolis neaera* Beddard—had been known from the Atlantic abyss. The genus is well represented in Antarctic polar regions, but is yet unknown from the Arctic. In fact, only one species is known from the Northern hemisphere—namely, *Serolis carinata* Lockington (Richardson, 1905). Here five species of abyssal serolids are described from the abyss of the South Atlantic.

Genus : SEROLIS Leach

Subgenus : SEROLIS Nordenstam, 1933

Type species: Serolis (Serolis) *paradoxa* (Fabricius, 1775).

Diagnosis: Uropoda two-branched (biramous, not spiniform). Tergum of seventh peraeonal somite vanished. Tergum of sixth peraeonal somite well demarcated from first abdominal segment in its entire length. Second article of maxillipedal palp cordate. (Modified after Nordenstam, 1933.)

Serolis (Serolis) neaera Beddard
Figure 65 A

Synonyms: Serolis neaera Beddard, 1884, pp. 331–332.
Diagnosis: *Serolis* with coxal plates marked off on

peraeonal somites 2–4 inclusive. Third article of maxillipedal palp small. Pleon with apex acute, dorsum with stout wide tooth at proximal end and a

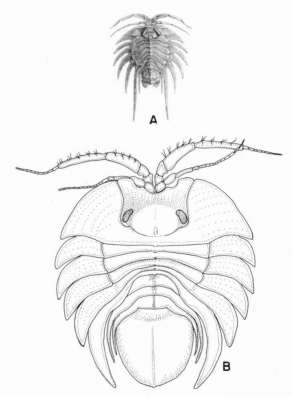

Figure 65. A: *Serolis (Serolis) neaera* Beddard, dorsal view. B: *Serolis (Serolis) margaretae*, n. sp., dorsal view female holotype.

smaller one near midpoint having a tooth on either side and a carina connecting with paired converging carinae near proximal tooth. Second pleonal epimera extending beyond posterior margin of pleon. Uropoda biramous, extending beyond apex of pleon.

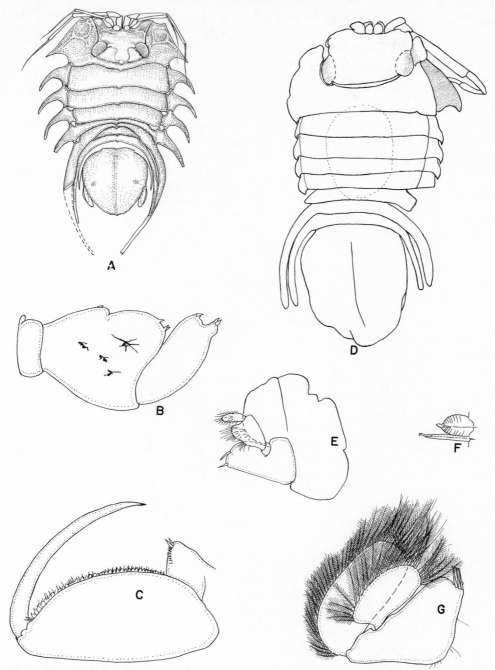

Figure 66. *Serolis (Serolis) macdonnellae*, n. sp. A: dorsal view female holotype; B: maxilliped embryo; C: first peraeopod; D: dorsal view embryo; E: maxilliped; F: peraeopodal seta; G: first pleopod.

Measurements: Largest male length 43 mm., greatest breadth 47 mm; female length 40 mm., greatest breadth 40 mm.

Type locality: South Atlantic, *Challenger* Station 320, 1079 meters, and Station 318, 3731 meters.

Distribution: This species was not captured by *Vema*.

Serolis (Serolis) *margaretae*, new species
Figure 65 B

Synonyms: None.

Diagnosis: Serolis with coxal plates marked off on peraeonal somites 2–5. Third article of maxillipedal palp small. Uropods biramous. Pleon with sharp pointed median extension of mid-dorsal carina, lateral carinae lacking. First peraeonal somite without spine at antero-lateral border, which is smooth. Eye lobes present, cephalon with low mid-dorsal tubercle at posterior end. Each peraeonal somite with a tubercle near posterior margin at midline. Pleon lacking postero-lateral angles. Epimera of sixth peraeonal somite extending slightly beyond apex of pleon.

Uropodal rami blunt, endopod one-fourth longer than exopod.

Measurements: Female holotype length 8.4 mm., width pleon 3.2 mm., plus three smaller female paratypes.

Type locality: South Atlantic, L.G.O. Biotrawl No. 200, types only, cat. no. I-226.

Distribution: Known only from type locality.

Affinities: The very short uropodal exopod distinguishes this species.

Serolis (Serolis) macdonnellae, new species
Figure 66

Synonyms: None.

Diagnosis: *Serolis* with coxal plates marked off on peraeonal somites 2–4 inclusive. Third article of maxillipedal palp small. Pleon with sharp median posterior extension of entire mid-dorsal carina; lateral carinae lacking; postero-lateral angles and dorsal sculpture lacking; a pit present on either side of midline dorsally. Cephalon with sharp separated antero-lateral angles; lateral area carinate. Eye lobes present. Uropodal rami blunt, exopod one-fifth shorter than endopod, not extending to pleonal posterior margin.

Measurements: Length holotype female 42 mm., width pleotelson 13 mm.

Type locality: South Atlantic, L.G.O. Biotrawl No. 49, type only, cat. no. I-193.

Distribution: Known only from type locality.

Affinities: Similar to *S. (S.) glacialis* Beddard but

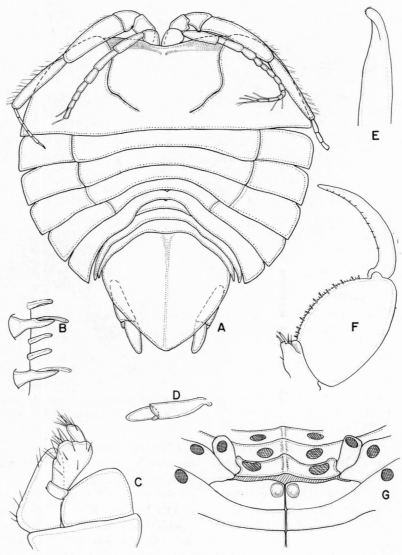

Figure 67. *Serolis (Serolis) vemae*, n. sp. A: dorsal view male holotype; B: peraeopodal seta; C: maxilliped; D: uropod; E: apex of second pleopod; F: first peraeopod; G: ventral view peraeon-pleon.

differing in the sculpture on the dorsum of the pleon.

Serolis (Serolis) vemae, new species
Figure 67

Synonyms: None.

Diagnosis: *Serolis* with coxal plates marked off on peraeonal somites 2–5 inclusive. Third article of maxillipedal palp small. Uropoda biramous, exopod minute, endopod thick projecting beyond posterior margin of pleon. Pleon without postero-lateral angles, apex pointed, mid-dorsal carina entire, lateral or transverse carinae lacking. Lateral borders of peraeon not pointed and produced but quadrate. Peraeonal somites 5 and 6 with a small mid-dorsal spine. Flagellum of second antenna shorter than last peduncular article. Flagellum of first antenna with ten articles.

Measurements: Holotype male 4.3 mm., width 1.7 mm.

Type locality: South Atlantic, L.G.O. Biotrawl No. 12, type only, cat. no. I-89.

Distribution: Also from L.G.O. Biotrawl No. 51, one female, cat. no. I-196.

Affinities: This species is unique, not falling into any of the subgroups mentioned by Nordenstam (1933).

Serolis (Serolis) maryannae, new species
Figure 68

Synonyms: None.

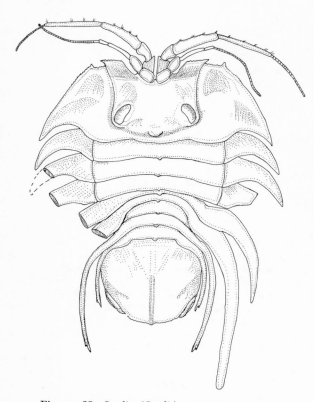

Figure 68. *Serolis (Serolis) maryannae*, n. sp., dorsal view female holotype.

Diagnosis: *Serolis* with coxal plates marked off on peraeonal somites 2–5. Third article of maxillipedal palp small. Uropoda biramous. Pleon with sharp pointed median posterior extension of mid-dorsal carina; lateral carinae lacking. First peraeonal somite with pronounced spine at antero-lateral angle. Eye lobes present, cephalon with mid-dorsal tubercle at posterior end. Each peraeonite except first somite with tubercle at posterior border at midline. Pleon lacking postero-lateral angles. Epimera of sixth peraeonal somite extending beyond apex of pleon by one times its length. Uropodal rami blunt, exopod one-third shorter than endopod, not extending to posterior margin of pleon.

Measurements: Female holotype length 18.8 mm., width pleon 7.2 mm.

Type locality: South Atlantic, L.G.O. Biotrawl No. 201, type only, cat. no. I-225.

Distribution: Known only from type locality.

Affinities: The serrated pleonal apex of this species is unique. Otherwise the species is very close to *S. (S.) macdonnellae*.

GLABROSEROLIS, new genus

Type species: *Glabroserolis specialis*, n. sp.

Diagnosis: Serolidae with uniramous uropoda. Coxal plates not marked off on any peraeonal somite. First antenna one-half the width of expanded peduncular article of second. Second article of maxillipedal palp quadrate, not cordate. Basipodites of pleopods 1–3 with projecting setiferous inner proximal angles.

Composition: Unique.

Glabroserolis specialis, new species
Figure 69

Synonyms: None.

Diagnosis: *Glabroserolis* with shield-shaped pleon devoid of carinae or postero-lateral angles. Endopod of uropod pointed, one-third longer than peduncle, not visible in dorsal view. Lateral borders of peraeon quadrate, not projecting. Flagellum of second antenna shorter than last peduncular article.

Measurements: Holotype female length 3.3 mm., width pleon 1.95 mm.

Type locality: South Atlantic, L.G.O. Biotrawl No. 53, type and one female, one fragment, cat. no. I-194.

Distribution: Known only from type locality.

Affinities: A unique species in a unique genus. To a certain extent the genus resembles *Spinoserolis* Nordenstam, but it lacks coxal plate demarcation entirely and has the unusually expanded peduncular articles of the second antenna.

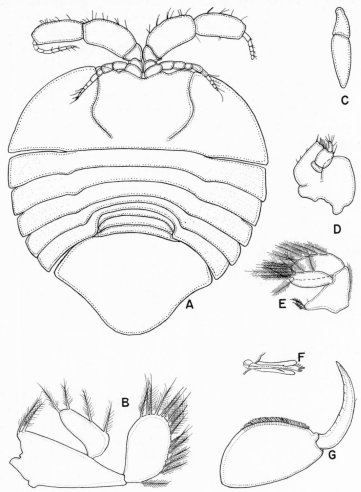

Figure 69. *Glabroserolis specialis*, n. sp. A: dorsal view female holotype; B: first pleopod; C: uropod; D: maxilliped; E: second pleopod; F: peraeopodal seta; G: peraeopod.

Subtribe: ANTHUROIDEA

Anthurids are seldom encountered in the abyss and are principally shallow water representatives. In the Atlantic four species, *Calathura brachiata* (Stimpson, *vide* Hansen, 1916), *Hyssura producta* Norman and Stebbing, *Ananthura abyssorum* (Norman and Stebbing), and *Anthelura truncata* (Hansen). The standard reference is Barnard's synopsis of the group. Here *Pseudanthura lateralis* Richardson is described from 1800 meters and a new species of *Leptanthura* is described from greater depth.

Diagnosis: Flabellifera with the individual peraeonal somites much longer than wide. Generally the uropoda arch over the telsonic somite (in all genera except *Pseudanthura*). The terminal abdominal segment (seventh) is probably a false telson or pseudotelson. First peraeopod generally subchelate.

A KEY TO THE GENERA OF
THE ANTHUROIDEA HAVING
ABYSSAL SPECIES
(After Barnard, 1925)

1. Mouth parts adapted for piercing and sucking . . 2
1. Mouth parts adapted for chewing 3
2. Uropoda lateral, exopod minute, not inflexed over pleotelson . . . . *Pseudanthura*
2. Uropoda with exopod inflexed over pleotelson . . 5
3. First pleopod indurated, operculiform . . . . *Hyssura*
3. First pleopod similar to second, not operculiform . 4
4. Peraeopods 2–3 not large . . . . *Anthelura*
4. Peraeopods 2–3 very similar to 1, large . . . . *Ananthura*
5. Maxilliped with three articles . . . . . . *Leptanthura*
5. Maxilliped with five articles . . . . *Calathura*

Genus: PSEUDANTHURA Richardson

Type species: *Pseudanthura lateralis* Richardson, 1911, pp. 523–524; — Barnard, 1920, pp. 343–344.

Diagnosis: Eyes absent. Mouth parts adapted for piercing and sucking. Telson not indurated, without statocyst. Maxilliped with four articles (palp with two articles). Peraeopods 4–7 with fifth joint not under-riding the sixth. Uropoda with small, lateral exopod; endopod and peduncle fused. All somites of pleon distinct dorsally and laterally. (Modified after Barnard 1925.)

Composition: The maxilliped in this genus has four articles not three, as indicated by Barnard (1925). The fusion of the uropodal endopod with the ped-uncle and the minute lateral exopods characterize this genus quite firmly. The genus contains only one species, and it ranges in depth from shallow water (930 meters) into the abyss (3200 meters).

Pseudanthura lateralis Richardson
Figure 70

Synonyms: *Pseudanthura lateralis* Richardson, 1911, pp. 524–525; — Barnard, 1920, pp. 344–345, Pl. XV; — 1925, p. 157.

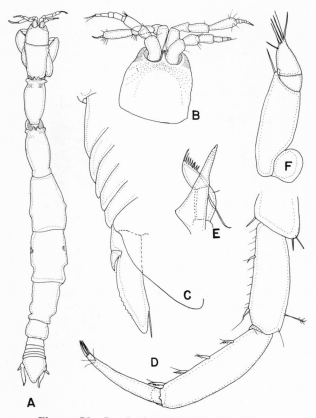

Figure 70. *Pseudanthura lateralis* Richardson, 1911. A: dorsal view male; B: cephalon; C: uropod; D: fifth peraeopod; E: man-dible; F: maxilliped.

Diagnosis: *Pseudanthura* with a pair of stout tubercles medially at anterior border of peraeonal somites 3 and 4. Lateral border of uropodal endopod finely serrated. Apex of pleon pointed, without teeth or setae.

Measurements: Male length 16 mm., female length 18 mm. (Barnard, 1920). Richardson gave the length as 20.5 mm.

Type locality: Coast of Soudan between Dakar and Praya, *Talisman* Station 80 (930 meters), Station 83 (1139 meters), and Station 101 (3200 meters) (Richardson, 1911).

Distribution: Near Dakar, West Africa (930–3200 meters) and Cape Point, North Africa, 86° E., distant 43 miles, 1620–1800 meters (Barnard, 1920, p. 345). L.G.O. Biotrawl No. 54.

Remarks: While I am reasonably certain that the species described here is equal to Barnard's specimens, it may not be the same as Richardson's species. Richard-son's (1911) description is incomplete and she gave no illustrations. The genus, however, is probably correct.

Genus: CALATHURA Norman and
Stebbing, 1886

Type species: *Calathura brachiata* (Stimpson, 1853).

Diagnosis: Mouth parts piercing and sucking. Eyes absent or feebly developed. Peraeon not strongly keeled dorso-laterally, with dorsal pits; seventh somite short. Pleon with distinct somites. Maxilliped with five articles. Peraeopods 4–7 with fifth joint triangular, underriding sixth. Pleopod 1 not indurated. Uropods with broad exopod inflexed over telson. (After Barnard, 1925.)

Composition: Restricted to the type species only by Barnard. The genus is known only from the northern hemisphere.

Calathura brachiata (Stimpson)
Figure 71

Synonyms: *Anthura brachiata* Stimpson, 1853, p. 43; — Richardson, 1905, p. 72 and references. *Calathura brachiata* (Stimpson), Norman and Stebbing, 1886, pp. 131–133, Pl. XXVI, Fig. 1; — Richardson, 1905, p. 72 and references; — Hansen, 1916, pp. 183–184, Pl. XV and references; — Barnard, 1925, p. 152. *Paranthura norwegica* Sars, 1873, p. 88. *Paranthura arctica* Sars, 1877, p. 347.

Diagnosis: Single species with generic characteris-tics sufficient to distinguish it (cf. Barnard, 1925, p. 152). Telson ovate-lanceolate, widest in the middle, apex acute, strongly concave dorsally in a longitudinal section, but plane in transverse section, a short narrow keel at base bearing a very fine median groove, followed by a very shallow ovate depression. (Barnard, op. cit., p. 152.)

Measurements: 45.5 mm. (Barnard, op. cit., p. 152).

Type locality: Duck Island, Bay of Fundy (Hargar, 1880).

Distribution: North Atlantic and Arctic, 5–735 fathoms (Barnard, op. cit., p. 152).

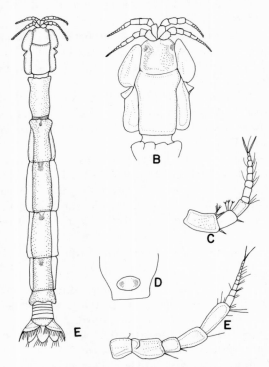

Figure 71. *Calathura brachiata* (Stimpson). A: dorsal view; B: cephalon; C: first antenna; D: statocyst; E: second antenna (Hansen, 1916).

According to Hansen (1916, p. 184), the species was collected at several *Ingolf* stations, and he reports the species from 2488 meters at latitude 48° 38′ N., west of Brittany (Norman and Stebbing, 1869, p. 133). It is doubtful that this abyssal record is correct, but without specimens it is impossible to tell.

Genus: **ANTHELURA** Norman and Stebbing, 1886

Type species: Anthelura elongata Norman and Stebbing, 1886.

Diagnosis: Eyes absent. Peraeonal somites without dorsal pits. Pleon distinct at least laterally. Telson not indurated, moderately convex. Antenna 1 typically with brush-like flagellum in male, pauci-articulate in female. Antenna 2 with flagellum pauci-articulate. Maxilliped five-jointed. Peraeopods 4–7 with fifth joint not underriding sixth. Pleopod 1 not indurated. Exopod inflexed over telson. (After Barnard, 1925.)

Composition: The genus contains the type, from 1332 meters in the North Atlantic; *Anthelura ramipies*

Barnard, from around 300 meters in the South Atlantic; and *Anthelura truncata* (Hansen) from the North Atlantic abyss. Here only the latter will be considered.

Anthelura truncata (Hansen)
Figure 72 A

Synonyms: Cyathura truncata Hansen, 1916, p. 182, Pl. XV. *Anthelura truncata* (Hansen), Barnard, 1925, p. 135.

Diagnosis: Anthelura with third palpal joint of mandible shorter than first, tipped with a few setae. Maxilliped without inner plate. Antenna 1 with two-jointed flagellum. Peraeopod 1 with fifth joint squarely projecting, palm slightly sinuous. Peraeopods 4–7 with fifth and sixth joints narrow. Telson broadly ovate, widest at basal third, with straight lateral

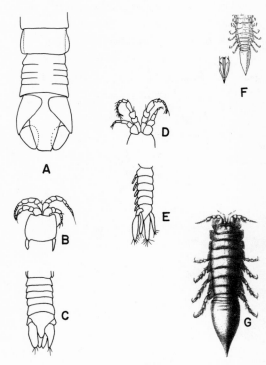

Figure 72. A: *Anthelura truncata* (Hansen), dorsal view of fragment. B–C: *Ananthura abyssorum* (Norman and Stebbing). B: cephalon; C: uropods. D–E: *Hyssura producta* Norman and Stebbing. D: cephalon; E: uropods. F: *Mesidothea magalura polaris* Gurjanova, dorsal view posterior. G: *Mesidothea megalura megalura* (G. O. Sars), dorsal view.

margins and truncate apex, dorsal surface convex. Uropod with endopod ovate, apex rounded, exopod ovate. (After Barnard, 1925.)

Measurements: To 10 mm. (Hansen, op. cit.).

Type locality: North Atlantic, *Ingolf* Station 24, Davis Strait, latitude 63° 06′ N., longitude 56° 00′ W., 2258 meters, temperature 2.4° C., five specimens.

Distribution; Also found at *Ingolf* Station 36, latitude 61° 50′ N., longitude 56° 21′ W., 2702 meters, temperature 1.5° C., two specimens (Hansen, op. cit.).

Genus: ANANTHURA Barnard, 1925

Type species: *Ananthura sulcaticauda* Barnard, 1925, p. 136.

Diagnosis: Anthuroidea with chewing mouth parts. Eyes feeble or absent. Peraeon not dorso-laterally keeled, dorsal pits in one species. Pleonal somites distinct. Telson lenticular in cross-section, somewhat indurated. Mandible with first and third palpal joints subequal, latter with a comb of setae. Maxilliped five-jointed with small inner plate which may not be present in all species. Peraeopods 2 and 3 nearly as large as peraeopod 1. Peraeopods 4–7 with fifth joint short but not underriding sixth. Pleopod 1 not indurated. Uropod with endopod long, subequal to peduncle, exopod closing over telson.

Composition: Besides the bathyal Atlantic type, Barnard (1925) included two additional species, *A. ovalis* Barnard from the Mediterranean and the Atlantic abyssal *Ananthura abyssorum* (Norman and Stebbing), which is here described.

Ananthura abyssorum (Norman and Stebbing)
Figure 72 B–C

Synonyms: *Anthelura abyssorum* Norman and Stebbing, 1886, pp. 127–128, Pl. 27. *Ananthura abyssorum* (Norman and Stebbing), Barnard, 1925, p. 137.

Diagnosis: *Ananthura* with antennal flagella multi-articulate. Palm of first peraeopod with about eight slender spine-like setae. Palm of second pair with three spines and a few setae. Carpus and propod of last peraeopod each furnished with two forked spines on anterior margin. Telson with acute apex and equal in length to uropods. (From Norman and Stebbing, op. cit. p. 127.)

Measurements: Length 9 mm.

Type locality: North Atlantic near entrance of Davis Strait, *Valorous* Station 8, latitude 59° 11′ N., longitude 50° 25′ W., 3199 meters.

Distribution: Known only from type locality.

Genus: HYSSURA Norman and Stebbing, 1886

Type species: *Hyssura producta* Norman and Stebbing, 1886.

Diagnosis: Anthuroidea without eyes. Mouth part adapted for chewing. Dorso-lateral keels and pits lacking from peraeon. Telson indurated, without statocysts. Antennal flagellum pauci-articulate. Mandible with third palpal joint subequal to first, with comb of setae. Maxilliped five-jointed, with inner plate. Peraeopods 4–6 with fifth, joint not underriding sixth. Somite 7 without peraeopods. Pleopod 1 not operculiform, not larger than others. Uropods with narrow rami, exopod folding down over telson.

Composition: The genus contains two deep sea species, *producta* and *profunda* Barnard.

Hyssura producta Norman and Stebbing
Figure 72 D–E

Synonyms: *Hyssura producta* Norman and Stebbing, 1886, pp. 128–129, Pl. 25; — Barnard, 1925, p. 137.

Diagnosis: *Hyssura* with narrow cylindrical telson. Endopod of uropod terete, longer than peduncle; exopod very narrow, terete. Peraeopods 4–6 with fourth joint twice as long as broad. (After Barnard, 1925.)

Measurements: Length about one quarter of an inch.

Type locality: North Atlantic, *Valorous* Station 11, latitude 56° 11′ N., longitude 37° 41′ W., 2651 meters.

Distribution: Known only from type locality.

Genus: LEPTANTHURA G. O. Sars

Type species: *Leptanthura tenius* (Sars) 1872, Barnard, 1925, p. 150.

Diagnosis: Anthuroidea with piercing and sucking mouth parts, eyes absent. No dorsal pits. Pleon with distinct sutures. Telson shorter than pleon, concave dorsally, thin, not indurated; single statocyst at proximal end. Antenna 1 with brush-like flagellum in male, rudimentary in female. Flagellum antenna 2 rudimentary in both sexes. Mandible with third palpal joint shorter than first, with two apical setae. Maxilliped three-jointed, second joint much the longest. Peraeopods 4–7 with fifth joint underriding sixth. Pleopod 1 not indurated. Uropods with endopod almost as broad as peduncle, exopod broadly oval, meeting at midline and folding down over telson.

Composition: Besides the shallow water type, the genus also contains *affinis* (Bonnier), 1410 meters; *glacialis* Hodgson, 1910, from around 300 meters; *orientalis* Barnard, intertidal?, *thori* Barnard, 952 meters; *laevigata* (Stimpson), from around 200 meters; *truncata* Richardson, 1911, from 888 meters; *chiltoni* (Beddard, 1886), from around 1400 meters; *diemenensis* (Haswell), littoral, and *hendili* Wolff from 6000 meters. Prior to this work an abyssal Atlantic species was unknown.

Leptanthura species
No figure

Two specimens, a male and a female of a species of *Leptanthura*, were found in L.G.O. Biotrawl No. 22. They were too damaged to permit specific identification even though the generic designation was possible. This record is given here only to indicate that the genus does penetrate the Atlantic abyss; previously only *L. hendili* Wolff from the Pacific was known from abyssal depth.

Subtribe : CIROLANOIDEA

Cirolanid type isopods morphologically retain the greatest number of truly primitive and embyronal characters. Nevertheless, this type is not known for certain from depths exceeding 2000 meters. Two species, both members of the typically pelagic genus *Eurydice*, have been caught in dredge hauls fishing the depths and the surface in the Atlantic. These are: *Eurydice grimaldi* Dollfuss, Stephensen, 1915 (0–2600 meters) and *Eurydice stygia* G. O. Sars, Hansen, 1916 (527–2356 meters).

The greatest depth from which Cirolanoidea are known is 1958 meters, based on the *Challenger* capture of the certainly benthic sphaeromid *Naesicopea abyssorum* Beddard from the South Pacific. The parasitic *Anilocra meridionalis* Searle, taken from 2000–2500

meters in the South Pacific, should probably be included among the pelagic species.

Anuropus, an exceedingly primitive genus (family: Anuropidae), has been identified as bathypelagic by Menzies and Dow (1958).

Bathynomous is doubtless a truly benthic genus. The greatest depth from which it has been reported is 1719 meters, and the shallowest is 357 meters. It is known mainly from the seas accessory to the oceans—e.g., Gulf of Bengal, Caribbean, South China Sea. Although very primitive, it has not succeeded in penetrating the abyss of the oceans. Perhaps it is best viewed as a relict descendant of the Mesozoic period. It is known as fossil from the Miocene of Japan (Imaizumi, 1953).

Tribe : VALVIFERA

Valviferans are in general alga feeders and are generally restricted to shelf depth, except for the Arcturidae, which contains filter-feeding types. These arcturids are quite common in shallow water, and one species, *Antarcturus spinosus* Beddard, has been reported from the abyss (2516 meters) in the South Atlantic Ocean. Four species of Antarcturus are known from

the Antarctic abyss, and one is known from the Indian Ocean abyss. One species was present in the *Vema* collections from the South Atlantic.

Besides the arcturids, *Mesidothea* has one subspecies which penetrates the abyss of the Arctic.

Diagnosis: Isopoda with the uropods valve-like, flexed under the pleotelson as an operculum.

Family : ARCTURIDAE

Diagnosis: Valvifera with biramous uropods. Peraeopods 2–4 directed toward the cephalon, provided with plumose setae, not prehensile. Last three peraeopods clinging or walking appendages.

Composition: Stephensen (1947) has presented a review of the arcturids. The majority of the species are found in cold water and at shallow depths. The poles are typified by their own genera, *Arcturus* from the high northern latitudes and *Antarcturus* from high southern latitudes. Stephensen (op. cit.) has also provided a key to the 30 species of *Antarcturus* known up to 1940.

Genus : ANTARCTURUS Zur Strassen, 1902

Synonyms: *Antarcturus*, Nordenstam 1933, p. 122; — Stephensen, 1940, p. 17.

Diagnosis: First peraeonal somite coalesced with cephalon, yet separated by a shallow groove. Lateral margins of the first peraeonai somite not prolonged

downward and forward; mouth organs visible in lateral view. Pleon with three somites anterior to pleotelson, which are indistinctly marked off by shallow grooves. Length of pleon not exceeding length of the last five peraeonal somites together. Flagellum of second antenna with four or five articles. First peraeopods prehensile. Antennae as long as or longer than body.

Type species: *Arcturus furcatus* Studer, 1884, pp. 12–15, Pl. I; — Zur Strassen, 1902, p. 686; — Nordenstam, 1933, p. 129.

Antarcturus species
No figure

A large fragmentary specimen of a species of *Antarcturus* which is perhaps closely related to *A. glacialis* (Beddard) but with sharper and fewer dorsal spines was collected by *Vema* at L.G.O. Biotrawl No. 214. The animal, with its pleon 9.7 mm. long, was poorly preserved and description of it is not indicated at this time. It is mentioned here only because of its abyssal nature.

Locality: South Atlantic, L.G.O. Biotrawl No. 214.

Genus: MESIDOTHEA Richardson

Type species: Mesidothea entomon (Linnaeus), Richardson, 1905, pp. 347–348.

Diagnosis: Valvifera with uniramous uropoda. First antenna with four articles. Flagellum with a single article. Flagellum of second antenna multiarticulate. Peraeopods 1–3 prehensile without plumose setae. Pleon consisting of five complete somites.

Composition: This genus formerly contained only two species—the blind *sabini* and the eye-bearing type, *entomon*. Gurjanova (1946, pp. 105–44) has provided a review of *Mesidothea*. She states, "A comparative analysis of species and forms of *Mesidothea* makes it possible to establish a continued row of morphological variations from the abyssal *M. megalura megalura* (G. Sars) through the intermediate *M. megalura polaris* Gurjanova, *M. sabini megaluroides* Gurjanova and *M. sabini sabini* to *M. sabini robusta* Gurjanova, and from *M. sibirica* (Birula) to *M. entomon vetterensis* Ekman, through the intermediate Far Eastern and Siberian estuary forms." This statement favors a recent penetration of the abyss by *Mesidothea*.

Mesidothea megalura polaris Gurjanova
Figure 72 F

Synonym: Mesidothea megalura polaris Gurjanova, 1946a, pp. 280–281, 295 (English).

Diagnosis: Mesidothea megalura with clearly pentagonal pleon, epimera upturned and body more rugose than in subspecies.

Measurements: 56 mm.

Type locality: Arctic Ocean, Sedov Station 100, latitude 81° 10′ N., longitude 137° 17′ E., 2500 meters one specimen (Gurjanova, op. cit.).

Distribution: Known only from the Arctic Ocean abyss. Not captured by *Vema.*

Mesidothea megalura megalura (G. O. Sars)
Figure 72 G

Synonyms: Chiridothea megalura G. O. Sars, 1879, p. 432; — Ohlin, 1901, p. 24, Figs. 4a–d. *Mesidothea megalura* (G. O. Sars), Hansen, 1916, p. 187. *Mesidothea megalura megalura* (G. O. Sars), Gurjanova, 1946a.

Diagnosis: Mesidothea megalura with the epimeral plates (coxal plates) not upturned. Body less coarse than *M. megalura polaris* Gurjanova and smaller in size. Pleon spear point-shaped, not pentagonal.

Measurements: Female 52 mm. long (Hansen, op. cit).

Type locality: North Atlantic, between Norway and Spitzbergen (Hansen, op. cit., p. 187).

Distribution: A cold water abyssal species in the North Atlantic. It was found by the *Ingolf* at Station 112, latitude 67° 57′ N., longitude 6° 44′ W., 2386 meters, temperature −1.1° C., two specimens; Station 118, latitude 68° 27′ N., longitude 8° 22′ W., 1996 meters, temperature −1.0° C., four specimens; Station 113, latitude 69° 31′ N., longitude 7° 06′ W., 2465 meters, temperature −1.0° C, seven specimens (Hansen, op. cit.). Not captured by *Vema.*

LIST OF ATLANTIC ABYSSAL BIOLOGICAL TRAWL SAMPLES OF THE LAMONT GEOLOGICAL OBSERVATORY

L.G.O. Biotrawl No. 1, *Vema*-7-1, 12 November 1955, 5104–5122 meters, latitude 20° 3.2′ N, longitude 68° 21.1′ W., Antilles Outer Ridge, north of the Puerto Rico Trench, EBTOC, species of isopods captured:

Abyssianira dentifrons Menzies
Echinothambema ophiuroides Menzies
Eurycope (Indeterminable)
Haploniscus unicornis Menzies
Ianirella vemae Menzies
Syneurycope hanseni Menzies

L.G.O. Biotrawl No. 2, *Vema*-7-2, 1 December 1955, 3425 meters, latitude 11° 16.6′ N., longitude 79° 14.4′ W., southwestern part of Colombia Abyssal Plain in western Caribbean, EBTOC, species of isopods captured:

No specimens captured.

L.G.O. Biotrawl No. 5, *Theta*-1-1, 8 September 1956, 3028 meters, latitude 27° 05–06′ N., longitude 15° 17.9–19.4′ W., Upper Continental Rise off the coast of Río de Oro, Africa, EBT, species of isopods captured:

No specimens captured.

L.G.O. Biotrawl No. 6, *Theta*-1-3, 11 September 1956, 4738 meters, latitude 26° 7–28.9′ N., longitude 22° 12.0–12.2′ W., northeast corner Cape Verde Abyssal Plain, EBT, species of isopods captured:

No specimens captured.

L.G.O. Biotrawl No. 7, *Theta*-1-4, 23 September 1956, 5779 meters, latitude 29° 17.6′ N., longitude 57° 20.3′ W., Abyssal Hills between Nares and Sohm Abyssal Plains, EBT, species of isopods captured:

Abyssijaera acarina, new species
Eurycope complanata Bonnier

L.G.O. Biotrawl No. 8, *Theta*-1-5, 25 September 1956, 4488 meters, latitude 31° 30.3–33.5′ N., longitude 64° 12.5′–65° 15.5′ W., Bermuda Apron southeast of Bermuda, EBT, species of isopods captured:

No specimens captured.

L.G.O. Biotrawl No. 9, *Theta*-1-6, 26 September 1956, 5166 meters, latitude 31° 41–43′ N., longitude 68° 08′ W., Bermuda Plateau near western edge of Bermuda Rise, EBT, species of isopods captured:

Desmosoma birsteini, new species
Eurycope (Indeterminable)
Storthyngura vemae, new species

L.G.O. Biotrawl No. 10, *Theta*-1-7, 27 September 1956, 5325 meters, latitude 32° 16.4–21.5′ N., longitude 69° 08.8–13.4′ W., Bermuda Rise near northwest boundary, EBT, species of isopods captured:

No specimens captured.

L.G.O. Biotrawl No. 11, *Theta*-1-8, 30 September 1956, 2238 meters, latitude 38° 33.1–35.7′ N., longitude 72° 32.1–34.4′ W., Upper Continental Rise southeast of New York, EBT, species of isopods captured:

No specimens captured.

L.G.O. Biotrawl No. 12, *Vema*-12-1, 6 April 1957, 5024 meters, latitude 38° 58.5′ S., longitude 41° 45′ W., northern part of Argentine Rise southeast of Río Grande LBT, species of isopods captured:

Abyssianira dentifrons Menzies
Acanthocope argentinae, new species
Eurycope (Indeterminable)
Haplomesus bifurcatus, new species
Haploniscus bicuspis (G. O. Sars)
Haploniscus minutus, new species
Haploniscus ovalis, new species
Haploniscus parallelus, new species
Haploniscus tridens, new species
Haploniscus (Indeterminable)
Ilyarachna argentinae, new species
Ischnomesus bidens, new species
Ischnomesus magnificus, new species
Ischnomesus paucispinis, new species
Ischnomesus (Indeterminable)
Macrostylis bipunctatus, new species
Nannoniscoides hirsutus, new species
Serolis (*Serolis*) *vemae*, new species
Stylomesus inermis (Vanhöffen)
Stylomesus simplex, new species
Stylomesus spinulosus, new species
Stylomesus (Indeterminable)
Xostylus parallelus, new species

L.G.O. Biotrawl No. 13, *Vema*-12-1, 15 April 1957, 4000 meters, latitude 40° 10′ S., longitude 6° 05′ W., Eastern Steps of Mid-Atlantic Ridge south-east of Tristan da Cunha, SBT, species of isopods captured:

No specimens captured.

L.G.O. Biotrawl No. 14, *Vema*-12-2, 30 April 1957, 3049 meters, latitude 30° 14.9′ S., longitude 13° 03′ E., Upper Continental Rise southeast of Port Nolloth, Union of South Africa, SBT, species of isopods captured:

Antennuloniscus dimeroceras (Barnard)
Eurycope ovaloides, new species
Haploniscus princeps, new species
Haploniscus rugosus, new species
Haploniscus trituberculatus, new species
Ilyarachna africana, new species
Ilyarachna triangulata, new species
Ilyarachna (Indeterminable)
Ischnomesus decemspinosus, new species
Storthyngura triplispinosa, new species

L.G.O. Biotrawl No. 15, *Vema*-12-3, 2 May 1957, 4935 meters, latitude 28° 25.2′ S., longitude 8° 28.5′ E., northern end of Orange Abyssal Plain, SBT, species of isopods captured:

Vemathambema elongata, new species

L.G.O. Biotrawl No. 16, *Vema*-12-4, 3 May 1957, 2970 meters, latitude 25° 33′ S., longitude 12° 27′ E., Upper Continental Rise off Walvis Bay, South Africa, SBT, Species of isopods captured:

Acanthaspidia bifurcata, new species
Desmosoma (Indeterminable)

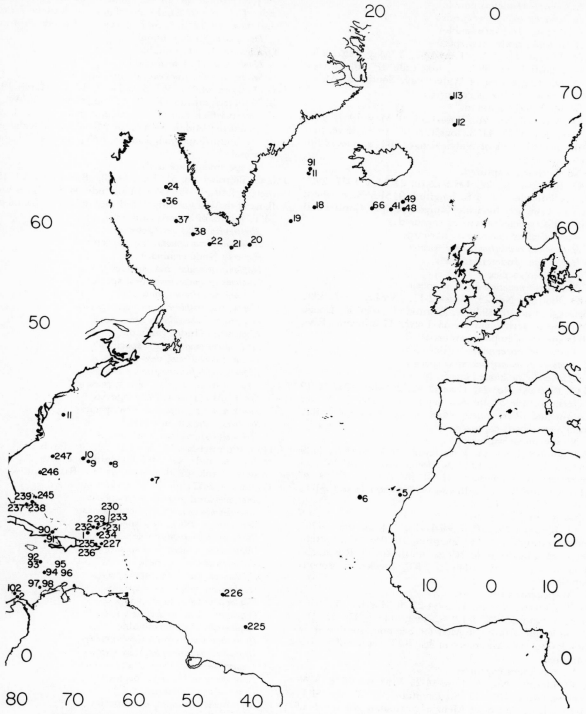

Figure 73. Chart of Lamont Geological Observatory Deep-Sea Biotrawl Stations in the North Atlantic. Stations north of 50° N. are *Ingolf* stations.

Eurycope (Indeterminable)
Haploniscus percavix, new species
Haploniscus spinifer Hansen
Nannoniscus (Indeterminable)
Spinianirella walfishensis, new species
L.G.O. Biotrawl No. 17, *Vema*-12-5, 4 May 1957, 126 meters, latitude 24° 18′ S., longitude 14° 07.5′ E., SBT, species of isopods captured:
  Desmosoma striata, new species

L.G.O. Biotrawl No. 18, *Vema*-12-6, 7 May 1957, 4047 meters, latitude 23° 00′ S., longitude 08° 11′ E., crest of Walvis Ridge Front Range west of Walvis Bay, Southwest Africa, SBT, species of isopods captured:
  Acanthocope unicornis, new species
  Acanthocope (Indeterminable)
  Desmosoma (Indeterminable)
  Haplomesus ornatus, new species
  Haploniscus spinifer Hansen

Haploniscus (Indeterminable)
Ischnomesus wolffi, new species
Ischnomesus (Indeterminable)
Notoxenoides vemae, new species

L.G.O. Biotrawl No. 19, *Vema*-12-7, 7 May 1957, 2701 meters, latitude 22° 58.5′ S., longitude 07° 00′ E., crest of Walvis Ridge west of Walvis Bay, Southwest Africa, SBT, species of isopods captured:

No specimens captured.

L.G.O. Biotrawl No. 20, *Vema*-12-8, 9 May 1957, 4945 meters, latitude 22° 41′ S., longitude 03° 16′ E., lower part of the western flank of Walvis Ridge, SBT, species of isopods captured:

No specimens captured.

L.G.O. Biotrawl No. 22, *Vema*-12-10, 21 May 1957, 2997 meters, latitude 5° 53.5′ S., longitude 9° 51.5′ E., northern wall of Congo Submarine Canyon, Upper Continental Rise, SBT, species of isopods captured:

Antennuloniscus dimeroceras (Barnard)
Haploniscus quadrifrons, new species
Haploniscus (Indeterminable)
Leptanthura species
Macrostylis hirsuticaudis, new species

L.G.O. Biotrawl No. 23, *Vema*-12-11, 23 May 1957, 3921 meters, latitude 6° 19.3′ S., longitude 8° 18.5′ E., Congo Cone near active canyon on Lower Continental Rise, SBT, species of isopods captured:

Antennuloniscus dimeroceras (Barnard)
Haploniscus quadrifrons, new species
Macrostylis abyssicola Hansen

L.G.O. Biotrawl No. 24, *Vema*-12-12, 24 May 1957, 3919 meters, latitude 5° 45′ S., longitude 8° 29′ E., Lower Continental Rise, north edge of Congo Cone, SBT, species of isopods captured:

No specimens captured.

L.G.O. Biotrawl No. 25, *Vema*-12-13, 27 May 1957, 4139 meters, latitude 4° 13.9′ S., longitude 0° 18′ W., an extension of Cameroun trend in Eastern Steps of Mid-Atlantic Ridge southwest of Annobon Island, SBT, species of isopods captured:

No specimens captured.

L.G.O. Biotrawl No. 26, *Vema*-12-15, 1 June 1957, 4707 meters, latitude 1° 52′ S., longitude 16° 04.5′ W., Eastern Steps of Mid-Atlantic Ridge northeast of Romanche Trench, equatorial Atlantic, SBT, species of isopods captured:

No specimens captured.

L.G.O. Biotrawl No. 46, *Vema*-14-22, 6 March 1958, 3705 meters, latitude ±55° 19′ S., longitude ±37° 57′ W., Archipelagic Apron of Menzies Seamont southwest of South Georgia, eastern Scotia Sea, SBT, species of isopods captured:

No specimens captured

L.G.O. Biotrawl No. 47, *Vema*-14-23, 6 March 1958, 3756 meters, latitude 55° 29′ S., longitude 37° 57′ W., SBT, Archipelagic Apron of Menzies Seamount southwest of South Georgia, eastern Scotia Sea, species of isopods captured:

Antennuloniscus ornatus, new species
Haploniscus tricornis, new species
Storthyngura (Indeterminable)
Stylomesus (Indeterminable)

L.G.O. Biotrawl No. 48, *Vema*-14-24, 7–8 March 1958, 3473 meters, latitude 56° 37′ S., longitude 34° 48′ W., Abyssal Hills eastern Scotia Sea southeast of South Georgia Island, SBT, species of isopods captured:

No specimens captured.

L.G.O. Biotrawl No. 49, *Vema*-14-25, 9 March 1958, 2741

meters, latitude 56° 43′ S., longitude 27° 41′ W., western side of the South Sandwich Island arc between Visokoi and Lesokov Islands, SBT, species of isopods captured:

Desmosoma (Indeterminable)
Eurycope (Indeterminable)
Haploniscus (Indeterminable)
Serolis (*Serolis*) *macdonnellae*, new species

L.G.O. Biotrawl No. 50, *Vema*-14-27, 17–18 March 1958, 3776 meters, latitude 57° 39′ S., longitude 13° 32′ W., on the scarp which marks the boundary between the Lower Step and the Middle Step of the Mid-Atlantic Ridge east of the South Sandwich Islands, SBT, species of isopods captured:

No specimens captured.

L.G.O. Biotrawl No. 51, *Vema*-14-28, 28 March 1958, 4588 meters, latitude 45° 34′ S., longitude 06° 02′ E., western flank of the Walvis Ridge northwest of Meteor Seamount, SBT, species of isopods captured:

Abyssianira dentifrons Menzies
Antennuloniscus armatus, new species
Eurycope (Indeterminable)
Haploniscus acutus, new species
Haploniscus spatulifrons, new species
Haploniscus tricornis, new species
Haploniscus trituberculatus, new species
Haploniscus tuberculatus, new species
Haploniscus (Indeterminable)
Hydroniscus ornatus, new species
Ianirella magnifrons, new species
Macrostylis bifurcatus, new species
Macrostylis bipunctatus, new species
Serolis (*Serolis*) *vemae*, new species
Storthyngura triplispinosa, new species
Stylomesus elegans, new species
Stylomesus granulosus, new species

L.G.O. Biotrawl No. 52, *Vema*-14-29, 30 March 1958, 4960 meters, latitude 41° 03′ S., longitude 07° 49′ E., south-western flank of the Schmidt-Ott Rise southwest of Capetown, SBT, species of isopods captured:

Antennuloniscus armatus, new species
Antennuloniscus rostratus, new species
Eurycope acutitelson, new species
Eurycope (Indeterminable)
Haplomesus ornatus, new species
Haploniscus elevatus, new species
Haploniscus parallelus, new species
Haploniscus polaris, new species
Haploniscus telus, new species
Haploniscus tricornoides, new species
Haploniscus (Indeterminable)
Ilyarachna multispinosa, new species
Ilyarachna nodifronoides, new species
Ischnomesus simplissimus, new species
Ischnomesus wolffi, new species
Ischnomesus (Indeterminable)
Macrostylis bifurcatus, new species
Macrostylis bipunctatus, new species
Syneurycope multispina, new species

L.G.O. Biotrawl No. 53, *Vema*-14-31, 4 April 1958, 4885 meters, latitude 36° 34′ S., longitude 14° 08′ E., Lower Continental Rise southwest of Capetown, SBT, species of isopods captured:

Acanthocope annulatus, new species
Acanthomunna beddardi, new species
Eurycope nodosa, new species
Eurycope (Indeterminable)
Glabroserolis specialis, new species
Haploniscus bicuspis (G. O. Sars)

Haploniscus nondescriptus, new species
Haploniscus percavix, new species
Haploniscus princeps, new species
Haploniscus rugosus, new species
Ianirella bifida, new species
Ilyarachna gurjanovae, new species
Ilyarachna simplex, new species
Ilyarachna indentifrons, new species
Ischnomesus simplissimus, new species
Ischnomesus (Indeterminable)
Macrostylis bipunctatus, new species
Macrostylis (Indeterminable)
Nannoniscus laevis, new species
Storthyngura symmetrica, new species
Storthyngura triplispinosa, new species
Stylomesus simplex, new species

L.G.O. Biotrawl No. 54, *Vema*-14-32, 6 April 1958, 1816 meters, latitude 34° 35′ S., longitude 17° 31′ E., SBT, species of isopods captured:

Antennuloniscus dimeroceras (Barnard)
Dendromunna spinipes, new species
Gnathia albescenoides, new species
Ilyarachna (Indeterminable)
Notoxenoides abyssi, new species
Pseudanthura lateralis Richardson
Spinianirella walfishensis, new species

L.G.O. Biotrawl No. 55, *Vema*-14-33, 6 April 1958, 706 meters, latitude 34° 26′ S., longitude 17° 32′ E., SBT species of isopods captured:

Gnathia vemae, new species
Haploniscus capensis, new species
Ilyarachna spinoafricana, new species

L.G.O. Biotrawl No. 76, *Vema*-14-48, 9 July 1958, 2526 meters, latitude 34° 14′ N., longitude 24° 10′ E., SBT, species of isopods captured:

Haplomesus tropicalis, new species

L.G.O. Biotrawl No. 90, *Vema*-15-5, 4 November 1958, 3378 meters, latitude 20° 30′ N., longitude 73° 16′ W., gap between Old Bahama Abyssal Plain and Hispaniola-Caicos Abyssal Plain, SBT, species of isopods captured: No specimens captured.

L.G.O. Biotrawl No. 91, *Vema*-15-6, 5 November 1958, 3897–4080 meters, latitude 19° 26′ N., longitude 75° 09′ W., south scarp of Cayman Trench, south of Guantanamo Bay, Cuba, SBT, species of isopods captured: none.

L.G.O. Biotrawl No. 92, *Vema*-15-7, 6 November 1958, 3094–3076 meters, latitude 15° 51′ N., longitude 75° 11′ W., escarpment west of Colombia Abyssal Plain, SBT, species of isopods captured: No specimens captured.

L.G.O. Biotrawl No. 93, *Vema*-15-8, 6 November 1958, 3071 meters, latitude 15° 51′ N., longitude 75° 11′ W., escarpment west of Colombia Abyssal Plain, SBT, species of isopods captured: No specimens captured.

L.G.O. Biotrawl No. 94, *Vema*-15-9, 7 November 1958, 4071 meters, latitude 14° 05′ N., longitude 75° 25′ W., Central part of Colombia Abyssal Plain, SBT, species of isopods captured:

Acanthocope (Indeterminable)
Eurycope (Indeterminable)
Heteromesus bifurcatus, new species
Mesosignum kohleri, new species

L.G.O. Biotrawl No. 95, *Vema*-15-10, 7 November 1958, 4071 meters, latitude 14° 05′ N., longitude 75° 25′ W., central part of Colombia Abyssal Plain, SBT, species of isopods captured:

Haplomesus tropicalis, new species

Mesosignum kohleri, new species
Storthyngura snanoi, new species

L.G.O. Biotrawl No. 96, *Vema*-15-11, 7 November 1958, 4076, meters, latitude 14° 05′ N., longitude 75° 25′ W., central part of Colombia Abyssal Plain, SBT, species of isopods captured:

Acanthocope (Indeterminable)
Mesosignum kohleri, new species

L.G.O. Biotrawl No. 97, *Vema*-15-12, 8 November 1958, 2868–2875 meters, latitude 11° 30′ N., longitude 75° 50′ W., Continental Rise northwest off Cartagena, Colombia, SBT, species of isopods captured:

Mesosignum kohleri, new species
Nannoniscus primitivus, new species

L.G.O. Biotrawl No. 98, *Vema*-15-13, 8 November 1958, 2875–2941 meters, latitude 11° 30′ N., longitude 75° 50′ W., Continental Rise northwest off Cartagena, Colombia, SBT, species of isopods captured:

Ilyarachna (Indeterminable)
Ischnomesus (Indeterminable)
Macrostylis caribbicus, new species
Mesosignum kohleri, new species
Mesosignum usheri, new species

L.G.O. Biotrawl No. 100, *Vema*-15-15, 9 November 1958, 1714 meters, latitude 10° 11′ N., longitude 78° 30′ W., SBT, species of isopods captured:

Haploniscus tropicalis, new species
Ischnomesus caribbicus, new species
Nannoniscus camayae, new species

L.G.O. Biotrawl No. 101, *Vema*-15-16, 9 November 1958, 1615–1533 meters, latitude 10° 11′ N., longitude 78° 30′ W., SBT, species of isopods captured:

Eurycope (Indeterminable)
Haploniscus tropicalis, new species

L.G.O. Biotrawl No. 102, *Vema*-15-17, 10 November 1958, 2076 meters, latitude 10° 13′ N., longitude 78° 33′ W., Continental Rise north of Colón, Panama, SBT, species of isopods captured: No specimens captured.

L.G.O. Biotrawl No. 103, *Vema*-15-18, 10 November 1958, 1906–1800 meters, latitude 10° 13′ N., longitude 78° 33′ W., SBT, species of isopods captured:

Desmosoma magnispinum, new species

L.G.O. Biotrawl No. 107, *Vema*-15-22, 10 November 1958, 975 meters, latitude 09° 46.3′ N., longitude 79° 37.5′ W., SBT, species of isopods captured:

Ilyarachna (Indeterminable)
Ischnomesus multispinis, new species
Nannoniscus (Indeterminable)

L.G.O. Biotrawl No. 199, *Vema*-15-115, 14 March 1959, 3275 meters, latitude 55° 18.2′ S., longitude 64° 08.6′ W., Estados Escarpment south of Staten Island, SBT, species of isopods captured: No specimens captured.

L.G.O. Biotrawl No. 200, *Vema*-15-116, 15 March 1959, 3813 meters, latitude 55° 42.9′ S., longitude 64° 21.6′ W., Continental Rise south of Staten Island, northwest Scotia Sea, SBT, species of isopods captured:

Ilyarachna scotia, new species
Serolis (*Serolis*) *margaretae*, new species
Syneurycope heezeni, new species

L.G.O. Biotrawl No. 201, *Vema*-15-117, 15 March 1959, 3839 meters, latitude 55° 31.2′ S., longitude 64° 07.5′ W., Continental Rise south of Staten Island, northwest Scotia Sea, SBT, species of isopods captured:

Antennuloniscus ornatus, new species
Eurycope antarctica Vanhöffen
Eurycope vicarius Vanhöffen

Eurycope (Indeterminable)
Ilyarachna (Indeterminable)
Munna (*Munna*) *argentinae*, new species
Serolis (*Serolis*) *maryannae*, new species
Syneurycope heezeni, new species
L.G.O. Biotrawl No. 202, *Vema*-15-118, 16 March 1959, 3776 meters, latitude 55° 44.2′ S., longitude 64° 11.5′ W., Continental Rise south of Staten Island, northwest Scotia Sea, SBT, species of isopods captured:
Storthyngura birsteini, new species
L.G.O. Biotrawl No. 203, *Vema*-15-119, 17 March 1959, 3959 meters, latitude 57° 04′ S., longitude 61° 25′ W., Northern Rift Mountains of the Triton Rift System in the western Scotia Sea south of Burdwood Bank, SBT, species of isopods captured:
No specimens captured.
L.G.O. Biotrawl No. 204, *Vema*-15-120, 20 March 1959, 4146 meters, latitude 57° 32.1′ S., longitude 55° 09.5′ W., Southern Rift Mountains of the Triton Rift System, western Scotia Sea south of Burdwood Bank, SBT, species of isopods captured:
No specimens captured.
L.G.O. Biotrawl No. 205, *Vema*-15-121, 22 March 1959, 3963 meters, latitude 54° 45.8′ S., longitude 52° 02′ W., Abyssal Hills south of the Scotia Ridge east of Burdwood Bank, SBT, species of isopods captured:
No specimens captured.
L.G.O. Biotrawl No. 206, *Vema*-15-122, 24 March 1959, 2526 meters, latitude 52° 10.8′ S., longitude 49° 04.9′ W., south side of Falkland Ridge near the north wall of the Malvinas Chasm, SBT, species of isopods captured:
No specimens captured.
L.G.O. Biotrawl No. 207, *Vema*-15-123, 25 March 1959, 2681 meters, latitude 50° 23.2′ S., longitude 47° 25′ W., central part of Falkland Ridge northeast of the Falkland Islands, SBT, species of isopods captured:
Abyssianira argentenensis, new species
L.G.O. Biotrawl No. 208, *Vema*-15-124, 26 March 1959, 2738 meters, latitude 49° 35′ S., longitude 48° 04.6′ W., 200 fathoms below the top of the Falkland Escarpment northeast of the Falkland Islands, SBT, species of isopods captured:
Haploniscus (Indeterminable)
Stylomesus elegans, new species,
L.G.O. Biotrawl No. 209, *Vema*-15-125, 27 March 1959, 5042 meters, latitude 49° 21.2′ S., longitude 47° 44.6′ W., lower part of Falkland Escarpment northeast of the Falkland Islands, SBT, species of isopods captured:
No specimens captured.
L.G.O. Biotrawl No. 210, *Vema*-15-126, 28 March 1959, 6079 meters, latitude 47° 57.5 S., longitude 48° 03′ W., southern part of Argentine Abyssal Plain, SBT, species of isopods captured:
Stylomesus inermis (Vanhöffen)
L.G.O. Biotrawl No. 211, *Vema*-15-127, 30 March 1959, 5933 meters, latitude 45° 44′ S., longitude 50° 45′ W., southwest flank of the Argentine Rise southeast of Bahía Blanca, Argentine Republic, SBT, species of isopods captured:
No specimens captured.
L.G.O. Biotrawl No. 212, *Vema*-15-128, 31 March 1959, 5843 meters, latitude 44° 53.3′ S., longitude 51° 26.5′ W., southwest flank of the Argentine Rise southeast of Bahía Blanca, Argentine Republic, SBT, species of isopods captured:
Antennuloniscus dimeroceras (Barnard)
Haploniscus tridens, new species
Ilyarachna (Indeterminable)

Nannoniscus oblongus G. O. Sars
Storthyngura digitata, new species
Storthyngura triplispinosa, new species
Stylomesus simplex, new species
L.G.O. Biotrawl No. 213, *Vema*-15-129, 31 March 1959, 5849 meters, latitude 44° 54′ S., longitude 51° 35.4′ W., southwest flank of the argentine Rise southeast of Bahía Blanca, Argentine Republic, SBT, species of isopods captured:
No specimens captured.
L.G.O. Biotrawl No. 214, *Vema*-15-130, 2 April 1959, 5293 meters, latitude 42° 00′ S., longitude 45° 01.5′ W., Southwest flank of the Argentine Rise southeast of Bahía Blanca, Argentine Republic, SBT, species of isopods captured:
Abyssianira dentifrons Menzies
Antarcturus species
Haplomesus ornatus, new species
Hydroniscus quadrifrons, new species
Ischnomesus elegans, new species
Storthyngura (Indeterminable)
Stylomesus inermis (Vanhöffen)
Stylomesus productus, new species
Stylomesus simulans, new species
L.G.O. Biotrawl No. 217, *Vema*-15-133, 24 April 1959, 3963–3954 meters, latitude 39° 55.4′ S., longitude 42° 38.8′ W., north central part of Argentine Rise, SBT, species of isopods captured:
Hydroniscus ornatus, new species
Ischnomesus (Indeterminable)
Macrostylis bipunctatus, new species
L.G.O. Biotrawl No. 218, *Vema*-15-134, 25 April 1959, 4166–4144 meters, latitude 27° 53.7′ S., longitude 39° 26′ W., Continental Rise southeast of Rio de Janeiro, SBT, species of isopods captured:
Eurycope (Indeterminable)
Haploniscus (Indeterminable)
Ilyarachna (Indeterminable)
Stylomesus regularis, new species
L.G.O. Biotrawl No. 219, *Vema*-15-135, 29 April 1959, 4303–4254 meters, latitude 20° 39′ S., longitude 34° 48.5′ W., Upper Continental Rise east of Valparaiso, South America, SBT, species of isopods captured:
No specimens captured.
L.G.O. Biotrawl No. 220, *Vema*-15-136, 3 May 1959, 3222–3336 meters, latitude 9° 45′ S., longitude 34° 24′ W., Continental Rise southeast of Recife, Brazil, SBT, species of isopods captured:
Ischnomesus (Indeterminable)
Syneurycope heezeni, new species
L.G.O. Biotrawl No. 225, *Vema*-15-141, 10 May 1959, 4674–4678 meters, latitude 5° 04′ N., longitude 41° 01′ W., southeast end of Guiana Abyssal Plain east of the Guianas, SBT, species of isopods captured:
No specimens captured.
L.G.O. Biotrawl No. 226, *Vema*-15-142, 14 May 1959, 4932 meters, latitude 10° 31′ N., longitude 45° 02′ W., inter-montane basin floor, western Mid-Atlantic Ridge north of the east-west Vema Trough, east of Trinidad, SBT, species of isopods captured:
No specimens captured.
L.G.O. Biotrawl No. 227, *Vema*-15-143, 25 May 1959, 3711–3761 meters, latitude 19° 01′ N., longitude 65° 39′ W., top of south wall of Puerto Rico Trench north of Arecibo, Puerto Rico, SBT, species of isopods captured:
No specimens captured.
L.G.O. Biotrawl No. 229, *Vema*-15-145, 1 June 1959, 5684 meters, latitude 22° 01.5′ N., longitude 66° 23.5′

W., Antilles Outer Ridge, north of Puerto Rico Trench, north of Puerto Rico, SBT, species of isopods captured:

Haploniscus (Indeterminable)
Hydroniscus quadrifrons, new species
Macrostylis vemae, new species

L.G.O. Biotrawl No. 230, *Vema*-15-146, 2 June 1959, 5814–5817 meters, latitude 22° 20′ N., longitude 65° 01′ W., Southern part of Nares Abyssal Plain north of the Virgin Islands, SBT, species of isopods captured:

No specimens captured.

L.G.O. Biotrawl No. 231, *Vema*-15-147, 4 June 1959, 5440–5410 meters, latitude 21° 18.7′ N., longitude 65° 13.4′ W., Antilles Outer Ridge, north of Puerto Rico Trench, north of Puerto Rico, SBT, species of isopods captured:

Antennuloniscus dimeroceras (Barnard)
Desmosoma (Indeterminable)
Eurycope (Indeterminable)
Haplomesus (Indeterminable), *tenuispinis* Hansen?
Haploniscus (Indeterminable)
Hydroniscus quadrifrons, new species
Ilyarachna (Indeterminable)
Macrostylis minutus, new species
Macrostylis vemae, new species

L.G.O. Biotrawl No. 232, *Vema*-15-148, 6 June 1959, 5172–5163 meters, latitude 21° 35′ N., longitude 67° 09′ W., Antilles Outer Ridge, north of Puerto Rico Trench, north of Puerto Rico, SBT, species of isopods captured.

Haploniscus (Indeterminable)
Hydroniscus quadrifrons, new species
Macrostylis minutus, new species

L.G.O. Biotrawl No. 233, *Vema*-15-149, 7 June 1959, 5291–5271 meters, latitude 21° 32′ N., longitude 66° 37′ W., Antilles Outer Ridge, north of Puerto Rico Trench, north of Puerto Rico, SBT, species of isopods captured:

Eurycope (Indeterminable)
Hydroniscus quadrifrons, new species
Ischnomesus (Indeterminable)

L.G.O.Biotrawl No. 234, *Vema*-15-150, 11 June 1959, 5477–5494 meters, latitude 20° 21.3′ N., longitude 66° 24′ W., Antilles Outer Ridge, north of Puerto Rico Trench, north of Puerto Rico, SBT, species of isopods captured:

Eurycope (Indeterminable)
Haplomesus insignis Hansen

Hydroniscus quadrifrons, new species
Ischnomesus armatus Hansen
Macrostylis minutus, new species
Macrostylis setifer, new species

L.G.O. Biotrawl No. 235, *Vema*-15-151, 12 June 1959, 6264 meters, latitude 18° 45.4′ N., longitude 66° 30′ W., south wall of Puerto Rico Trench north of Fajardo, Puerto Rico, SBT, species of isopods captured:

No specimens captured.

L.G.O. Biotrawl No. 237, *Vema*-15-153, 21 June 1959, 2370–2357 meters, latitude 25° 01.5′ N., longitude 77° 47′ W., floor of the tongue of the ocean west of New Provident Island, SBT, species of isopods captured:

Eurycope (Indeterminable)

L.G.O. Biotrawl No. 238, *Vema*-15-154, 21 June 1959, 2668–2623 meters, latitude 25° 15′ N., longitude 77° 42′ W., western end of Northeast Providence Channel (Bahamas) at the entrance to the tongue of the ocean south of the Berry Islands, SBT, species of isopods captured:

No specimens captured.

L.G.O. Biotrawl No. 239, *Vema*-15-155, 22 June 1959, 3727 meters, latitude 25° 28′ N., longitude 77° 15′ W., axis of Northeast Providence Channel (Bahamas) north of Nassau, SBT, species of isopods captured:

No specimens captured.

L.G.O. Biotrawl No. 245, *Vema*-15-161, 4 July 1959, 4759 meters, latitude 26° 11′ N., longitude 76° 27.5′ W., Blake–Bahama Abyssal Plain near the mouth of the Northeast Providence Channel (Bahamas), SBT, species of isopods captured:

No specimens captured.

L.G.O. Biotrawl No. 246, *Vema*-15-162, 8 July 1959, 3963–3950 meters, latitude 30° 30′ N., longitude 75° 55′ W., Outer Ridge east of the Blake Plateau, SBT, species of isopods captured:

Macrostylis truncatex, new species

L.G.O. Biotrawl No. 247, *Vema*-15-163, 9 July 1959, 4680 meters, latitude 32° 34′ N., longitude 74° 21.5′ W., northern end of the Outer Ridge east of the northern part of the Blake Plateau southeast of Cape Hatteras, SBT, species of isopods captured:

No specimens captured.

LIST OF OTHER ABYSSAL ATLANTIC AND ARCTIC STATIONS FROM WHICH ISOPODS WERE COLLECTED

Albatross Station 2084, North Atlantic, off Georges Bank, 2361 meters, 40° 16.5′ N., 67° 05′15″ W., temp. 40° F., species of isopods captured:
Heteromesus spinescens Richardson

Albatross Station 2105, North Atlantic, off Virginia, 2557 meters, 37° 50′ N., 73° 03.5′ W., temp. 41° F. (Richardson, op. cit.), species of isopods captured:
Heteromesus spinescens Richardson

Albatross Station 2208, North Atlantic, south of Block Island, 2155 meters, 39° 33′ N., 71° 16′15″ W., temp. 38.4° F., species of isopods captured:
Heteromesus granulatus Richardson
Heteromesus spinescens Richardson

Albatross Station 2571, North Atlantic, southeast of Georges Bank, 2480 meters, 40° 09′30″ N., 67° 09′ W., temp. 37.8° F. (Richardson, op. cit.), species of isopods captured:
Heteromesus granulatus Richardson
Heteromesus spinescens Richardson
Ianirella lobata Richardson

Albatross Station 2572, North Atlantic, southeast of Georges Bank, 3235 meters, 40° 29.0′ N., 66° 04′ W., temp. 37.8° F (Richardson, op. cit.), species of isopods captured:
Haploniscus excisus Richardson
Heteromesus granulatus Richardson
Ianirella lobata Richardson
Rhacura pulchra Richardson
Storyngura truncata (Richardson)

Albatross Station 2573, North Atlantic, southeast of Georges Bank, 3186 meters, 40° 34′18″ N., 66° 09′ W., temp. 37.3° F. (Richardson, op. cit.), species of isopods captured:
Ianirella lobata Richardson

Albatross Station 2714, North Atlantic, south of Martha's Vineyard, 3337 meters, 38° 22′ N., 70° 17′30″ W., temp. ? (Richardson, 1908a), species of isopods captured:
Heteromesus spinescens Richardson

Albatross Station 2043, North Atlantic, Cape May to Nantucket, 39° 49′ 00″ N., 68° 28′ 30″ W., 2680 meters, temp. 38.5° F., species of isopods captured:
Storthyngura magnispinis (Richardson)

Albatross Station 2221, North Atlantic, Cape Hatteras to Nantucket, 39° 05′ 30″ N., 70° 44′ 30″ W., 2788 meters, temp. 36.9° F., species of isopods captured:
Storthyngura truncata (Richardson)

Atlantis Station 15, North Atlantic, c. 40° N., 30° E., species of isopods captured:
Haploniscus percavix, new species

Challenger Station 318, South Atlantic, 3731 meters, 42° 38′ S., 56° 29′ W., species of isopods captured:
Serolis (Serolis) neaera Beddard

Ingolf Station 18, North Atlantic, south of Denmark Strait, latitude 61° 44′ N., longitude 30° 29′ W., 1135 fathoms (2137 meters), temp. 3.0° C. (Hansen, op. cit.), species of isopods captured:
Haplomesus angustus Hansen

Ingolf Station 22, North Atlantic, latitude 58° 10′ N., longitude 48° 25′ W., 3474 meters, temp. 1.4° C. (Hansen, op. cit.), species of isopods captured:
Haploniscus spinifer Hansen
Haplomesus tenuispinis Hansen
Macrostylis abyssicola Hansen
Syneurycope parallela Hansen

Ingolf Station 24, North Atlantic, Davis Strait, latitude 63° 06′ N., longitude 56° 00′ W., 1199 fathoms (2258 meters), temp. 2.4° C. (Hansen, op. cit), species of isopods captured:
Anthelura truncata (Hansen)
Desmosoma gracilipes Hansen
Desmosoma intermedium Hult
Desmosoma simile Hansen
Eurycope complanata Bonnier
Eurycope furcata G. O. Sars
Haplomesus modestus Hansen
Haplomesus quadrispinosus (G. O. Sars)
Haplomesus tenuispinis Hansen
Ianirella laevis Hansen
Munna (M.) acanthifera Hansen
Nannoniscus analis Hansen
Nannoniscus inermis Hansen
Storthyngura magnispinis (Richardson)

Ingolf Station 36, North Atlantic, Davis Strait, latitude 61° 50′ N., longitude 56° 21′ W., 1435 fathoms (2702 meters), temp. 1.5° C. (Hansen, op. cit.), species of isopods captured:
Anthelura truncata (Hansen)
Desmosoma coarctatum (G. O. Sars)
Desmosoma gracilipes Hansen
Desmosoma insigne Hansen
Eurycope complanata Bonnier
Eurycope nodifrons Hansen
Eurycope parva Bonnier
Haploniscus spinifer Hansen (?), n. sp. ?
Haplomesus insignis Hansen
Haplomesus quadrispinosus (G. O. Sars)
Heteromesus longiremis Hansen
Ianirella laevis Hansen
Ilyarachna bicornis Hansen
Ilyarachna spinosissima Hansen
Ischnomesus armatus Hansen
Storthyngura magnispinis (Richardson)

Ingolf Station 37, North Atlantic, Davis Strait, latitude 60° 17′ N., longitude 54° 05′ W., 3229 meters, temp. 1.4° C., species of isopods captured:
Macrostylis abyssicola Hansen

Ingolf Station 38, North Atlantic, south of Davis Strait, latitude 59° 12′ N., longitude 51° 05′ W., 3521 meters, temp. 1.3° C. (Hansen, op. cit.), species of isopods captured:
Desmosoma longispinum Hansen

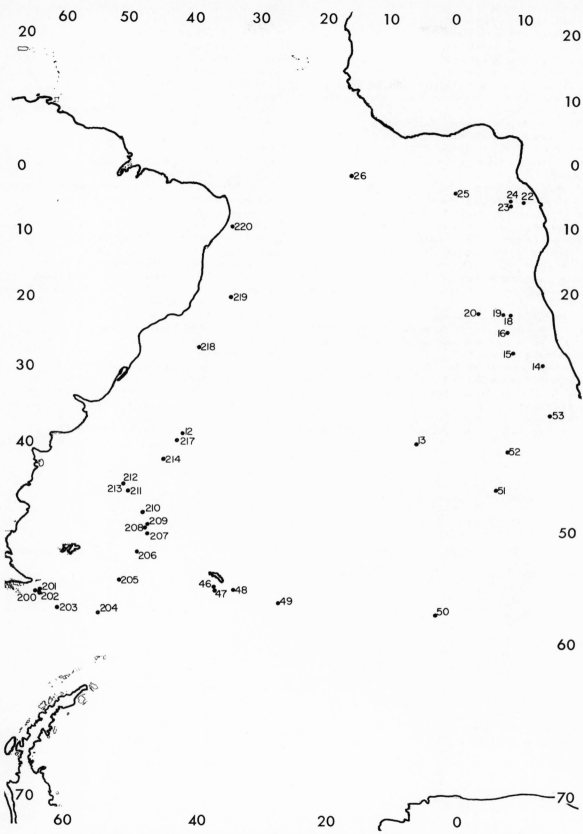

Figure 74. Chart of Lamont Geological Observatory Deep-Sea Biotrawl Stations in the South Atlantic.

Haplomesus quadrispinosus (G. O. Sars)
Hydroniscus abyssi Hansen
Ilyarachna spinosissima Hansen
Ischnomesus profundus Hansen
Macrostylis abyssicola Hansen
Nannoniscus armatus Hansen

Ingolf Station 112, North Atlantic, latitude 67° 57′ N., longitude 6° 44′ W., 2386 meters, temp. —1.1° C., species of isopods captured:

Mesidothea megalura megalura (G. O. Sars)

Ingolf Station 113, North Atlantic, south of Jan Mayen, latitude 69° 31′ N., longitude 7° 06′ W., 2465 meters, temp. —0.1° C. (Hansen, op. cit.), species of isopods captured:

Eurycope hanseni Ohlin
Haplomesus quadrispinosus (G. O. Sars)
Haploniscus bicuspis (G. O. Sars)
Gnathia stygia (G. O. Sars)
Ilyarachna longicornis (G. O. Sars)
Mesidothea megalura megalura (G. O. Sars)
Nannoniscus spinicornis Hansen

Plankton expedition Station 158, North Atlantic, latitude 7.5° N., longitude 21.3° W., 4000 meters, species of isopods captured:

Acanthaspidia decorata Hansen

Porcupine Station 19, North Atlantic, west of Donegal, latitude 54° 53′ N., longitude 10° 56′ W., 2486 meters, species of isopods captured:

Thambema amicorum Stebbing

Sadko Station 10, Arctic Ocean, latitude 80° 02′ N., longitude 3° 19′ E., 2380 meters (Gurjanova, 1946a), species of isopods captured:

Eurycope incisa Gurjanova

Sedov Station 100, Arctic Ocean, latitude 81° 10′ N., longitude 137° 17′ E., 2500 meters (Gurjanova, op. cit.), species of isopods captured:

Ilyarachna derjugini Gurjanova
Mesidothea megalura polaris Gurjanova

Talisman Station 31, north of San Miguel in the Azores, 22 August 1883, 2995 meters, species of isopods captured:

Heteromesus similis Richardson

Talisman Station 76, North Atlantic, latitude 25° 1′ N., longitude 19° 15′ W., 2638 meters (Monod, 1926a), species of isopods captured:

Gnathia caeca Richardson

Talisman Station 134, 24 August 1883, 4060 meters, Azores, species of isopods captured:

Ilyarachna abyssorum Richardson

Talisman Station 135, 25 August 1883, 4165 meters, Azores, species of isopods captured:

Ilyarachna abyssorum Richardson

Talisman Station 139, coast of Soudan between Dakar and Praya, 3200 meters (Richardson, 1911), species of isopods captured:

Pseudanthura lateralis Richardson

Thor Station, North Atlantic, south of Iceland, latitude 60° 11′ N., longitude 19° 36′ W., 1899 to 2143 meters (Hansen, op. cit.), species of isopods captured:

Ianira hanseni, new species
Munna (*Munna*) *acanthifera* Hansen

Valorous Station 8, North Atlantic, near entrance of Davis Strait, latitude 59° 10′ N., longitude 50° 25′ W., 3199 meters, species of isopods captured:

Ananthura abyssorum (Norman and Stebbing)

Valorous Station 11, North Atlantic, latitude 56° 11′ N., longitude 37° 41′ W., 2651 meters, species of isopods captured:

Hyssura producta Norman and Stebbing

BIBLIOGRAPHY

Barnard, K. H. 1920. Contributions to the crustacean fauna of South Africa. No. 6. Further additions to the list of Marine Isopoda. Ann. So. African Mus. 17, part V, no. 11, pp. 319–438, pls. XV–XVII.

——— 1925. A revision of the family Anthuridae (Crustacea, Isopoda), with remarks on certain morphological peculiarities. Linnean Soc., Jour. (Zool.) 36: 109–160.

Beddard, F. E. 1884. Preliminary notice of the Isopoda collected during the voyage of H.M.S. "Challenger." Part I. Serolis Proc. Zool. Soc. London, May, 1884, pp. 330–341.

——— 1886. Preliminary notice of the Isopoda collected during the voyage of H.M.S. "Challenger." Part II. Munnopsidae. Proc. Zool. Soc. London, December, 1885, pp. 916–925.

——— 1886a. Preliminary notice of the Isopoda collected during the voyage of H.M.S. "Challenger." Part III. Proc. Zool. Soc. London, No. 7, pp. 97–122.

——— 1886 b. Report on the Isopoda collected by H.M.S. "Challenger" during the years 1873–76, part 2, "Challenger" Reports, Zoology, vol. 17, 175 pp., 25 pls.

Birstein, J. A. 1957. Certain peculiarities of the ultra-abyssal fauna at the example of the genus Storthyngura (Crustacea Isopoda Asellota). Akad. Nauk. SSSR. 36 (7): 961–985 (summary in English).

——— 1960. The family Ischnomesidae (Crustacea, Isopoda, Asellota) in the north-western part of the Pacific and the problem of amphiboreal and bipolar distribution of the deep sea fauna. Zool. Zhurnal SSSR. 39 (1:) 3–28 (summary in English).

——— 1961. Microthambema tenuis n. gen., n. sp. (Isopoda, Asellota) and relations of some asellote isopods. Crustaceana 2 (2): 132–141.

Bonnier, J. 1896. Edriophthalmes, in Résultats Scientifiques Campagne "Caudan" dans le Golfe de Gascogne. Ann. Univ. Lyon 26: 527–689. Paris.

Dollfus, A. 1901. Etude préliminaire des Gnathiidae recueillis dans les camp. de l'Hirondelle et de la Princesse Alice. Bull. Soc. Zool. France 26: 239–246.

Fabricius, J. C. 1775. Systema entomolologiae (not seen by writer).

Gurjanova, E. 1933. Contributions to the Isopod Fauna of the Pacific Ocean. II. New Species of Gnathiidea and Asellota, pp. 79–88 (Russian), 89–91 (English). Expl. Mers U.S.S.R. Leningrad, no. 19.

——— 1946a. New Species of Isopoda and Amphipoda from the Arctic Ocean. Vol. 3. Compendium of Results of Drifting Expedition of Ice-Breaker "Cedov" 1937–1940 (English summary). Chief Office of Northroad, Moscow.

——— 1946b. Individual and age variability of the marine assel and its importance in evolution of the genus Mesidothea Rich. Trav. Inst. Zool. Acad. Sci. URSS 8: 105–144.

Hansen, H. J. 1895. Isopoden, Cumaceen u. Stomatopoden der Plankton-Expedition. Erg. Plankt. Exp. Humb. Stft. 2, 4 (3), pp. 1–105.

——— 1897. Reports on the dredgings of the Albatross, XXII. Isopoda. Bull. Mus. Comp. Zool., Harvard 31: 95–129.

——— 1916. Crustacea Malacostraca III (V). The Order Isopoda, in the Danish Ingolf Expedition, vol. 3, part 5, 262 pp., 16 pls. Bianco Luno, Copenhagen.

Harger, Oscar. 1880. Report on the marine Isopoda of New England and adjacent waters. Rept. U.S. Commissioner of Fish and Fisheries, 1878, part 6, pp. 297–462, pls. 1–13. Washington, D.C.

Hedgpeth, J. W. 1957. Obtaining ecological data in the sea. Mem. Geol. Soc. America, 1: 53–86, 11 figs., in Treatise on marine ecology and paleoecology. Geol. Soc. America Memoir 67, vol. 1, Ecology, 1296 pp., J. W. Hedgpeth, ed.

Hodgson, T. V. 1910. Crustacea IX: Isopoda. National Antarctic Expedition 1901–1904, vol. 4 (3), Zoology and Botany, 77 pp., 10 pls.

Hult, J. 1936. On some species and genera of Parasellidae. Arkiv. f. Zoologi. (Stockholm) 29A (6): 1–14.

——— 1941. On the soft-bottom isopods of the Skager Rak. Zool. Bidrag f. Uppsala, vol. 21, 234 pp.

Imaizumi, R. 1953. Note on Bathynomus sp. (Crustacea) from the Miocene of Japan. Short Papers, Tohoku University, no. 5, pp. 84–87, pl. 12. Sendai, Japan.

Leach, W. E. 1813–1814. Crustaceology. Edinburgh Encyclopedia, 7: 221–277, Appendix, pp. 429–434 (Brewster's ed.).

Menzies, Robert J. 1952. Some marine asellote isopods from Northern California, with descriptions of nine new species. Proc. U.S. Natl. Mus. 102 (3293): 117–159.

——— 1956a. New abyssal tropical Atlantic isopods with observations on their biology. American Museum Novitates, no. 1798: 1–16.

——— 1956b. New bathyal Isopoda from the Caribbean with observations on their nutrition. Breviora, Harvard Univ. no. 63: 1–10.

——— (in press). The Zoogeography, ecology, and systematics of the Chilean marine Isopods. Lund University, Lund, Sweden, Repts. Swedish Chilean Expedition.

Menzies, Robert J., and Thomas Dow. 1958. The largest known bathypelagic isopod Anuropus bathypelagicus n. sp., Ann. Mag. Nat. Hist., Ser. 13, 1: 1–6.

Menzies, Robert J., and Michael Tinker. 1960. Haploniscus robinsoni, a new species of asellote deep sea isopod from the eastern tropical Pacific Ocean. Pacific Naturalist, 1 (18): 1–4.

Monod, T. 1926a. Les Gnathiidae. Mem. Soc. Sci. Nat. Maroc. no. 13, 667 pp.

——— 1926b. Tanaidacés, Isopodes et Amphipods, in Zoology, Rapports Scientifiques Résultats Voyage de la Belgica, 1897–1899, Exped. Antarctique Belge, pp. 1–66.

Nierstrasz, H. F. 1941. Isopoda Genuina III. Gnathiidea, Anthuridea, Valvifera, Asellota, Phreatocoidea, in Siboga Exped. Monographie XXXII d, E. J. Brill, pp. 235–308. Leiden.

Nordenstam, A. 1933. Marine Isopoda of the families Serolidae, Idotheidae, Pseudidotheidae, Arcturidae, Parasellidae, and Stenetriidae mainly from the South Atlantic. Further Zool. Res. Swed. Antarctic Exped. 1901–1903, 3, (1): 1–284. Stockholm.

——— 1955. A new isopod from the deep-sea. Rep. Swedish Deep-Sea Exped., vol. 2, Zoology, no. 16, pp. 205–212.

Norman, A. M. and T. R. R. Stebbing. 1886. On the

crustacea Isopoda of the "Lightning," "Porcupine," and "Valorous" Expeditions. Trans. Zool. Soc. 12 (4): 77–141, pls. XVI–XXVII.

Ohlin, A. 1901. Arctic crustacea collected during the Swedish Arctic Expedition 1898 and 1899 under the direction of Professor A. G. Nathorst. 1. Leptostraca, Isopoda, Cumacea. Bih. Sv. Vet. Akad. Hand 1, 26 afd. 4, 12: 1–54.

Richardson, H. E. 1904. Contributions to the Natural History of the Isopoda. Proc. U.S. Nat. Mus., 27: 1–89.

———— 1905. A monograph on the isopods of North America. Bull. U.S. Nat. Mus., no. 54, 727 pp.

———— 1908a. Some new Isopoda of the superfamily Aselloidea From the Atlantic Coast of North America, Proc. U.S. Nat. Mus. 35 (1633): 71–86.

———— 1908b. Description of a new isopod of the genus Eurycope from Martha's Vineyard. Proc. U.S. Nat. Mus., 34 (1598): 67–69.

———— 1910. Marine Isopods collected in the Philippines by the U.S. Fisheries steamer "Albatross" in 1907–1908. Dept. Commerce Lab. Bu. Fish. Doc. 736, pp. 1–44. Washington.

———— 1911. Les Crustacés Isopodes du Travailleur et du Talisman. Bull. Mus. Paris, no. 7, pp. 518–534.

Sayce, O. A. 1900. Janirella, a new genus of isopod from fresh-water, Victoria. Proc. Roy. Soc. Victoria (N.S.) 13: 124–130, pls. XVIII–XIX.

Sars, G. O. 1864. Om en anomal Gruppe af Isopoder. Forh. Vidensk. Selsk, Christiania Aar 1863. Christiania.

———— 1868. Beretning om en i Sommeren 1865 foretagen Reise vid Kysterne af Christianias ôg Christiansands Stifter. Nyt Mag. F. Naturvid. Band 15, Hft. 1. Christiania. (Not seen by writer, copied from Hult, 1941.)

———— 1870. Dybvandscrustaceer Fra Lofoten. Forh. Vidensk. selsk. Christiania Aar 1869. Christiania. (Not seen by writer.)

———— 1873. Bidrag til Kundskaben om Dyrelivet paa vore Havbanker. Forh. Vidensk. selk. Christiania, 1872. (Not seen by writer.)

———— 1877. Prodromus Descriptionis Crustaceorum et Pycnogonidarum, que in Expeditione Norvegica Anno 1876 observavit. Arch. f. Math. og Naturvid, vol. 2. Christiania.

———— 1885. Crustacea, I.—Norw. N. Atl. Exped. Zool. (1876–1878) 1: 1–276. Christiania.

———— 1886. Crustacea II. Den Norske Nordhavs—Expedition 1876–1878, XV. Zoologi, Christiania. (Not seen by writer.)

———— 1897–1899. An account of the Crustacea of Norway. Vol. II. Isopoda, 2: 1–270. Bergen.

Searle, H. E. (Richardson). 1914. Isopoda. Bull. Mus. Comp. Zool., Harvard Coll., Cambridge, Mus. 58 (8): 361–372.

Schott, G. 1926. Geographie des Atlantischen Ozeans, 2nd ed., C. Boysen, pp. 1–368, 27 pls., Hamburg.

Stebbing, T. R. R. 1893. A history of recent Crustacea. Intern. Sci. Ser., vol. 71, 466 pp., D. Appleton & Co., New York.

———— 1912. On the Crustacea Isopoda of the "Porcupine" Expedition. Trans. Zool. Soc. London 20, part 4, no. 1: 231–239, pls. XXIV–XXVI.

———— 1912. Abstract "On the Crustacea Isopoda of the Porcupine Expedition." Proc. Zool. Soc. London, 1912, p. 42.

Stephensen, K. 1913. Report on the Malacostraca collected by the Tjalfe Exped. Vid. Meddel. Naturh. Foren. Kbhv. 64: 99.

———— 1915. Isopoda, Tanaidacea, Cumacea, Amphipoda (Excl. Hyperiidea), vol. II (Biology) D. I., in Rept. Danish Oceanographical Expeds. 1908–1910 to the Mediterranean and adjacent seas, no. 3, pp 1–25.

———— 1947. Tanaidacea, Isopoda, Amphipoda, and Pycnogonida, in Scientific Res. Norwegian Antarctic Exped. 1927–1928, no. 27, pp. 1–90.

Tattersall, W. M. 1905 (1906). The marine fauna of the coast of Ireland, part V, Isopoda. Rept. Sea and Inland Fisheries of Ireland 1904. Part II, Scientific Investigations. Dublin.

———— 1911. Die Nordischen Isopoden, in Nordisches Plankton, Brandt and Apstein, vol. III, no. VI, pp. VI 181–VI 313. Lipsius and Tischer, Kiel and Leipzig.

Vanhöffen, E. 1914. Die Isopoden der deutschen Südpolarexpedition 1901–1903, vol. 15, Zoology 7 (4): pp. 449–598, G. Reimer, Berlin.

Wolff, T. 1956. Isopoda from depths exceeding 6000 meters. Galathea Report, 2: 85–157, Copenhagen. Scientific Results of the Danish Deep-Sea Expedition Round the World 1950–52.

Contribution a la connaissance du genre
Makrokylindrus Stebbing (Crustacea Cumacea)

Espèces nouvelles recüeillies au cours des Campagnes
du Lamont Geological Observatory de New York

par MIHAI C. BĂCESCU
Musée d'Histoire Naturelle, Bucharest, Rumania

INTRODUCTION

Le matériel des Cumacés abyssaux, dont l'étude nous a été si aimablement confiée par le Dr. Robert J. Menzies, comprend, entre autres, le genre *Makrokylindrus*, qui y est particulièrement bien représenté, à en juger par les captures antérieures. Voici une première raison pour laquelle nous avons commencé par ce genre l'étude de la riche collection du L.G.O.; une seconde, en est le fait qu'un de ses représentants détient le record de profondeur pour un Cumacé ± identifié: 7160 mètres! Il s'agit de "*Diastylis*," figuré par Bruun (1953)—en realité un *Makrokylindrus* n. sp. Il serait très intéressant de savoir si le Cumacé capturé par le *Viteaz* par 8006 mètres de fond (Wolff, p. 110) n'appartient pas, lui aussi, à ce genre.

Tel qu'on le conçoit actuellement, le genre *Makrokylindrus* compte 20 espèces, le *M. costata* et le *M. fistularis* y compris. Comme le font récemment remarquer Fage (1951) et Lomakina (1958), il n'existe pas de limite nette entre les genres *Diastylis* et *Makrokylindrus*. En effet, on y trouve tous les intermédiaires entre le *Makrokylindrus* de type *tubulicauda* (*M. fragilis*, *M. fagei* n. sp.)—dont l'immense telson cylindrique[1] finit par deux grosses valves anales, surplombées d'une minuscule proéminence postanale, occupant à peine 1/5–1/7 de la longueur totale du telson—et les espèces à telson court (*M. insignis*, *M. longicauda*, *M. acanthodes*) ou celles à partie postanale très longue (*M. erinaceus*, *M. mystacinus*), aux

[1] Réalisé par le *Dimorphostylis australis* Hale également.

valves anales mal définies; quelques-unes des dernières espèces ne diffèrent pas trop de certaines *Diastylis*. Il y est donc question d'un genre encore mal défini, accepté surtout en raison de commodité systématique (vu le grand nombre d'espèces du genre *Diastylis*) plutôt qu'en vertu de bons critériums morphologiques.

Dans les études ultérieures, il faudra accorder plus d'attention, croyons-nous, aux caractères dimorphiques, à la forme et à l'articulation des *valves* anales (mentionnées déjà par Calman, Bonnier, Stebbing, Zimmer, etc.), lorsqu'on établit l'appartenance d'une espèce de ce genre; il faudra également considérer plus rigoureusement les espèces aux thoracomères 3 et 4 coalescents (*M. cingulatus*, *M menziesi* n. sp, *M. dubius* Bonnier, synonymisée avec *M. josephinae*).

Nous ne nous attardons plus à ce sujet, parce que nous y reviendrons sans faute. Pour le moment, nous allons considérer, sous une clef, toutes les espèces placées dans ce genre, y compris les espèces nouvelles.

Voir à ce sujet surtout les travaux de Stebbing (1912, 1913), Fage (1929), et Lomakina (1958). Le dernier en est dû au distingué cumacéologue, le professeur Louis Fage, à qui nous devons d'importantes précisions quant à la systématique de ce genre, ou aux synonymies (*M. spinventris* Hansen, *M. dubius* Bonnier), et quant à l'inclusion de plusieurs espèces jadis décrites comme des *Diastylis* (1951).

SYSTÉMATIQUE

Makrokylindrus wolffi,[2] n. sp.
Figures 1, 2

Collection du Lamont Geological Observatory. Station 53 (4 Avril 1958), Afrique du S-O. (latitude 36° 34′ S., longitude 14° 08′ E). Biotrawl, par 4885 mètres, 1 ♀ P = 12.5 mm.—type de l'espèce.

Carapace translucide, assez élastique, allongée, sa longueur dépassant le double de la partie libre du thorax; elle est 1.5 fois plus longue que haute et un peu moins 1.5 fois, que sa largeur (Fig. 1 A, B). Vue d'en haut, la carapace présente deux grosses gibbosités latérales et une petite crête médiane, sur la partie basse du plateau occupé par le lobe oculaire, bien exprimé; yeux absents (Fig. 1 B), pseudorostre aigu, quoique moins allongé que chez le *M. josephinae*, p. ex., orné d'une rangée de petits tubercules (plus gros pourtant, à côté de ceux que la carène latéro-ventrale orne). On voit partout de petits tubercules épars, apparement sans aucun ordre.

Le thorax a tous les somites libres, dépourvu de phanères, contrastant avec la carapace. La dernière

patte se dirige en bas, bien que son insertion soit plutôt latéro-inférieure. Le cinquième tergite à bord antéro-supérieur finement dentelé.

Les pléonites ± lisses dessus; des tubercules épineux sur la face dorsale du troisième et quatrième pléonites et sur les côtés du cinquième pléonite (Fig. 1 A). Le dernier pléonite est presque de le même longueur que le précédent, le telson dépassant leur longueur; ce dernier est cylindrique, sa partie post-anale représentant moins d'un tiers du tout (Fig. 1 C). Les deux gros piquants apicaux exceptés, le telson est dépourvu de tout phanère ou de toute ornamentation; par conséquent, vu d'en haut, l'aspect du telson rappelle bien une plume. L'anus présente deux petites valves latérales (Fig. 1 D).

A_2 trapue (Fig. 2 A), le flagellum court tri-articulé, le flagellum long quadri-articulé; A_1 (Fig. 2 B) à deux articles.

La troisième patte-mâchoire présente une base très allongée, armée d'un seul piquant distal; son bord interne, orné de 12 à 14 soies plumeuses; le méro- et le carpopodites armés d'un piquant; quatre soies sur l'apex extérieur de sa base (Fig. 2 C).

Le premier péréiopode est cassé; sa base courte

[2] Dédié au distingué carcinologiste danois, Dr. Torben Wolff, auteur de très belles synthèses sur la faune hadale.

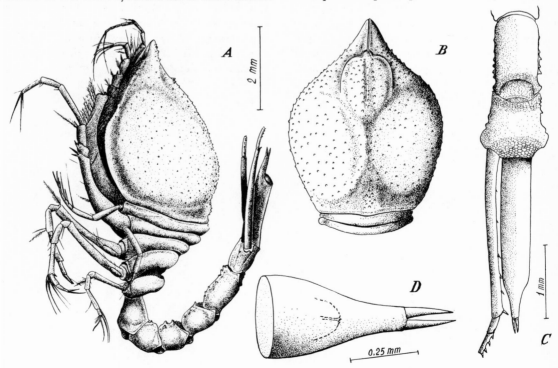

Figure 1. *Makrokylindrus wolffi*, n. sp. (♀ = 12.5 mm.). A: vue de profil; B: vue dorsale; C: telson et les deux derniers pléonites, vue ventrale; D: bout du telson, grossi.

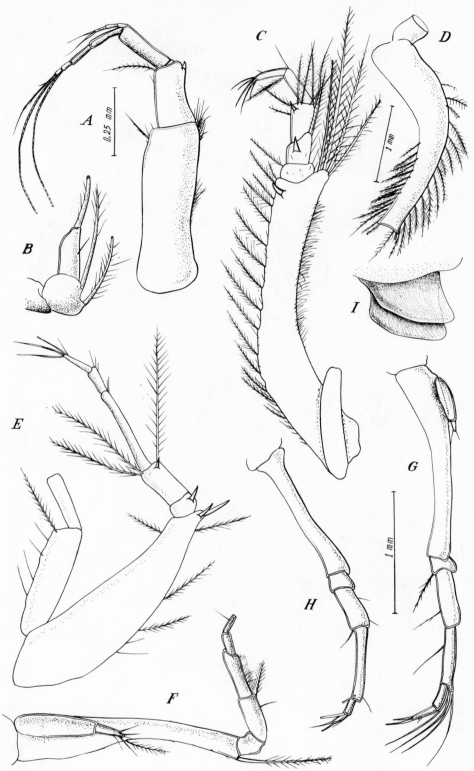

Figure 2. *Makrokylindrus wolffi*, n. sp. (♀ ad. = 12.5 mm.). A: A₂; B: A₁; C: maxillipède 3; D: base de la première patte; E, F, G, H: péréiopodes 2, 3, 4, 5; I: lobes médianes sur le sternite des péréiopodes 1. (L'échelle de G s'applique aux C, E, F, H, et I également; celle de A, à B également.)

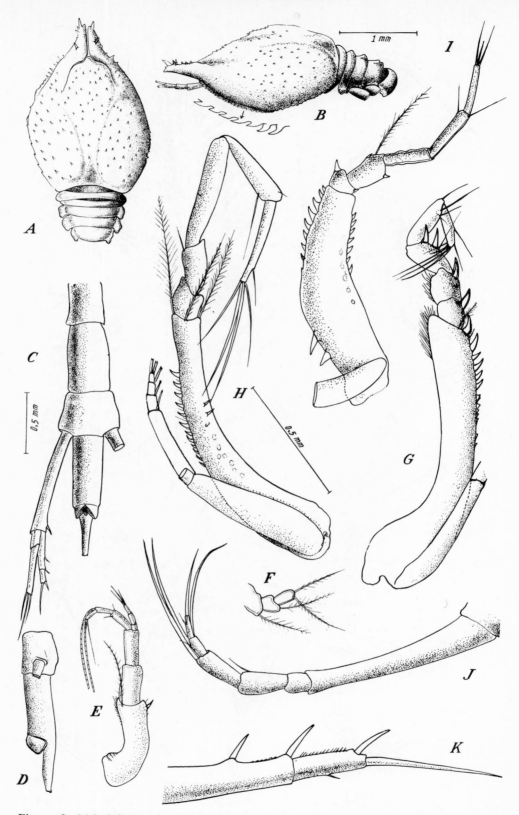

Figure 3. *Makrokylindrus lomakinae*, n. sp. (♀ juv. = 6.6 mm.). A: céphalothorax, vue dorsale; B: idem, de profil (en bas, la dentelure du plis antéro-inférieure de la carapace, grossie; C: partie distale du pléon; D: telson, vue latérale; E: antennae; F: antennule; G: maxillipède 3; H: péréiopode 1; I: péréiopode 2; J: péréiopode 5; K: endopodite de l'uropode. (L'échelle de H s'applique aux E, F, G, I et J également; celle de D, à C également.)

est inerme (Fig. 2 D), le second péréiopode (Fig. 2 E) faiblement armé : un piquant sur le metro-et l'ischiopodite et deux sur l'apex de la base. Péréiopodes 3 et 4 avec des exopodites rudimentaires (Fig. 2 F, G). Cinquième patte (Fig. 2 H) d'aspect banal, à insertion latéro-ventrale.

L'uropode atteint la longeuer des trois derniers segments abdominaux, son pédoncule, armé de huit à dix petites épines, atteint presque l'insertion des deux piquants apicaux du telson ; les branches cassées (Fig. 1 C).

La femelle porte quatre paires d'oostégites ; ceux-ci se présentent, pourtant, d'une manière un peu différente ; leurs ébauches occupent la ligne sternale médiane, entre le maxillipède 3 et le péréiopode 3, sous forme de lobes charnus, juxtaposés, et bien éloignés des coxas des pattes, auxquelles coxas elles appartiennent cependant (Fig. 2 I) ; en arrachant une patte, l'oostège correspondent ne se détache pas, pareillement à la plupart des Cumacés ; on dirait des formations qui n'ont rien à faire aux oostégites. On n'y trouve d'oostégites que pour deux ou trois espèces de *Makrokylindrus* ; aussi ne pouvons-nous anticiper aucune comparaison.

Observations : On ne connaît, à l'heure actuelle, que deux *Makrokylindrus* à telson armé de deux piquants apicaux seulement : *M. josephinae* Sars et surtout *M. inermis* Fage. De la première, notre espèce se distingue par les péréionites et l'abdomen glabres et par la faible armature des péréiopodes ; de la seconde, par la carapace plus allongée, à convexité faible, parsemée de tubercules.

De plus, le carpopodite de la seconde patte est presque deux fois plus long que le dactylo- et le propodites, pris ensemble (subégaux chez la *M. inermis* ; à comparer notre Fig. 2 à la Fig. 76 de Fage, 1929).

Deux autres espèces (*M. fragilis* et *M. acanthodes*) ont déjà été mentionnées pour les eaux de l'Afrique du Sud, mais à des profondeurs bien moins grandes (805 mètres).

commence presqu'à la base du pseudorostre. Les cinq thoracomères libres n'ont pas de phanères ni de tubercules, l'abdomen, idem (Fig. 3 A, C).

Le telson, parfaitement cylindrique dans sa partie proximale, s'effile brusquement, au-dessus des valves anales, pour former une partie post-anale 1.5 fois plus courte que le cylindre pré-anal (Figs. 3 C, 4 D) ; les phanères de l'apex manquent. Les A_1 (Fig. 3 F) et A_2 banales ; les fouets de l'A_2 ont trois articles chacun (Fig. 3 E). La troisième patte-mâchoire, à ectopodite fin et long, presente une base fortement armée, sur la moitié distale ; de forts piquants sur le carpo- (2), méro-, et l'ischiopodites (1) (Fig. 3 G). Le péréiopode 1, également grêle, à une base armée de deux séries de piquants, dont l'extérieure compte 12 à 14 épines, finit par trois longs articles (Fig. 3 H). La seconde patte, armée également de deux rangées d'épines, présente, en plus, deux forts piquants sur ses côtés internes et inferieurs et deux petits piquants sur les ischium et méros (Fig. 3 I). Le péréiopode 5 banal, à six articles (Fig. 3 J). L'uropode plus long que le telson ; sa hampe dépasse un peu les valves anales ; l'ectopodite plus long que l'endopodite ; celui-ci, bi-articulé (Fig. 3 K), à trois piquants et de fines serrulations ou poils sur le côté interne.

Association : Capturé sur un fond très riche en Cumacés, semble-t-il, vu que la station comptait plus de 60 individus, surtout des *Diastylis*, *Campylaspis* et *Bathycuma*.

Observations : Seules deux espèces placées dans le genre *Makrokylindrus* ont seulement deux articles à l'endopodite de l'uropode—à savoir, *M. insignis* et *M. mystacinus* Sars, toutes deux ouest-européennes. Le manque de deux grosses cornes latéro-antérieures de la carapace distingue cette espèce aussitôt de la première, et le manque d'une carène latérale et d'épines sur la carapace de la seconde ; enfin, la forme brusquement rétrécie du telson la distingue également de n'importe laquelle de ces deux espèces.

Makrokylindrus lomakinae,[1] n. sp.
Figure 3

Collection du Lamont Geological Observatory, Washington. Station 53 (4 Avril 1958), Afrique du S.-O., par 4893 mètres, latitude 36° 34′ S., longitude 14° 08′ E. Biotrawl, 1 ♀ juvénile = 6 mm.

Carapace allongée et assez large (Fig. 3 A), hérissée de petits piquants ; pseudorostre bien long, ayant une série de piquants plus forts, le plus long surplombant son bout (Fig. 3 B). Carène latéro-inférieure, bien individualisée par une série de denticulations (voir la flèche, Fig. 3 B) ; la carène

Makrokylindrus americanus, n. sp.
Figure 4

Collection du Lamont Geological Observatory. Station 122 (14 Novembre 1958), latitude 07° 25′ N., longitude 79° 23′ O. (Océan Pacifique, les eaux de l'Amérique tropicale ouest). Biotrawl, 1748 mètres. 1 ♂ juvénile = 6.3 mm.

Carapace ± globuleuse, moins 1.5 fois plus longue que haute, hérissée d'épines courtes sur les côtés surtout. Une rangée régulière d'épines, plus longues, festonne le pli inféro-latérale, derrière le pseudorostre. Celui-ci, bien pointu, a quelques petits tubercules épineux s'appuyant sur un lobe oculaire bien exprimé (Fig. 4 A).

Le tégument sans calcaire, translucide, élastique. Les cinq thoracomères libres présentent quelques petits

---

[1] Dédié au Dr. N. V. Lomakina, de Léningrad, qui nous a récemment fait connaître la riche faune cumacéologique du Pacifique N.-O.—entre autres, deux espèces de *Makrokylindrus*.

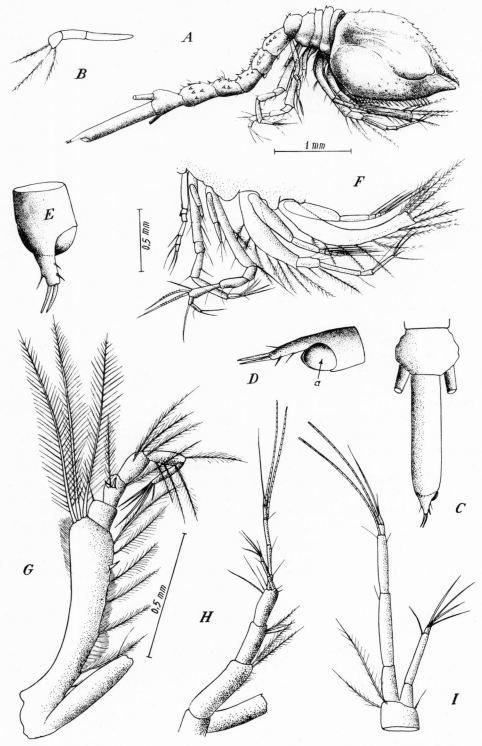

Figure 4. *Makrokylindrus americanus*, n. sp. (♂ juv. = 6.3 mm.). A: de profil (carapace un peu tournée du côté dorsal); B: A₂, en plein bourgeonnement; C: telson et le pléonite précédent (vue dorsale); D, E: telson, de profil et d'en haut, pour mieux voir les valves anales (a); F: les péréiopodes 1 à 5; G: maxillipède 3; H: antennule; I: idem, ses flagels grossis. (L'échelle de F, s'applique aux B, C, et H également; celle de G, aux D et E également.)

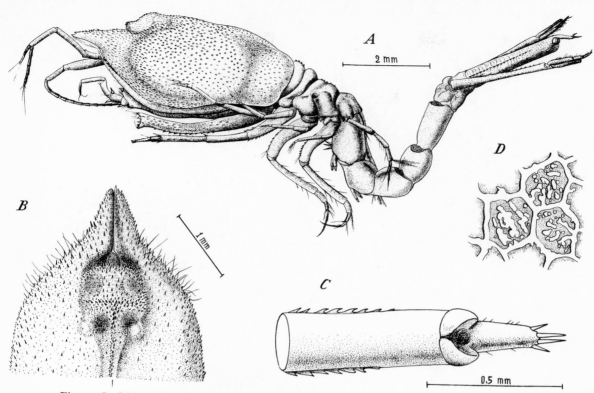

Figure 5. *Makrokylindrus menziesi*, n. sp. (♂ P = 14.5 mm.). A: de profil; B: moitié antérieure de la carapace, vue dorsale; C: telson vu d'en bas; D: détails de la structure des téguments.

piquants dorsalement et de longues soies sur le cinquième. Pléomères hérissés d'épines courtes, disposées ± clairement en deux séries dorsales et deux latérales; deux épines plus fortes sur les bords postérieurs de chaque somite (Fig. 4 A).

De longs poils sur la face tergale des pléonites. Telson un peu plus long que les trois derniers pléonites, pris ensemble, présentant une très longue partie cylindrique pré-anale (presque quatre fois la longueur de la petite partie post-anale); celle-ci est brusquement rétrécie au niveau des valves anales (Fig. 4 C, D) et porte, outre les deux longues épines apicales (1/3 de toute sa longueur), une épine et une paire de soies latérales (Fig. 4 E).

Les uropodes sont manquants.

A_1 présente une hampe tri-articulée, banale, et deux branches, tri-, respectivement cinq-articulées (Fig. 4 H, I). A_2 à peine au commencement (Fig. 4 B), n'atteint même pas la longueur de l'A_1.

La patte-mâchoire a une base courte, ornée de six longues soies plumeuses, de faibles dentelures et de longues soies, sur son bord extérieur. Une seule épine arme cet article; trois longues soies plumeuses sur son apex et deux épines sur le carpe caractérisent également le maxillipède 3 (Fig. 4 G).

Les pattes sont, toutes, presque sans épines, même sur leurs bases (à l'exception du bord distal de la base du péréiopode 1). Le talon des péréiopodes 3 et 4

plus accusé (Fig. 4 F); ces pattes ont de très courts ectopodites (caractère juvénile?). La cinquième patte est deux fois moins robuste que la quatrième (Fig. 4 F) (caractère juvénile également?).

Capturée en compagnie d'*Eudorella* sp. (six exemplaires), une dizaine de *Leucon* (trois espèces différentes) et plusieurs espèces de *Campylaspis*.

Observations: Bien que juvénile, la morphologie du telson, associée à l'ornementation des somites et à la faible armature des appendices, singularise suffisamment cette espèce parmi les autres *Makrokylindrus*; tout au plus le *M. armatus* (Norm.) rappelle quelque peu le *M. americanus*.

C'est la seconde espèce établie pour les eaux qui baignent le continent américain, de même que pour le Pacifique Est.

Makrokylindrus menziesi,[4] n. sp.
Figures 5, 6

Collection du Lamont Geological Observatory. Station 137 (23 Novembre 1958), latitude 09° 20.5' N., longitude 89° 34' O. (Océan Pacifique, les parages des Îles Galápagos). Biotrawl, par 3469–3493 mètres. 1 ♂ P = 14.5 mm.

[4] Dédié au Professeur R. J. Menzies, qui a récolté une bonne partie de Cumacés abyssaux qu'il a bien voulu nous envoyer, en vue de cette étude.

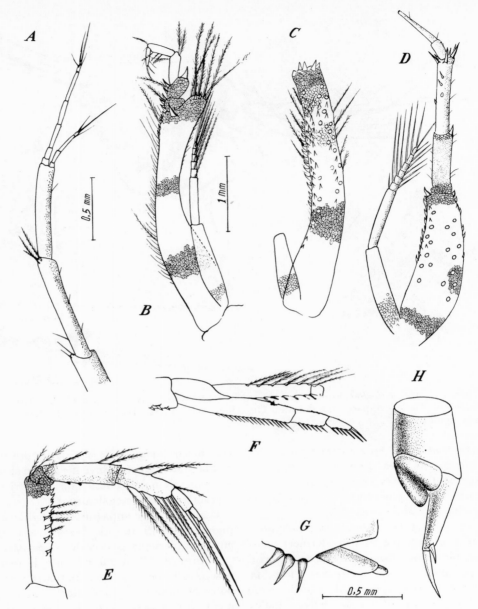

Figure 6. *Makrokylindrus menziesi*, n. sp. (♂ P = 14.5 mm.). A: A₂; B: maxillipède 3;
C: base du péréiopode 1; D: péréiopode 2; E: péréiopode 5; F: les deux branches de
l'uropode, grossies; G: la "crête" des épines sur la sternite du premier pléonite et le pléopode
1, de la phase pré-adulte; H: bout du telson, de profil. (L'échelle de B s'applique aux C
et D également; celle de A, à E et F, et celle de G à H également.)

Carapace translucide, mince, élastique, hérissée de longs poils sur sa moitié antérieure (Fig. 5 A) et armée de courts piquants partout, surtout sur les côtes ou sur les zones proéminentes de la région du lobe oculaire (Fig. 5 B). Elle est deux fois plus longue que haute ou large; vue de profil, elle présente une brusque élévation à la hauteur du lobe oculaire et deux autres, moins accusées, un peu plus loin (Fig. 5 B).

Le pseudorostre allongé et armé d'épinules ± égales; la crête inférieure de la carapace ne possède que de faibles dentelures, aussitôt derrière le pseudo-rostre, puis des tubercules à peine visibles.

Les thoracomères 3 et 4 sont coalescents; le cinquième presente une articulation latérale du péréiopode 5, dirigée postérieurement. Les plonites n'ont d'autres phanères que les trois piquants, sur la face sternale du premier somite (Fig. 6 G); le tout paraît granulé, à cause de nombreux petits tubercules, parsemés un peu partout.

Le telson atteint la longueur des trois derniers pléomères; sa partie cylindrique est plus longue que la base de l'uropode, étant au moins trois fois plus longue que la partie post-anale; celle-ci, apparemment articulée, surplombe les grosses valves anales

(Fig. 5 C) et finit par deux épines apicales, suivies de deux autres subapicales, plus petites; quelques petites soies ornent également ses bords (Figs. 5 C, 6 H).

La partie cylindrique est armée de chaque côte d'une rangée d'écailles transformées en piquants courts (Fig. 5 C).

Les téguments présentent, partout, une structure réticulaire, chaque pentagon ou hexagon étant sillonné de petits canaux irréguliers, de petits trous circulaires, etc.; le tout donne à la patte mâchoire, p. ex., une beauté particulière, rappelant les centaines de galeries de Bostrychidae juxtaposées (Fig. 5 D). Un pareil sillonnement du reticulum tégumentaire n'est figuré que pour le *M. longipes* par Bonnier (1896, p. 550, Pl. 29, Fig. 4 C).

On voit les écailles ± hexagonales typiques seulement vers le milieu des articles aplatis des appendices; on peut surprendre la transformation de ces écailles en tubercules, puis en grosses épines vers les côtés et, surtout, sur leurs bords distaux (Fig. 6 C, D).

A_1 (Fig. 6) longue aux branches tetra-, respectivement hexa-articulées. A_2, non encore complètement développée, présente seulement 22 articles à son fouet.

Le maxillipède 3 a six soies plumeuses sur la partie antéro-extérieure, doublées d'une couronne de quatre à cinq piquants, et sur le bord intérieur de la base une rangée d'épines. Cette patte-mâchoire se singularise parmi les autres *Makrokylindrus* par ses trois forts piquants sur la face sternale: l'un sur le bord distal de la base, deux autres sur l'ischium et le méropodite (Fig. 6 B), outre la rangée de trois, respectivement deux épines sur le bord intérieur.

La base du premier péréiopode (le seul qui reste sur place) est fortement épineuse sur le bord extérieur et distal (Fig. 6 C); le second péréiopode à une base armée, sur la partie distale, des deux côtés, présente, en outre, une agglomération de quatre à cinq épines sur la partie distale du carpe et une à deux sur le méros (Fig. 6 D). Les autres pattes ont également des tubercules épineux (Fig. 6 E); leurs ectopodites sont longs et grêles; deux paires de pléopodes, pas tout à fait développés.

L'uropode à l'endopodite tri-articulé, l'article proximal de beaucoup plus long et massif que les deux autres, armé d'une vingtaine d'épines à peu près; les autres, en ont six, respectivement cinq épines longues, regulièrement disposées. L'exopodite bien fourni d'épines et de soies (Fig. 6 F) est cassé distalement.

Observations: *M. menziesi* a été capturée en compagnie d'*Eudorella* sp. L'espèce a les appendices bien cassants en dépit d'une carapace élastique. Bien qu'apparentée à *M. cingulatus* (Calman, 1905)—par la coalescence de thoracomères 3 et 4, par l'insertion dorsale du péréiopode 5, par son aspect général et l'armature de la carapace—*M. menziesi* n'en est

pas moins une espèce différente. Elle en diffère, non seulement par le manque des tubercules disposés le long d'une crête circulaire au millieu de la carapace et par l'absence de la rangée des longues épines qui festonnent sa partie inférieure, mais aussi par l'absence d'épines sternales au premier pléonite et d'épines latérales sur les autres pléonites, par l'armature de l'apex du telson, par la présence de 15 à 20 petites épines sur la hampe de l'uropode (au lieu de huit), etc. Il s'agit là d'une sorte de réplique américaine est-pacifique, de cette espèce de l'Archipel Malais, issue d'un ancêtre commun avec *M. cingulatus*. De *M. fistularis* notre espèce diffère par sa carapace rugueuse (celle de *M. fistularis* est lisse et striée longitudinalement), et par les uropodes plus longs que le telson.

Nous croyons qu'une caractéristique morphologique si importante, comme la coalescence des thoracomères 3 et 4, qu'on rencontre chez *M. longipes* (syn. *M. spiniventris*?), *M. fistularis*, *M. cingulatus*, et *M. menziesi* Băcescu, doit être considérée plus attentivement; il s'agit là d'un groupe d'espèces formant une série génétique bien délimitée dans le cadre du genre *Makrokylindrus*, d'un valeur de sous-genre au moins, pour lequel nous proposons le nom de *Coalescuma*, n. sg.

Makrokylindrus fagei, n. sp
Figure 7 A–M

Collection du Lamont Geological Observatory. Station 58 (29 Avril 1958), latitude 28° 28′ S., longitude 44° 22′ E. (S-O. Madagascar). Biotrawl, par 2275 mètres, 1 ♂ sub-adulte = 9 mm. Type de l'espèce.

Corps allongé, tégument ± cassant, réticulé, parsemé partout de petits tubercules (Fig. 7 A). Carapace ovale, sans autre dépression que celle du pseudorostre. Bien que rugueuse sur toute son étendue, la carapace ne présente pas la rangée de longues épines inféro-latérales qui caractérisent certaines espèces de *Makrokylindrus*, la *M. tubulicauda* (Calman) emend. Fage notamment, avec laquelle elle a certaines affinités; le bord frangé ou "pectiné" de la carapace est bien expimé, soit qu'on s'adresse au ♂ figuré par Fage (1929, Pl. III, Fig. 78), soit au ♀ juvénile de Calman (1905a, Pl. V, Fig. 82). A leur place, sur les bords inférieurs de la carapace de notre espèce, on voit une série plus dense de tubercules cassants, à peine plus longs que ceux implantés sur le dos du corps; les plis inféro-médianes de la carapace sont beaucoup plus élastiques et assez éloignés; l'espace qu'ils laissent est occupé par les bases du maxillipède 3 et du péréiopode 1. Sur la partie dorsale du céphlo-thorax, on ne saurait distinguer aucune rangée régulière de tubercules; ceux-ci sont plus longs sur le pseudorostre et sur le lobe oculaire, bien contouré; c'est vers le bord postérieur de la carapace, seulement, qu'ils prennent l'aspect de

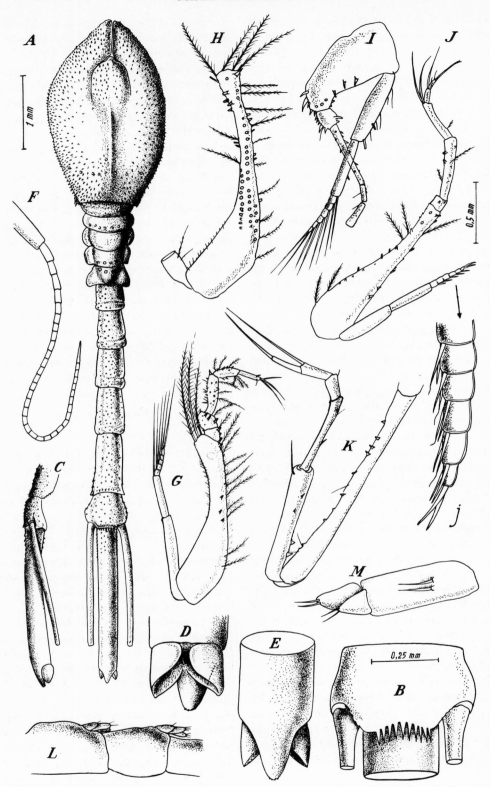

Figure 7. *Makrokylindrus fagei*, n. sp. (♂ P = 9 mm.). A: vue dorsale; B: l'extrémité du pléon, grossie (vue d'en haut); C: extrémité du pléon, de profil; D: bout du telson, d'en bas, pour mieux voir les valves anales; E: idem, d'en haut; F: fouet de l'A₂ incomplètement developpé; G: maxillipède 3; H: base du péréiopode 1; I, J, K: péréiopodes 2, 3, et 5; j: partie distale de l'exopodite du péréiopode 3; on y voit les phanères polymorphiques, différents de ceux ornant les exopodites des autres péréiopodes; L: pléonites 1 et 2, avec les pléopodes immatures; M: pléopode 1. (F–M, à la même échelle que J; D–E, à la même échelle que B.)

vraies épines; ils sont de plus en plus minuscules vers le milieu de la carapace.

Les lobes pseudorostraux arrondis, courts, surmontés chacun d'une épine plus grande.

Les thoracomères distincts, bien que la suture entre le troisième et le quatrième en soit moins accusée; les deux premiers possèdent de petites épines, disposées en série transversale. Sur la Fig. 7 A on a exagéré un peu la longueur du premier thoracomère, l'animal étant dilacéré. Le dernier pléonite présente une frange de lamines sur son bord dorsal et postérieur surplombant le telson (Fig. 7 B).

Le telson très long, plus long que les trois derniers pléonites pris ensemble (Fig. 7 A), est parfaitement cylindrique, un peu rugueux dans son quart proximal seulement; on y distingue trois à quatre rangées de minuscules tubercules, plus espacés, sur le bord tergal surtout (Fig. 7 C).

Un trait bien caractéristique de notre espèce est la présence d'une partie post-anale très courte, aplatie, sans aucun phanère apical: on dirait un petit ongle, dépassant à peine les grandes valves anales, nettement articulées (Fig. 7 C, D, E); elle ne possède pas "les deux épines apicales" (Fage, 1929, p. 37) ou "a pair of very minute spinules" (Calman, 1905a, p. 46), si clairement figurées, d'ailleurs, par Calman et Fage.

L'A_2 incomplètement dèveloppée (Fig. 7 F). Les pièces buccales n'ont rien de particulier. Le maxillipède 3, bien qu'abondamment hérissè d'épines tronquées (plutôt des tubercules) même sur le propodos, ne présente pas la série d'épines régulièrement croissantes sur le bord inférieur de sa base, comme c'est le cas pour *M. tubulicauda* (Fage, 1929, Fig. 82, Pl. III); outre la double garniture de minuscules soies, la base porte deux séries de soies plumeuses et de courtes épines-tubercules. Le fouet de l'exopodite du maxillipède 3 a cinq articulations (quatre chez *M. tubulicauda*).

Tous les péréiopodes portent de nombreuses épines et tubercules surtout sur leurs bases. Ces bases sont très élargies proximalement chez les péréiopodes 1 à 4 (Fig. 7 H, J, K,) portant plusieurs rangées de tubercules (sur le bord ventral surtout). Le péréiopode 2 (Fig. 7 I) a un méros fin et fortement rugueux, puis de longues épines sur l'ischium et sur la partie distale de la base. Les exopodites des péréiopodes, aux fouets sept à huit-articulés, ont des soies plumeuses banales aux péréiopodes 1 et 2, tandis que ceux des troisième et quatrième paires (Fig. 7 J) y ont une sorte d'épinules, alternant avec des épines flagellées (ou plutôt laminées). Le péréiopode 5 (Fig. 7 K) diffère des autres par sa base cylindrique, armée de rares tubercules. Les pléopodes ne sont pas pleinement développés (Fig. 7 L, M). La base de l'uropode a la proportion de celle de *M. tubulicauda*, mais elle est presque nue; ses branches sont cassées.

Observations: *M. fagei* fait partie du groupe *M. tubulicauda*. Les traits communs en sont la morphologie du telson et le gonflement proximal des basipodites des péréiopodes 1 à 4. Si on compare la morphologie de notre Cumacé aux descriptions de Calman et de Fage, on voit qu'il s'agit là d'une espèce à part; elle en diffère premièrement par une plus faible "fourrure" d'épines; sous ce rapport, son tégument, plutôt rugueux qu'épineux, ressemble plus aux figures de Calman (1905a) qu'à celles de Fage; il ressemble plus encore au tégument *M. cingulatus* (Calman, 1905b). Il en diffère également par le manque de la "corbeille" filtrant sur le bord inférieur de la carapace, présente même chez les petits, lorsqu'il s'agit de *M. tubulicauda* (Calman, 1905a, Fig. 82), puis par le manque de la série d'épines sur la base du maxillipède 3 et des épinules sur l'apex du telson.

De *Makrokylindrus* sp. capturée par *Galathea* (Bruun, 1953, p. 191), faisant partie du groupe *tubulicauda*, notre espèce en diffère également par les péréiopodes beaucoup plus courts et trapus; de ces deux espèces à la fois, elle s'éloigne encore par sa petite taille; en effet, bien que le type de *M. tubulicauda* soit une ♀ juvénile d'à peine 5.4 mm., l'espèce doit être beaucoup plus grande, vu le manque total du péréiopode 5 à cette taille là. Le fait est confirmé d'ailleurs par Fage (1929), qui décrit des ♂♂, moins evolués que le notre, quoi qu'ils depassent 15 mm.; quant au *Makrokylindrus* sp. de *Galathea*, c'est un géant de 30 mm.

Le seul individu de *M. fagei* a été capture dans une riche coenose de Cumacés (20 exemplaires environ), parmi lesquels dominent les *Campylaspis*, *Diastylis*, et *Leucon*.

CONCLUSIONS ET CLÉ POUR LE G. MAKROKYLINDRUS

Sur les 54 stations ayant des Cumacés et envoyées par L.G.O., dont 18 ont été exécutées par des fonds dépassant 4000 mètres (4000 à 6328 mètres précisément), six recélaient des *Makrokylindrus*. On y découvrait chaque fois *un seul individu* et *une espéce unique* (la Station 53 à part, avec ses deux espèces); cela indique une répartition assez vaste, mais associée à une densité bien faible, par rapport à d'autres genres de Cumacés abyssaux de la Collection L.G.O., tels que *Eudorella, Bathycuma, Leucon, Campylaspis*, certaines *Diastylis*, tous, richement représentées dans les dites stations, vu même comme cobiontes de nos espèces.

Les données concernant la présence de ce genre —l'Atlantique peut bien en être excepté—sont trop pauvres encore pour nous permettre une discussion sur sa distribution géographique. En effet, de l'immense aquatorium des océans Pacifique et Indien, on n'a rapporté que six, respectivement trois espèces, et, précisons-le, dans des points isolés aux extrémités est et ouest de ces océans (Kurile, Sonda, Galápagos, Archipel de la Malaisie, et les parages du Madagascar). On peut aisément se figurer la riche moisson de nouveautés que nous réserve la campagne internationale des recherches de toute l'étendue de l'Océan Indien, dans les années à venir, quant à ce genre abysso-hadal.

Onze des espèces connues proviennent des eaux atlantiques, baignant les côtes européennes ou ouest-marocaines, dont deux, de la Mer Mediterranée également. Six seulement on été draguées dans d'autres régions de l'océan mondial.

Cette dispersion inégale tient, sans aucun doute, du fait qu'on a mieux étudié les parages profonds de l'Atlantique plutôt que ceux des autres océans, témoins notre présente contribution: sur cinq espèces nouvelles, deux proviennent des eaux ouest-américaines et trois des parages sud-africains; il faut y ajouter encore le *Makrokylindrus* n.sp. capturée par le *Galathea* (Sonda). La préférence du genre pour les eaux abyssales, voire hadales, n'en ressort pas moins, vu les profondeurs de capture de ces espèces. Deux en ont été recueillies par presque 5000 mètres (4885 mètres), une à 3500 mètres, et les trois autres entre 1300 et 1700 mètres à peu près. Les stations du L.G.O. se placent donc parmi les plus profondes pout le *Makrokylindrus*, vu que, jusqu'à présent, une seule station du *Galathea* les dépasse (7160 mètres).

Parmi les anciennes captures, les plus profondes sont celles du Golfe de Gascogne (4380 mètres), d'ou on a pêchè *M. tubulicauda* (Calman) et *M. mystacinus* Sars. Suit de près la capture de *M. abyssi* Lomakina (3940 mètres).

L'absence totale des yeux, les téguments translucides et élastiques, dépourvus presque complètement de calcaire; la présence $\pm$ constante de gros piquants à la face sternale des péréiopodes et du maxillipède 3; et, surtout, la présence de la rangée de longues épines qui pendent comme une frange —réalisant une sorte de corbeille filtrant autour de la partie inférieure de la carapace de certaines espèces (*M. cingulatus, M.* n. sp. du *Galathea*, etc.); enfin un abdomen toujours redressé et la convergence dans la morphologie du telson, sont, croyons-nous, autant d'adaptations aux fonds, à demi-liquide (moux) des abîmes océaniques, réalisées par les espèces de *Makrokylindrus*.

Pour nous rendre mieux compte de la position systématique de ces espèces nouvelles, nous avons dressé plus bas une première clef dychotomique de toutes les espèces (25) placées dans le genre *Makrokylindrus* Stebbing.

Aux listes antérieures (Stebbing, Hansen, Zimmer, Fage), nous ajoutons *M. fistularis* (Calman) et *M.* n. sp. de *Galathea*, puis nous allons considérer séparément les espèces *M. spiniventris* Hansen, de *M. longipes* (Sars) et *M. dubius* (Bonnier), de *M. josephinae* (Sars). Jusqu'à ce qu'une étude morphologique plus approfondie nous apporte la preuve qu'une même espèce peut avoir des somites thoraciques coalescentes (*M. spiniventris* et *M. dubius*) ou libres (*M. longipes, M. josephinae*), toute synonymie définitive est exclue; et cela parce que ce n'est pas là un trait dimorphique ($\female$), comme on l'avait cru (Zimmer, Fage), mais une particularité morphologique—réclamée par une raison phylogénétique encore obscure—qui affecte les $\male\male$ également; le cas de $\male\male$ de *M. cingulatus* et *M. menziesi* ($\female\female$ non encore connues) ou bien celui de *M. dubius* ou de *M. fragilis*—chez lesquelles cette coalescence est propre aux deux sexes—est assez éloquent. Si cette coalescence était une caractéristique femelle, elle devrait être présente chez la $\female$ juvénile de *M. longipes* de Bonnier, synonymisée à tort avec *M. spiniventris* Hansen (vu que cet auteur souligne, avec vigueur une pareille structure, lorsqu'il parle de sa *Diastylopsis dubia*, en lui avançant même la valeur d'un trait générique [Bonnier, p. 561]).

TABLE DES ESPÈCES DES MAKROKYLINDRUS STEBBING, 1912

1 (38). Tous les thoracomerès sont libres, ± mobiles; l'insertion du thoracopode 5 latéro-ventrale; l'apex du telson dépasse évidemment les valves anales (A. Sous-genre *Makrokylindrus* Stebbing, 1912) 2

2 (3). Carapace à deux cornes antéro-latérales (comme chez *l'Eocuma* à peu près) 1. *M. insignis* (G. O. Sars, 1877) (Atlantique E., Méditerranée, 360–1100 mètres)

3 (2). Carapace ovale, sans cornes antéro-latérales 4

4 (13). Telson plus long que les trois derniers pléonites 5

5 (10). La partie post-anale du telson très courte (1/7–1/9 de sa longueur totale) et dépassant à peine les valves anales 6

6 (7). Tous les péréiopodes extrêmement fins, les carpus et méros presque filiformes 2. *Makrokylindrus* n. sp. (Capturée par *Galathea* dans la fosse de Sonda, 7160 mètres, Vol. 2, Fig. 4, p. 191)

7 (6). Seulement le péréiopode 1 un peu allongé, les autres normaux, aux méros et carpus courts 8

8 (9). Apex du telson armé de deux petites épines. Carapace et surtout les tergites des thoracomères épineux; une rangée régulière d'épines sur le bord inférieur de la base du maxillipède 3. *M. tubulicauda* (Calman, 1905) emend. Fage 1929 (Atlantique E., 700–4380 mètres)

9 (8). Apex du telson complètement inerme; carapace et tergites des somites libres, tout au plus rugueux, sans épines; des tubercules et soies plumeuses sur le bord de la base respective 4. *M. fagei*, n. sp. (S.-O. Madagascar, 2275 mètres).

10 (5). La partie post-anale du telson plus longue (1/4 à 1/5 de la longeur totale), dépassant de beaucoup les valves anales, se présente brusquement rétrécie et armée de deux à quatre épines terminales 11

11 (12). Seulement deux épines minuscules sur l'apex du telson 5. *M. josephinae* (G. O. Sars, 1871) nec. syn. *M. dubius* Bonnier (Atlantique, 364–1500 mètres)

12 (11). Hormis les épines apicales (qui touchent un tiers de la longueur de la lame), on y voit trois à quatre épines sousterminales 6. *M. americanus*, n. sp. (Pacifique E. [Amèrique tropicale], 1748 mètres)

13 (42). Telson moins long que les trois derniers pléonites.[a] La partie post-anale du telson plus longue (moins 1/4 du tout, le plus souvent), armée de deux épines apicales au moins (le plus souvent quatre ou plus), dépassant de beaucoup les valves anales 14

14 (33). Telson plus long que la base de l'uropode 15

15 (16). Telson finement poilu sur les bords de sa partie post-anale sans autres phanères que les deux épines apicales; des denticulations sur les bords latéraux du pénultième segment abdominal 7. *M. erinaceus* (G. O. Sars, 1887) (O. Espagne, 3700 mètres)

16 (15). Telson glabre; pas de denticulation sur le dit segment 17

17 (22). L'endopodite de l'urupode plus court que l'exopodite, bi- ou tri-articulé 18

18 (21). Endopodite bi-articulé 19

19 (20). L'article distal de cet endopodite deux fois plus court que le proximal, portant une forte épine terminale, deux fois sa longeur. Partie post-anale du telson brusquement rétrécie (Fig. 3 C) 8. *M. lomakinae*, n. sp. (Afrique du S., 4885 mètres)

20 (19). L'article distal de l'endopodite de l'uropode à peu près de la même longueur que l'autre, armé d'une minuscule épine terminale. Partie post-anale du telson s'amincissant graduellement 9. *M. mystacinus* (G. O. Sars, 1887) (Madère, G. Gascogne, 3700–4380 mètres)

21 (18). Endopodite tri-articulé; telson à deux épines apicales et trois paires sous-apicales. Deux fortes épines surplombant les lobes pseudo-rostraux 10. *M. armatus* Norman, 1876 (Détroit de Davis, 3295 mètres)

22 (17). L'endopodite de l'uropode plus long que l'exopodite, tri-articulé 23

23 (26). Telson étranglé un peu au niveau de l'anus. 24

24 (25). La partie post-anale garde presque la même largeur que la partie pré-anale; elle est arrondie au bout et armée de quatre paires d'épines un peu arquées; le rest du telson glabre 11. *M. abyssi* Lomakina, 1955 (Mer de Behring, 394 mètres)

25 (24). La partie post-anale, plus gonflée au niveau de l'anus que dans le reste du telson, se rétrécit après, étant armée de deux épines apicales seulement et finement serrée sur les côtes. Le telson entier est hirsute 12. *M. serricauda* (T. Scott, 1912) (N.-O. Angleterre, 140 mètres)

26 (23). Telson ± cylindrique, sa partie post-anale s'étirant en pointe de plume (on n'y voit ni étranglement, ni serrulation 27

27 (30). Le bout du telson armé de deux fortes épines apicales seulement 28

28 (29). Tégument du céphalothorax lisse. Cinq épines sur la base de l'uropode, base qui dépasse à peine le niveau de l'anus 13. *M. inermis* Fage, 1929 (Açores, 1550 mètres)

29 (28). Tégument rugueux; de courtes épines sur les lobes pseudo-rostraux et sur les pléonites. Deux épines sur la base de l'uropode, qui touche presque l'apex du telson 14. *M. wolffi*, n. sp. (Afrique du S.-E., 4888 mètres)

30 (27). Outre les deux épines apicales, on en compte au moins trois à cinq paires de sous-apicales. Des épines seulement sur le 1/3 antérieur de la carapace, le reste de tégument nu 31

[a] C'est dans ce groupement 13 qu'on doit placer l'espèce *costata* Bonnier (1896, p. 553) si elle s'avérait, comme le suppose Fage, une *Makrokylindrus*. Elle s'en distingue aisément par les quatre arcs latéro-transversaux de tubercules sur la carapace.

31 (32). Avec trois à quatre paires d'épines sous-apicales
15. *M. longipes* (G. O. Sars, 1871). nec. Bonnier
(= *M. spiniventris* Hansen)
(Atlantique E., Meditérranée, 15 à 1227 mètres)

32 (31). Telson avec cinq paires d'épines sous-apicales
16. *M. viteasi* Lomakina, 1958
(Dépression Kurilo-Kamtchatka, 2840 mètres)

33 (14). Telson plus court que l'uropode ou l'égalant à peine[b] 34

34 (35). Les deux branches de l'uropode ± égales, thoracomères et pléonites armés de fortes épines sur leur faces tergales
17. *M. acanthodes* (Stebbing, 1912)
(Afrique du S., 805 mètres)

35 (34). L'endopodite de l'uropode bien plus court que l'exopodite; les dites somites lisses ou armés également 36

36 (37). Thoracomères et pléonites parfaitement inermes, lisses; des exopodites réduits aux péréiopodes 3 et 4 ♀
18. *M. longicaudatus* Bonnier, 1896
(Atlantique N.-E., 650–1287 mètres)

37 (36). Thoracomères, et pléonites surtout, recouverts de forts piquants; pas d'exopodites aux péréiopodes 3 et 4 ♀
19. *M. anomalus* (Bonnier, 1896)
(France O., Açores, 950–1550 mètres)

38 (1). Au moins deux thoracomères coalescents (3 et 4), chez les ♀♀ surtout, paraît-il; l'insertion du dernier thoracopode latéro-dorsale (Fig. 5 A); la partie post-anale du telson très courte, parfois dépassant à peine les valves anales (B. Sous-genre *Coalescuma*, n. sg[c]) 39

39 (44). La carapace dépourvue de la frange d'épines inféro-latérales (♂, ♀); trois à cinq piquants médians sur la face sternale du premier pléonite (Fig. 6 G) 40

40 (41). Deux à quatre piquants sur les côtes des deux premiers pléonites; six à huit épines arment le bout du telson

[b] La position des trois espèces de la section No. 33 dans le cadre du genre *Makrokylindrus*, d'accord avec Fage (1951, p. 114, pour le *M. dubius* au moins), est à reconsidérer lorsqu'on sera en possession d'un matériel plus abondant.

[c] Il ne s'agit-là nullement d'une simple ankylose de l'articulation entre les péréionites 3 et 4, dont on peut suivre la ligne en fer à cheval entre les dites somites, allongées d'une manière insolite, traits qui ont abouti à la création, par Smith, du genre *Diastylopsis*—mais d'une vraie coalescence, avec suppression de toute trace d'articulation de ces somites-là sur la face tergale au moins.

20. *M. spiniventris* Hansen, 1920 (syn. *M. longipes* Bonnier, nec. Sars)
(Atlantique de l'E., G. Gascogne, 950 mètres)

41 (40). Pas de piquants sur les côtes des deux premiers pléonites 42

42 (43). Le bout du telson avec seulement deux minuscules épinules apicales, qui mesurent à peine 1/8 de la longueur de la partie post-anale. Trois soies plumeuses sur l'angle externe et distal de la base du maxiliipède 3, faiblement armées
21. *M. dubius* (Bonnier, 1896) (nec. syn. *M. josephinae* Sars?)
(G. Gascogne, 650–950 mètres)

43 (42). Le bout du telson armé de quatre épines; deux sous-apicales et deux autres plus fortes sur l'apex (celles-ci couvrent plus d'un quart de la longueur totale de la partie post-anale du telson (Fig. 5 C). Six soies sur la base du maxillipède 3, bien armée d'épines
22. *M. menziesi*, n. sp.
(Pacifique de l'E., parages de Galàpagos, 3493 mètres)

44 (39). La carapace avec ou sans frange inférieure d'épines; la face sternale du premier pléonite ♂ dépourvue d'épines 45

45 (46). Le telson d'une exceptionnelle longeur dépasse l'extrémité même des branches de l'uropode. L'apex du telson ± inerme, ne dépassant pas les valves anales. Carapace lisse, striée longitudinalement
23. *M. fistularis* (Calman, 1911)
(Siam, 20–50 mètres)

46 (45). Le telson plus court, n'atteignant presque pas le niveau du troisième article de l'endopodite de l'uropode; l'apex du telson dépasse clairement les valves anales; un pli ± transversal sur la carapace, un peu avant son milieu, avec ou sans frange d'épines sur son bord inférieur 47

47 (48). Tégument lisse; deux grosses épines sur l'apex du telson, sans frange d'épines
24. *M. fragilis* Stebbing, 1912
(Afrique du S., 805 mètres)

48 (47). Tégument couvert de tubercules; quatre fines épines au bout du telson, deux apicales et deux sous-apicales, plus petites; avec une rangée d'épines
25. *M. cingulatus* (Calman, 1905)
(Archipel Malais, 2795 mètres)

BIBLIOGRAPHIE

Bonnier, J. 1896. Edriophthalmes. Résultat scientifique du "Caudan." Campagne du Caudan, pp. 527–689.

Bruun, A. F., Sv. Greve, H. Mielsche, et R. Spärck. 1953. Galatheas Jordomsejling, 1950–1952. Kobenhavn.

Calman, W. T. 1905a. Cumacea of west coast of Ireland. Fish. Irel. Sci. Invest., 1904. App. 1. part 4, pp. 3–52.

——1905b. The Cumacea of the Siboga Exp. 4, 27 pp., 2pl.

——1911. On new or rare crustacea of the order Cumacea from the collection of the Copenhagen Museum. Part II. Fam. Nannastacidae and Diastilidae. Trans. Zool. Soc. London, vol. 18, part 4.

Fage, L. 1929. Cumacés et Leptostracés. Résultats Campagnes Monaco, vol. 77.

——1951. Cumacés. Faune de France, no. 54. Paris.

Hansen, H. J. 1920. Crustacea Malacostraca. IV. Danish Ingolf Exp., vol. 3. Copenhagen.

Lomakina, N. B. 1958. Kumovîe raki (Cumacea) Morei SSSR. Acad. Nauk Moskva, 302 pp.

Sars, G. O. 1871. Nya arter of Cumacea samlade under K. Svenska Korvetten Josephines Expedition i Atlantiska Oceanen ar 1869, af. F. A. Smitt och A. Ljungman. Vet. Akad. Förh. 1: 71–81.

——1887. Report on the Cumacea collected by H.M.S. Challenger during the years 1873–1876. Rep. "Challenger" Zool., vol. 19.

Stebbing, T. R. R. 1912. The Sympoda (Part VI of S. A. Crustacea, for the Marine Invest. in South Africa). Ann. S. African Mus., 10: 129–176.

——1913. Cumacea (Sympoda). Das Tierrich (ed. Fr. Schultze), 39Lief.: 210 pp.

Wolff, Torben. 1960. The hadal community, an introduction. Deep Sea Research, 6: 95–124. London,

Zimmer, C. 1941. Cumacea in Bronn's Cl. Ord. Tierreich. vol. 5, 1 Abt., part 4. Buch. Acad. Verlags, Leipzig.